REPAIRING RECORD CHANGERS

REPAIRING
Record Changers

A practical guide to all models, including
PORTABLE PHONOGRAPHS,
HIGH-FIDELITY UNITS,
and
MAGNETIC TAPE RECORDERS

E. Eugene Ecklund, **Head, Special Products Engineering Section, Instrument Division, Allen B. DuMont Laboratories, Inc.**

McGRAW-HILL BOOK COMPANY, INC.

New York   Toronto   London   1955

Preface

This book presents the basic information needed to repair record changers. The everyday mechanical motions involved are first explained one by one. Next, the levers, cams, gears, and other actions that produce these motions in record changers are taken up. By considering only one motion at a time and learning the easy practical way to correct its troubles, the reader gains confidence along with competence.

For years the serviceman has been faced with the problem of obtaining basic record-changer information. The few service manuals that were available often did not teach. As an analogy, they gave a map of a maze of streets along which the serviceman could travel with little idea of where to go or how to get there. Now at last the serviceman can be independent of such information. Only rarely will such service manuals be needed.

The book is intended for home study, for reference, and as a classroom text in vocational and trade schools. The practical how-to-repair approach allows the reader to apply his newly found knowledge to his own changers and to others right from the start.

For men working in service organizations, whether as drivers, helpers, or apprentices, the book offers an opportunity for rapid upgrading. The radio and television serviceman will benefit by broadening his knowledge.

Manufacturers of record changers and combination radio or television sets can use the text for company-sponsored training courses, helping ambitious employees to progress in a minimum time to take over test and troubleshooting positions of greater responsibility.

Just as in radio and television servicing, a thorough knowledge of the basic fundamentals is very important for fixing record changers. Each manufacturer has a different arrangement of mechanical parts reflecting the taste of the designer, much the same as each house reflects the ideas of its architect. As a result, the variety is almost endless, even though the changers may have the same basic form of operation.

Knowing the basic fundamentals or motions makes it easy to figure out the operation of a particular record changer. The actions can then be isolated and the faulty operation spotted. This leads to a quick and sure repair that usually involves nothing more than adjusting a screw, bending a lever, or cleaning some parts.

This how-to-fix knowledge is built up in a convenient, logical sequence. The serviceman is first introduced to the clean, pleasant atmosphere of servicing record changers both in the shop and in the home. The instruction is entirely practical throughout, even down to details of the tools and workbench required. With his equipment ready, the serviceman can start getting practical experience after studying only the first few chapters.

Replacing needles and pickup cartridges can be a big business, particularly if given proper attention. Since these two parts are the causes of most of the troubles in record changers, they are studied first. The reader is thus ready to start making actual repairs by the time he has finished the first five chapters.

Next comes a study of motors and motor drives. The three main changing actions—tripping the change cycle, dropping the record, and cycling the pickup arm so the next record will play—are discussed separately for simplicity. The mechanisms discussed are those most likely to be encountered. Causes of trouble and practical how-to-fix details are provided while the mechanism is fresh in the reader's mind.

Special, deluxe, and auxiliary features such as automatic shutoff, special 45-rpm changers and spindles, and various amplifier techniques are similarly handled. A summarizing chapter then introduces simpler and faster methods of troubleshooting and checking the record changer.

Magnetic tape recorders, now becoming increasingly popular, offer additional repair business. A separate chapter is devoted to these machines and their problems. Since no changing mechanism is involved, magnetic recorders are even easier to repair than record changers.

Since new changer designs use the same basic motions, often in simpler forms, this book prepares for the future as well. The basic knowledge combined with experience will assure recognition in a field currently mastered only by few.

Appreciation is expressed to the many firms whose cooperation aided materially in preparation of this book, including Admiral, Audio Devices, Columbia Records, Dubbings, Electrovox, General Cement, General Industries, General Electric, International Resistance Co., Merix Chemical, M. A. Miller Mfg., Pacific Transducer, Philco, Radio Corporation of America, Howard W. Sams & Co., J. P. Seeburg, Shure Brothers, Mark Simpson Mfg., V-M Corp., Webster-Chicago, Westinghouse Electric, and Zenith Radio. Specific credit is given for illustrations wherever possible.

Credit is also given to Charles Agel, whose effort started this book prior to interruption by more pressing personal affairs. Special credit and sincere thanks go to John Markus, whose inspiration, guidance, and critical editing have followed the project from conception to production.

Finally, deep appreciation to my wife Shirl and our children Ellen, Norm, and Jan—to Shirl for persistent typing, and to them all for their understanding of the many short week ends and fatherless evenings during the writing of this book.

E. Eugene Ecklund

Contents

1

Handling Record-changer Service Calls

Value of Record-changer Knowledge. In recent years the use of record changers, wire recorders, and tape recorders has become more and more popular. Almost every home that has a radio or television set in it also has a record changer. Sometimes the automatic record changer is included as part of a combination radio. Sometimes it is a separate piece of equipment that is plugged into or used with a radio.

Record changers are not as troublesome as radio or television sets, but so many changers are now being used in homes and in industry that servicemen encounter them quite frequently. Unfortunately, however, many servicemen don't know how to fix record changers. It is truly surprising how many top-notch radio and television servicemen are actually turning down record-changer repair jobs even though the modern changer is simple in design and quite easy to fix.

The serviceman is not totally at fault here because only a few trade schools thoroughly cover the repairing of record changers. Besides, there has previously been no common source of basic information. Manufacturers' information is available on individual models, and there are books which compile data on a number of individual models, but there has been no source which thoroughly discusses the common fundamentals involved.

It also seems that mechanics of gears and gadgets for some reason tends to confuse the serviceman. Although the serviceman encounters each of the mechanical elements of a changer in everyday life and work, the combining of all these in an automatic record changer seems to discourage and even scare him.

1

Confidence a Prime Requisite. One of the most important features in any type of service work is confidence. This can be gained only through a thorough knowledge of the subject. When a serviceman recognizes the basic actions involved, he has a familiar starting point for tackling any record-changer problem. This is the basis of confidence.

Easy and Profitable Work. Record-changer servicing is a good source of income. There are servicemen who specialize in this field exclusively. Virtually every record changer in use requires a new needle. A proper approach to the problem is almost certain to result in a sale. In addition, many of these same record changers require a new pickup cartridge for proper results. This adds to the income.

There is no servicing job quite as simple as changing a needle or a cartridge. Record-changer servicing as a whole is relatively clean and physically easy. Manufacturers use women in assembly and test, as shown in Fig. 1. The work is just as easy for you once you know how.

Wire and Tape Recorders. The existence of many wire and tape recorders adds to the service business. Although wire recorders are being manufactured in smaller quantities, tape recorders are becoming increasingly popular. Both of these recorders are discussed in a separate section of the book. Although the operation of tape and wire recorders differs considerably in appearance from that of the disc-type record changer, the mechanical actions are very much the same, though fewer.

Customer Relations. Needless to say, good customer relations are important in any business. The impression which a serviceman leaves with the customer can mean added profits and a much more pleasant job.

Customer relations are services extended to the customer which are not of a technical nature. The important point in all contacts with the customer is to try to appreciate his point of view. The prime qualities expected are courtesy, consideration, honesty, and value.

Respect for the Customer's Property. Home is a man's castle. What may be a piece of junk to one person may be a prize possession to another. This point of view must be borne in mind in all transactions. Walking on the sidewalk rather than on the grass, using the doorknob rather than the woodwork when entering or leaving, closing the door rather than slamming it shut or leaving it ajar, wiping the feet rather than tracking in dirt or moisture—all are simple but important considerations.

Your hat should be removed in front of women and in the house. Any jacket or coat which is taken off should be neatly placed in a spot where it will not cause concern. When work is done in the home, newspapers or a cloth should be laid on the floor before placing the tools or the record changer there. Tools should generally be returned to the toolbox rather than placed on the floor. They should not be placed on top of furniture, as this is almost a sure way of scratching it. Caution should be used so that tools which are tucked into the pocket will not accidentally scratch the furniture or the wall.

Fig. 1. Record-changer repairing is light, clean work generally requiring only adjustment of a screw or bending a piece of thin metal

Another point to avoid is using furniture as a base when writing out invoices or receipts. A wood finish is usually soft, and an impression may be left in the surface. A magazine placed under the paper will solve this problem.

Considerations for the Work Area. In most instances it will be found that pictures, vases, clocks, and other ornaments are placed on the record changer, radio, or television set. These should be moved to a spot where there is no possible danger of damage. Furniture which might get in the way should also be moved before beginning work. Anything which is moved at the beginning of the job should be returned to its original position.

Where record changers are being repaired in the home, it may be a good idea to request the use of a card table. The record changer may then be placed on the card table, taking caution to first place a newspaper or other means of protection over the card table's surface. The card table will provide a convenient means of work.

Upon completing the job, any scraps, including newspapers, should be cleaned up. If necessary, a vacuum cleaner should be requested. If the customer advises the serviceman not to bother because he or she will clean up, this is perfectly acceptable, but the serviceman should first offer to do it. If the serviceman becomes dirty from working, he should ask permission to wash up in the kitchen. This will prevent any dirt or grease from being carried about the customer's home or on to the next job.

Personal Attitude. A cheerful disposition is a big asset in servicing. A smile goes a long way. It helps to put both the serviceman and the customer at ease.

The customer's questions often are prompted by ignorance, and a word of explanation is in order. However, it is never desirable to try to impress the customer, either by the use of technical terms or by boasting. The facts should be stated simply. If the answer is unknown, this fact should be acknowledged. If questions are of a general nature, a general answer should be given, indicating that specific examples do not always follow the general case. If specific answers are not possible, it is permissible to give your personal opinion, saying frankly that others may not fully agree with it.

Endorsement of Products. Caution must be used in evaluating a product or in condemning it. An approach should be used which avoids a definite opinion or answer. It is usually possible to say something good about any product. In general, it is not wise to say positively that any one product is the best. Even if such a feeling is in order, it may get you into trouble. For example, to remark that product A is the best available may bring repercussions if the customer talks to a neighbor or friend who owns product B—the owner of product B may be a present or future customer.

Customer Information of Considerable Value. Conversation with the customer regarding the nature of the trouble is very helpful and often essential. At the time of the customer's request for service it is often possible to obtain much information which will be of later value. The type of trouble involved, whether or not such trouble exists constantly or intermittently, whether or not it occurs on all records and all sizes of records, and whether or not the difficulty occurs only with the phonograph as opposed to the radio operation—all will assist the serviceman in making an intelligent approach.

If the trouble occurs in the phonograph only and is concerned with poor tone or volume, it is quite probable that the needle or the cartridge is at fault. If the changer-operating difficulty occurs with only a few records, it is possible that they have badly worn center holes, are of nonstandard dimensions, or lack a changing groove. Discussion of the problems with the customer both before leaving the shop and after arriving at the home can therefore be of considerable value to the serviceman.

Customer Operation of Record Changer. When making a call to service an unfamiliar record player, it is often advisable to have the customer start the operation. This enables the serviceman to get his bearings and saves embarrassment. Moreover, it is possible that the customer is operating the record player in an improper manner, which will become apparent by his actions.

Confident Appearance. At all times the serviceman should exhibit an air of confidence. If a questionable point occurs, he may stall for time by engaging the customer in conversation or by operating the record changer in a manner which will not damage the unit. This enables the serviceman to view the situation and to think out the problem with which he is faced without letting the customer become aware of the complications involved.

Personal Appearance. The serviceman should be presentable at all times. A neat appearance breeds neat work, which is appreciated by both customers and fellow workers. Much effort has been extended to raise the electronic serviceman to a professional status. To succeed, the serviceman must play the part.

Summary. It is not intended that this short discussion give all the details of conduct pertaining to service calls. The basic considerations have been pointed out, including the more frequent problems confronted. The prime principle is to be aware of the customer and to give him 100 per cent consideration. There is no substitute for being observant and thoughtful.

QUESTIONS

1. Are record players as troublesome as radio or television sets?
2. What is one of the simplest of servicing jobs that will help virtually every record changer in use?
3. Is the wire recorder more popular than the tape recorder?
4. What considerations should you give to a customer's property?
5. Why should you be cautious in endorsing products?
6. What personal traits should you emphasize?

2

How a Record Changer Works

Mechanical Record Player. The mechanical phonograph was the forerunner of our modern record players and changers. In this unit everything was accomplished mechanically from the spinning of the record to the reproduction of the sound.

When recording, the desired sounds were collected by means of a horn, as in Fig. 1, and guided to a thin diaphragm, which was free to vibrate when the sound waves reached it. By use of a lever a pointed stylus was connected to the center of the diaphragm and thereby caused to vibrate.

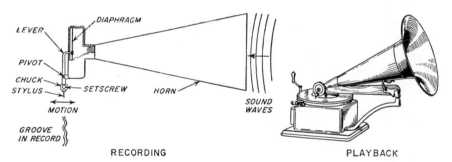

RECORDING   PLAYBACK

Fig. 1. Early method of recording and reproducing sound. Grooves are cut in recording by a stylus with a sharp cutting edge. Records are played back with a needle, which has a rounded point

The stylus rested lightly upon a disc or record coated with wax on the upper surface. This record was rotated on a turntable at a predetermined speed while the needle was moved across the disc surface. Thus the stylus cut a spiral groove in the wax coating. As the sounds caused vibration of the stylus, the spiral groove became wavy. These waves were proportional in both amplitude and frequency to the original sound waves.

To reproduce the recorded sounds, the process merely had to be reversed. The turntable and record were rotated at the original speed by means of a spring motor. A rounded-edge needle was allowed to follow the wavy groove thus causing the diaphragm to vibrate. This vibration, in turn, moved the surrounding air, producing sounds that were concentrated by a megaphone-like horn or sound box and then passed on to the listener.

The soft wax-coated disc could not withstand very many playings because the friction of the needle as it followed the groove soon caused the record waves to disappear. Consequently, the original wax disc was used only as a mold or pattern from which other records were made, of harder, longer-lasting materials. The main disadvantages of the mechanical system, however, were the limitations in volume and sound fidelity.

Modern Mechanical Record Player. The old phonographs are rarely in use today, and it is unlikely that you would be called upon to repair one. However, their exact counterparts, the portable phonographs, which are generally packaged in luggage-type cases, are in widespread use in the home, at beaches, vacation spots, or places where electric current is not available.

Operating the Mechanical Record Player. The following procedure is generally used in operating a mechanical, or portable, phonograph. The crank is removed from its storage hole or clamp, and inserted in the crank hole on the side of the case. Before the machine can be wound, the brake lever must be placed in the STOP position so that its leather shoe is in contact with the inside surface of the rim of the turntable. This stops the movement of the turntable. The motor spring is then wound until the crank stops. The spring should not be forced beyond this point because any further strain is apt to break it or one of its associated parts.

A needle must be placed in the chuck of the sound box and the thumb screw tightened to hold it secure. After a record is placed on the turntable, the brake lever should be moved to the START position. This allows the motor to rotate since the shoe no longer contacts the turntable rim. In a few seconds the motor will attain its proper speed. The sound-box head may then be placed gently on the record so that the needle contacts the record in the space between its outer edge and the first grooves. At this point the starting groove engages with the needle and carries it forward to the playing grooves.

Control of Turntable Speed. Mechanical record players have a speed scale and pointer. On one side of the center line the speed-indicating scale is marked FAST, the other side is marked SLOW. Under normal conditions the pointer is set at the center line of the scale, which provides the correct speed of the record.

In order to check the speed of the turntable, a stroboscope disc can be used and the speed pointer adjusted accordingly. The stroboscope disc will be discussed in detail later. An alternative is to adjust the speed to produce the most pleasing sound.

When the record has been played, the brake lever should be moved to the STOP position. The sound box should then be removed from the record and placed on its rest. In some machines an automatic device is used which throws the brake to the STOP position at the conclusion of the record.

In some of the old record players an electric motor was substituted for a spring motor. In this case the stopping and starting of the motor was done with an electric on-off switch. Automatic stop switches were sometimes used, eliminating the necessity of turning off the motor.

Electronic Record Players. The mechanical phonograph has been outmoded by the modern electronic record player. About the only similarity between the two devices lies in the physical character of the record. The recording process utilizes a microphone which converts the desired sounds into electrical energy which then is amplified by vacuum tubes. Next, the resulting signals are fed to a recording head which converts them into mechanical vibrations. These vibrations, through the medium of a recording stylus, produce the wavy groove on the surface of the rotating disc.

To reproduce the original sounds, the record is rotated again at its original speed, and a needle following the wavy groove produces mechanical vibrations, which are converted into electrical energy by a pickup mechanism. The resulting electrical energy may then be amplified by vacuum tubes to any desired level, and finally reconverted to sound by a loudspeaker. A volume control is provided in the audio amplifier to control the level of the sound reproduced by the loudspeaker. In most cases the power required for turning the record is supplied by an electric motor. Since synchronous a-c motors are used in these players, speed regulators are generally unnecessary.

Operation of Modern Record Players. The operation of a modern record player is quite simple. The motor must be turned on by means of a switch, a record placed on the turntable, and the pickup arm lifted from its rest position and gently lowered into the playing grooves of the record. The volume control of the record player, amplifier, or radio, depending on which is used, will have to be regulated to give the desired amount of sound. At the conclusion of the record, if there is no automatic stopping device, the motor must be turned off. The pickup then should be removed from the record and placed on its rest.

This same system is used when the radio and record player are combined into one unit, called a radio-phonograph combination. Some of these record players are put into portable cases and look very much like the mechanical portable except that they are all electric, incorporating their own amplifiers and speakers in the design. Others, table-model phonographs, are installed in wooden cabinets. Whatever the case may be, the operation of all these units is similar.

Wireless Record Players. Several manufacturers designed their record players so that they could be played through a radio with no connection to it. This was accomplished by means of an oscillator that was built into the record player. This oscillator sent out a signal capable of being picked up by the tuning portion of a radio in the same manner as this tuning portion picks up a signal broadcast by a radio station.

Wireless record players were used mostly when the record player was placed at a distance from the radio. This idea was once very popular and still is used sometimes, even though a record player attached directly to an amplifier is much better. Like radio signals, signals from the oscillator are subject to man-made and atmospheric disturbances, and the quality of tone through a direct hookup is much better.

The operation of wireless equipment is the same as previously described except that the radio must be tuned to the proper dial setting to receive the oscillator signal.

Automatic Record Changers. The desire to have continuous music for a long period of time without constantly operating the record player resulted in the development of the automatic record changer. Once placed in operation, several records are played in succession, requiring no further attention until the last one is finished. Selection of the records and proper operation of the pickup arm are accomplished automatically.

Because of the popularity of these record changers many electric portables, many table-model phonographs, and almost all radio combinations use them. The automatic changers operate in various ways, but they all accomplish the same job regardless of the manner in which it is done.

Types of Records. The early record changers were designed for use with standard or 78-rpm (revolutions per minute) records only. At that time 33⅓-rpm records were used solely for motion picture and transcription purposes. Only recently did the 33⅓-rpm microgroove, or long-playing (LP), record become available for domestic use. The 45-rpm record followed shortly thereafter. As a result record changers that are designed for 78 rpm only, for 78 rpm and 33⅓ rpm, and for all three speeds are now in use. The single-speed 45-rpm changer is also used extensively as a separate plug-in unit because of its significant differences and low cost. Other speed combinations are used in small quantities, also.

Operation of Record Changers. A general over-all procedure for the operation of record changers will follow. Because of the many different methods used by the various manufacturers to do the same job, detailed procedures will be indicated in later chapters.

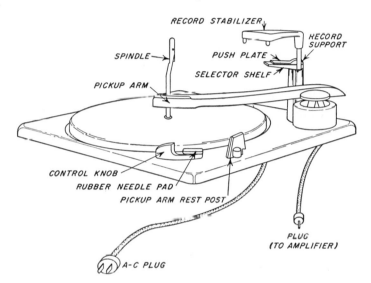

Fig. 2. One style of automatic record changer, showing those points which are important to operation

Before an automatic changer is operated, the buttons, levers, and adjustments should be studied thoroughly. This saves damaging of records, needle, pickup cartridge, or other parts of the mechanism. One general style of record changer is shown in Fig. 2.

The usual record changer can be operated in either the manual or automatic method. When the control knob is turned to MANUAL, or M, the machine will operate as an ordinary electric record player. The operating procedure is then as previously described.

Automatic Record-changer Operation. When the control is moved to AUTOMATIC, or A, the machine operates as an automatic record changer. Assume that an automatic record changer is being set up to play a stack of

10-inch records. The record support, or supports, must be placed in the 10-inch position and the stack of records put in place over the spindle. Any stabilizer arm or record weight should then be placed on the top of the stack. If there are any levers that can be placed in a position marked 10, or if there are any buttons marked 10, they should be moved into position. This will generally affect the record supports.

When playing standard 78-rpm records, make certain that the cartridge or needle is set in the STANDARD or 78 position. This adjustment will be located on the pickup arm, near the needle. The motor drive mechanism should also be set in the 78 position. This is located on the base of the changer. The motor may then be started, and the lever or button marked REJECT operated. The mechanism now will start through its automatic cycle.

Some changers will turn themselves off and move the pickup arm to its rest position when the final record has been played. In this case, it is only necessary that the record supports be moved out of the way and the records taken off the turntable.

On record players which keep repeating the last record instead of stopping automatically, the pickup arm should be lifted up from the surface of the record when it starts replaying and then placed in its rest position. The motor switch must then be shut off, the record supports moved out of the way, and the stack of records removed from the turntable.

A similar procedure is followed for playing a stack of 12-inch 78-rpm records except that the supports, levers, and buttons must be placed in the 12 position.

Likewise, other record speeds require adjustment of the pickup or of the needle and drive mechanism to the 33⅓ or 45 position as required. The LP or 33⅓–45 position of the pickup is used for both speeds since the same needle is used for both. In some cases the same pickup or needle position may be used for all records owing to the use of a compromise needle. In some cases it is necessary to insert a special plug-in spindle before playing 7-inch 45-rpm records.

If a changer is made for one speed and one record size, it is obviously unnecessary to make the preliminary adjustments.

Removing Pickup from Record. Many record changers are designed to be childproof. Since not all are designed this way, it is necessary to use caution in handling the pickup arm. When the pickup arm is removed from the record, if it has gone more than one-third of the way across the record, the REJECT button should first be pushed. Then the mechanism should be allowed to swing the pickup arm up and off the record and back down again into the starting groove, before it is manually removed. Thus the whole cycle has been completed and the pickup arm is free, with no danger of initiating the change cycle.

The motor switch should never be turned off while the pickup arm is still going through a part of the change cycle.

Ten- and twelve-inch records should never be placed on the record support arms to be played at the same time unless it is definitely known that the machine is an intermix record changer. An intermix record changer is designed to play both 10- and 12-inch records intermixed in a stack. It can be recognized by the absence of controls marked 10 and 12.

Use of Reject Control. The purpose of the REJECT control is to actuate cycling of the record changer. This causes the bottom record of the stack to drop in position for playing, and then moves the pickup arm into the starting groove of the record. If the REJECT button is pushed while a record is being played, the pickup arm is automatically raised and moved out of the way by the mechanism before the next record is dropped.

Intermix Record Changer. In the case of the intermix record changer the previously described precautions on setting the record supports may be neglected. Ten- and twelve-inch records may be stacked at random and placed on the record supports.

Records. The purpose of a record is to store sounds. The record changer and the associated amplifier and speaker equipment provide a means of taking the recorded information from the record and converting it back into audible sounds.

Recordings are generally made on both sides of a record. Where the record contains popular songs or music, a different selection is recorded on each side of the record. With microgroove recordings one side of the record may contain several musical selections. With these records the sequence in which the music is played is generally of little consequence.

With classical music or even the semiclassical types such as operettas the musical score is of rather long duration. Here it is not usually possible to get the entire selection on a single side of a record. With the standard 78-rpm records it is then generally necessary to use several records to present the complete group or sequence of music. Such records are assembled into albums for sale. Albums consist of two to possibly eight records recorded on both sides. Even with long-playing 33⅓-rpm records it is sometimes necessary to use two or more records for a classical selection.

Records for Manual Operation. If the records are played manually, it is convenient to start the musical sequence on one side of one record and to continue it on the other side so that the operator need only turn the record over to continue the sequence. The third portion is contained on another record and the fourth portion on its reverse side.

Records for Automatic Operation. In the usual record changer only one side of the record is played. Upon completion, another record drops onto the turntable and one side of it is played. As a result, it is necessary that the first part of the musical sequence be placed on one record and the second part on another record. The third part would likewise be placed on a third record.

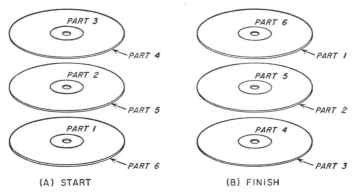

(A) START   (B) FINISH

Fig. 3. The recording sequence of a three-record album for use with an automatic record changer. When the first three parts have been played, the stack must be turned over to play the other three parts

The initial arrangement of a three-record album is illustrated by Fig. 3A. For convenience it is desirable that the stack of records can be removed intact and merely turned over on the record changer, as in Fig. 3B, to complete the playing of a long musical composition. This arrangement of records is said to be made for the drop-type record changer. Since virtually all record changers and record albums currently being made are of this type, it is generally not necessary to specify. On the other hand, it is possible that a record dealer may overlook this fact and sell your customer an album of older records made for manually operated phonographs. Here all you can do is explain why record albums have been made two ways and suggest that the customer try to exchange his album for the other type.

Functions Recorded on a Disc. In addition to the grooves which contain the music, a record generally has other desirable features which are necessary in the operation of a record changer.

Except for a few very old 78-rpm records, practically all records have a lead-in groove at the outer edge of the record. This groove starts at the extreme outer edge and leads in to the point where the reproduction portion begins. This portion of the record is a band approximately $\frac{3}{16}$ inch wide next to the edge of the record. It provides a convenient area in which the operator may set the needle down on the record. By placing the needle down in this area, the operator is assured that the very first notes of the recorded portion will be played. This portion is known as the starting groove.

The starting groove moves inwardly in a spiral manner much more rapidly than do the recorded grooves of the reproduction portion. This limits the time that the operator is required to wait before the record begins. Modern records designed for use with automatic record changers require this starting groove since, due to mechanical tolerances, the set-down or indexing mechanism does not drop the pickup arm at absolutely the same place each time the record changer operates. The set-down point is bound to vary slightly due to mechanical tolerances in the manufacturing process.

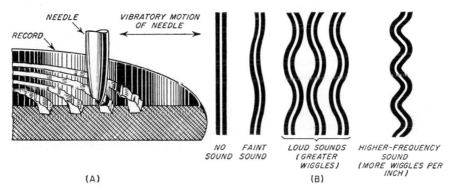

Fig. 4. An enlarged view of a record and needle illustrates the nature of the sound track. (A) Wiggles in groove contain the sound. (B) The number of wiggles determines the frequency, and the amount of wiggle determines the volume

Recorded Sounds. The reproduction portion of a record occupies the prime area since this is the purpose of the disc. It contains a continuous series of grooves in the otherwise smooth disc. This is illustrated in Fig. 4. With modern records the depth of the groove is held constant but it waves from side to side as the pitch of the music changes. The number of times it moves from side to side in each second of time determines the frequency or tone of the reproduction. The relative loudness is determined by the amount of lateral variation of the groove. Actually a single tone is only held for a very small portion of a second. In addition, several tones may be superimposed on one another since they can occur simultaneously. As a result, the variations from side to side are constantly changing.

The recorded portion of the record varies in width from about 1 inch to 3½ inches on the commercially available records. The amount of space allotted to reproduction is dependent upon the size of the record, the width of the groove, and the desired quality of the sound. The term playing grooves will be used to designate this area.

Finishing Groove. At the end of the reproduction portion is a finishing groove. Since the playing of the record started at the outer edge, this finishing groove is on the inside. This groove has a fast-leading spiral in much the same manner as the starting groove. With the manual record used in earlier times, this groove led rapidly inward for about ³⁄₁₆ to ½ inch and then stopped in a continuous circle so that the needle stayed in the same groove until the pickup arm was lifted from the record.

The present-day record also makes use of the finishing groove. In this case, however, not only does the groove lead in at a rapid speed, but when it reaches its maximum excursion (smallest diameter), it then moves outward to the start of the finishing groove. A groove with a continuous spiral in and out results. This finishing groove is used in conjunction with the pickup arm to operate the mechanism which causes the record changer to trip and change records.

Characteristics of the Grooves. Early records had grooves that varied up and down. As the pitch at any instant changed, the groove changed in depth. As a result of the appearance of this up and down cut in the record, the groove was often called a hill and dale type of recording. Because of commercial disadvantages of this vertical type of groove the lateral or sideways variation came into being and is now used predominantly. The vertical cut is today used in some professional recording equipment, chiefly for recorded radio programs. Commercial recordings all utilize the lateral type of groove.

The number of grooves per inch varies depending upon the type of record and the playing time for the selection. In order to standardize on records, the area used for the reproduction portion has been defined. For flexibility there may be more than one standard for a record size. Seven-inch 45-rpm records, for example, are made in two ways: one with about ⅞ inch recorded portion and the other (extended play) about 1³⁄₁₆ inches.

Within the limits of any one standard size, a relatively long reproduction requires a large number of grooves, whereas a short recording requires a relatively small number of grooves. The needle radius and therefore the shape of the groove is determined by industry-wide standards. Also the relative loudness of the record is determined by the amplitude or amount of lateral variation in the groove. Since the maximum number of grooves in a given space is determined by the width of the groove and the lateral variation, a limit is set as to the maximum number of grooves which can be recorded.

The number of grooves used per inch is known as the pitch. For the standard 78-rpm record the cutting pitch varies from approximately 88 grooves per inch to 112 grooves per inch. In order to present more playing time in a given recorded area, recordings are made at slower speeds and with smaller groove sizes. These are often known as the long-playing or microgroove type of record. The 45-rpm record is made only in the 7-inch size and has from about 120 to 275 grooves per inch. The 33⅓-rpm records use from about 120 to 300 grooves per inch. It is interesting to note that at least one recording group uses a variable number of grooves so that where the volume is low a greater number of grooves per inch are used. When the recorded volume and therefore the amplitude of the lateral cut increases, the number of grooves is decreased. This allows a greater over-all number of grooves to be cut in the reproduction portion of the record.

Characteristics of Recorded Sounds. The sounds that can be heard and that are normally recorded can range from a low of around 30 cycles to a high of around 15,000 cycles. Only a few special high-fidelity records cover this entire range, however.

Because of the characteristics of the human ear, not all sound frequencies are of equal effect. Hearing varies from individual to individual, and many older people cannot even hear frequencies above 10,000 cycles. Furthermore, there are technical factors that actually make it desirable to use a limited frequency range on the average commercial record and in record-playing equipment. One important factor is the inherent noise produced by the needle traversing the surface of the record. This noise occurs at audible frequencies above 10,000 cycles per second. Another is the high cost of loudspeakers that are capable of reproducing extremely low and extremely high frequencies.

Taking into consideration the human limitations, the drawbacks of surface noise, the limitations of the loudspeaking device, and the cost of constructing equipment capable of reproducing the upper and lower frequency extremes, it is common practice to restrict the range of reproduction.

Various recording standards have been devised, and record manufacturers use several of these. Basically, two characteristics are available for use in recording; constant amplitude and constant velocity. These are shown in Fig. 5. With a constant input, constant-amplitude recording gives an equal lateral excursion for all frequencies. Constant-velocity recording moves the stylus the same lineal distance for all frequencies. This gives a lateral amplitude which changes with the frequency; the higher the frequency, the smaller the amplitude.

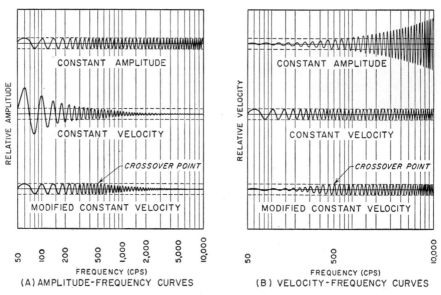

Fig. 5. Illustration of recording characteristics. Comparison of A and B shows difference in appearance when plotted for relative amplitude and relative velocity

To have constant amplitude, the needle must travel further at high frequencies than at low frequencies. This requires additional power at the higher frequencies. Constant velocity, on the other hand, limits the number of grooves per inch because the lateral amplitude is large for the low frequencies.

In general, records are made with constant-amplitude recording for the low frequencies. At some frequency, called the crossover point, this is changed to constant velocity.

Noise is a high-frequency phenomenon. Since it is desirable to keep it to a minimum in relation to the wanted high-frequency audio, the latter is increased in level when recording. Then when the record is played back, the high frequencies can be reduced in level and the noise will be subdued. This increase in level is usually something between constant amplitude and constant velocity.

The various standards are designed so that it is relatively easy to compensate for such variations by means of special tone controls. The standards differ in the amount of such compensation. In Fig. 6 the recording characteristic used by RCA for Victor records is compared to the characteristic used by the Columbia Broadcasting System for their Columbia records.

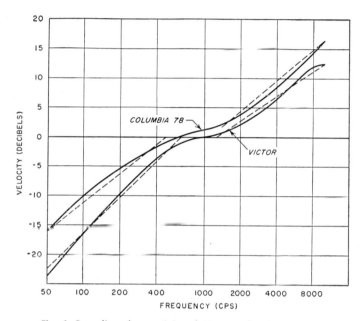

Fig. 6. Recording characteristics of Victor and Columbia discs

To understand these curves, it is necessary to define the scales used. Loudness or signal level is described by the term decibel which is the ratio of one level to another. The abbreviation db is usually used for decibel. In amplifiers it is customary to work with either power levels or voltage levels. A ratio of one is used as reference and is equal to zero db.

A voltage ratio of two to one is equal to 6 db. A voltage ratio of ten to one is equal to 20 db. Other values are indicated in Table 1. Decibels of power ratios are similarly indicated. The other scale of the curves is in frequency. However, it is customary to speak of decibels change per octave, so it is necessary to define an octave. An octave is a frequency ratio of two to one.

It will be noted that the Victor records have a high-frequency rise of approximately 4 db per octave above about 1,000 cycles per second (cps). The Columbia records have a rising compensation of about 5 db per octave over this range. Both characteristics tend to level off somewhat in the neighborhood of 600 to 1,000 cycles per second. Below this the Victor characteristics drop off at about 6 db per octave, while the Columbia records drop off at about 5 db per octave.

Table 1. Power and Voltage Ratios Expressed in Db

Power Ratio P_1/P_2	Voltage Ratio E_1/E_2	Decibels (db)
1	1	0
1.26	1.12	1
1.58	1.26	2
1.99 (roughly 2)	1.41	3
2.51	1.58	4
3.16	1.78	5
3.98 (roughly 4)	1.99 (roughly 2)	6
5.01	2.24	7
6.31	2.51	8
7.94	2.82	9
10.00	3.16	10
12.6	3.55	11
15.8	3.98	12
19.9	4.47	13
25.1	5.01	14
31.6	5.62	15
39.8	6.31	16
50.1	7.08	17
63.1	7.94	18
79.4	8.91	19
100.0	10.00	20

Restoration of the audio response to its original form is done in the amplifier. This is called compensation and is provided in the form of bass or treble boost. Where the amplifier is a standard unit, a preamplifier is often used to compensate for the cartridge and record characteristics. Some expensive amplifiers have a switch which allows selection of the compensation so as to match the particular record being played. Most amplifiers, however, have only a single compensation circuit which is a compromise between that required for the various recording standards. Most listeners will not be able to discern the difference. However, if the listener is a high-fidelity enthusiast or complains of the difference between different make records, this knowledge becomes of importance.

Needle Pressure and Shape. The information which is recorded in a disc is picked up by means of a needle which rides in the groove. The manner in which the needle fits into the groove is important since if it fits incorrectly or exerts too much pressure, it will cause undue wear either to the record or to the needle. On the other hand, insufficient pressure will result in weak volume and possibly a tendency for the needle to skip grooves or slide across the record.

The pressure of the standard 78-rpm needle should generally be between ¾ and 1¼ ounces. The pressure of the needle for microgroove recordings should be between 5 and 7 grams.

The pressure which the needle exerts is due primarily to the weight of the pickup-arm assembly. As a result, it is necessary to balance this in a rather delicate manner. Although the needle pressure in itself is not very great, the force per square inch of needle surface is rather tremendous because it makes contact with the record at only two points. The included angle of the needle is approximately 45 degrees. The needle rides in a groove which has an included angle of almost 87 degrees.

Pickup, Amplifier, and Speaker. The needle serves as a means of transmitting the groove variations to the pickup. The pickup is an electro-mechanical cartridge which converts the mechanical variations to electrical variations. An exact transfer is desired in order to faithfully reproduce the recorded portion, but this is not always possible and variations may exist.

The electrical variations produced by the cartridge are an audio signal of very low intensity and cannot drive a loudspeaker. An amplifier is therefore required to build up the strength of the audio signal. The loudspeaker is another electro-mechanical device used to convert electrical energy to mechanical energy. The mechanical motion of the loudspeaker cone pushes the air so as to produce audible sound.

In the process of recording it is not possible to handle the full range of volume actually used by a large orchestra. At very low volume, noises from the record surface and within the amplifier may mask the desired sound. If the maximum volume is recorded, the spacing between record grooves must be large or the grooves will break through to each other. For these reasons the recording is restricted or compressed at the two extremes of volume. Quality amplifiers, as used in listening to operatic recordings, sometimes include an expander circuit to restore the volume range to the original relationship.

QUESTIONS

1. How do you operate a mechanical record player?
2. How do you operate an automatic record changer?
3. What is the proper way to remove a pickup arm from the record?
4. Name two types of record albums.
5. What determines the tone of a record?
6. What determines the loudness of a record?
7. Name the functions of various areas of a record.
8. Do modern records have grooves that vary sideways or up and down?
9. What is the pitch of a record?
10. How high and how low do records go in frequency?
11. What is the crossover point?
12. In what manner do the recording characteristics of the various record manufacturers vary?
13. Why is it important that the needle properly fit the record groove?
14. How is the output of the pickup cartridge converted to sound?

3

Getting Acquainted with Record-changer Actions

Introduction. In order to provide continuous reproduction without interrupting the listener, an automatic method of changing records is desired. To accomplish this, methods must be used to carry out the motions that a person would use when changing records. When one record is completed, the pickup arm must be removed from the record, another record must be placed on the turntable, and the pickup arm must be set down at the beginning of the next record.

Turntable Rotation. Whether the record player is of the manual type or of the automatic-changing type, it is necessary to have a means of rotating the turntable. The turntable is driven by means of a motor and some sort of drive mechanism, and turns in a clockwise direction.

The motor may be a spring-driven type necessitating manual windup, or an electrical type. The spring-driven motor is common in older machines and in inexpensive or portable manual players. Since the spring-driven motor must be wound up frequently, it is not suitable for use in the automatic changer.

The drive mechanism between the motor and the turntable may be one of several varieties. The most obvious method of driving the turntable is direct drive with a slow-speed motor. In this method the motor shaft is connected directly to the turntable. Since the turntable has a large mass (or weight), a powerful motor is required.

A more common method is the rim-drive system. Here the motor has a small wheel connected to its shaft. This wheel pushes against the rim of the turntable as shown in Fig. 1. When the motor and drive wheel turn, the turntable is caused to rotate. This also gives speed reduction, permitting use of smaller and less expensive high-speed motors.

Other methods are variations of this, using gears or belt drive instead of friction or direct coupling. For example, a rim-drive machine may operate by connecting the motor shaft and the turntable drive wheel with a small belt, as shown in Fig. 2.

Operation of the motor is controlled by means of a switch. If the motor is electrical, an on-off switch is used to complete or interrupt the circuit. If the motor is spring-driven, it can be stopped by means of a heavily loaded friction unit holding the turntable from rotating, in much the same manner as a person might stop it by holding his hand against it. Where a constant-speed arrangement is not used, a speed adjustment is usually provided.

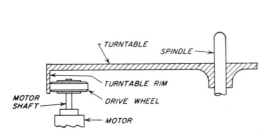

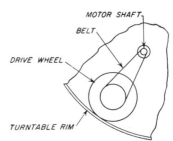

Fig. 1. Rim-drive principle of rotating the turntable

Fig. 2. Belt connection between wheels in the turntable drive mechanism

Initial Record-changing Cycle. When a stack of records is put on a record changer and the machine is started, mechanical action must cause the pickup arm to swing clear of the turntable prior to dropping the first record. The pickup arm then must be caused to set down at the beginning of the record.

Normal Changing Cycle. Upon completion of a record the changing mechanism must be actuated so as to start operation. This action is called trip. The remainder of the cycle must then be carried out as usual with the pickup arm lifting and moving to the side, the next record dropping, and the pickup arm then indexing itself at the beginning of the record. The turntable keeps rotating during all of this so the cycle does not affect it. In fact, usually the rotation of the turntable is an integral part of the change cycle.

Various methods are used by the many record-changer manufacturers to accomplish the actions described above. This also applies to reject action, automatic shutoff, and other features of modern record changers.

Basic Mechanical Movements. The various actions of a record changer are nearly always mechanical in nature. A number of different types of mechanical movements are utilized in conjunction with one another to obtain the results desired. Recognition of these movements and an understanding of how they work makes it possible to do repair work without the continual need of manufacturer's information.

The various mechanical movements can be broken down into a few basic types. This is true not only of record changers, but of mechanics in general. The movements used in record changers are: the lever, link, wheel and axle, gear, pulley, cam, clutch, ratchet, roller, spring, and screw. In addition, the effects of friction and gravity will also be discussed.

In mechanics there are three basic desires: (1) translating motion from one type to another, (2) changing direction of motion, and (3) obtaining a mechanical advantage. Although the first two are self-explanatory, it is desirable to discuss the third, namely, mechanical advantage.

Mechanical Advantage. Mechanical advantage is a term applied to the act of making work easier. For example, a crowbar provides an advantage in removing a nail from a piece of wood. A lever is helpful in budging a heavy object. A pulley is of advantage in raising or pulling a heavy object. Mechanical advantage is the ratio of the weight of the object moved to the force required to move it.

Lever. A lever is a long object which is useful in moving a desired piece. An example is shown in Fig. 3. The point at which the lever pivots is called the fulcrum. In practice the fulcrum may be located anywhere along the length of the lever arm.

In Fig. 3A the fulcrum is located at the center. If we assume that the lever is free to move, then a force exerted on the left-hand end in a downward direction will result in the right-hand end moving in an upward direction. If the fulcrum is in the exact center, the distance that the two ends move will be the same. If a 50-pound weight is placed on the right extremity and this end is resting on the ground, a force of over 50 pounds would be required at the other end to make the lever arm move.

Suppose the fulcrum is moved a little further toward the right-hand edge, as in Fig. 3B. The distance on the left-hand side of the fulcrum is now larger than that on the right-hand side. As a result, the left-hand edge must now move a further distance to obtain the same movement of the right-hand side as was obtained in the previous example. Experience has shown that if the lever has any appreciable weight, the left-hand side will swing down. This is due to the fact that the weight on the left side is greater than that on the right. Extending this same principle, if a 50-pound weight were now placed on the right-hand side, it would take less effort on the left-hand end to move it.

The amount of effort needed to move one end of a lever is called the moment. To figure the value of the moment, just multiply the force in pounds by the distance in feet from the fulcrum to the point at which the force is exerted.

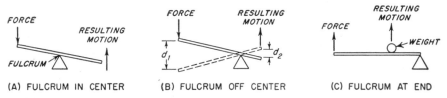

(A) FULCRUM IN CENTER   (B) FULCRUM OFF CENTER   (C) FULCRUM AT END

Fig. 3. A lever is one of the simplest of mechanical actions

If the levers shown in the previous figure are to remain at equilibrium (or stand still), the moments must be equal. Thus, in the first example the force on the left-hand side times the distance from it to the center must equal the weight on the right-hand side times the distance from it to the center. Since the fulcrum in Fig. 3A is at the middle, the force must equal the weight.

Suppose that in Fig. 3B the distance on the left of the fulcrum is 3 feet and the distance on the right of the fulcrum is 1 foot. If the weight on the right-hand end is 150 pounds, the moment is 150×1. The force required on the left end to obtain equilibrium would then be 50 pounds since $50 \times 3 = 150 \times 1$.

The mechanical advantage of the lever is the weight divided by the force. In the first example, then, the mechanical advantage is $50 \div 50$, or 1. In the second example, the mechanical advantage is $150 \div 50 = 3$. The mechanical advantage may also be described by the distance which the force moves divided by the distance which the weight moves.

In similar fashion, the fulcrum can be located at the end, as shown in Fig. 3C. The same formulas for moment and mechanical advantage apply. The only difference is that now both the force and the weight move in the same direction. To clarify this, consider a problem where the distance from the fulcrum to the weight is 1 foot. If the weight is 150 pounds, its moment is $150 \times 1 = 150$. The moment for the force end must also be 150. For force $\times 3$ to equal 150, the force must be 50 pounds.

Use of Lever. The lever arm is used frequently in record changers. One use is to lift the pickup arm during the changing cycle. Figure 4 shows the manner in which it is done. The record arm is pivoted near the left end and this point is considered the fulcrum. A rod extends up through the base of the record changer a short distance from the pivot or fulcrum. A small upward movement of this rod results in a rather large movement of the arm at the end in which the pickup is located. This, then, is a use of the lever with the fulcrum at the end.

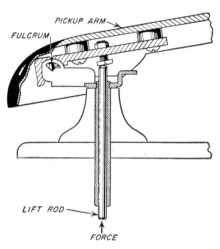

Fig. 4. Example of use of a lever with the fulcrum near the end. A relatively small movement of the lift rod will cause considerable movement at the right end where the pickup cartridge and needle are located

A use of the lever with the fulcrum at the center is shown in Fig. 5. In this instance the lever or rocker arm, as it is called, is not a straight piece but is bent. In order that the record may fall to the turntable during the changing cycle, it is desirable to have the upper right-hand end of the lever move a short distance to the left. Thus it pushes the record off the shelf of the spindle. This movement is accomplished by exerting a downward force at the left-hand end of the rocker arm, which causes the lever to rotate slightly counterclockwise about the fulcrum.

Link. A link is used to connect two lever arms and thus join or transmit their motion. Suppose that two lever arms on opposite sides of a record changer are to have identical actions. For this, two levers of equal length, with identical fulcrums, can be joined by a link, as shown in Fig. 6. If the lower end of lever arm *A* is moved to the right, the upper end will move to the left. Since the upper end is joined to the link and the link in turn joined to lever arm *B*, the link and the upper portion of lever arm *B* will also move to the left. The bottom of lever arm *B* will then move to the right in exactly the same manner as did the corresponding portion of lever arm *A*. Thus, the link has transmitted energy from *A* to *B*.

The link may be used with many other types of mechanical motion. It is useful in a two- or three-shelf changer. In these changers the records are supported by shelves on the tops of either two or three posts. In order that the record may drop, the shelves are rotated so they slide out from under the record. The motions of the shelves are tied together by means of one or more links as shown in Fig. 7.

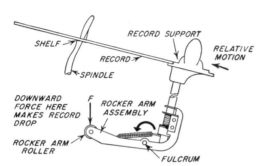

Fig. 5. Example of use of a lever with the fulcrum in the middle. The downward force on the left end of the rocker arm (lever) causes the assembly to rotate slightly counterclockwise around the fulcrum. This is used for record dropping

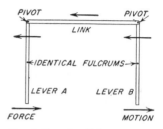

Fig. 6. Use of a link to connect two levers. Movement of the bottom of lever A to the right causes the top to move to the left. This pulls the link and the top of lever B to the left, and the bottom of lever B moves to the right

Wheel and Axle. When a wheel and axle are rigidly fastened together, one rotates when the other rotates. This is another basic mechanical motion. Thus, a downward force F applied to the left-hand edge of the wheel in Fig. 8A will cause an upward pull on the right-hand side of the axle.

If the distance through which the wheel moves is quite short, the wheel and axle combination can be compared to a lever. Their mutual center is the fulcrum. In Fig. 8B a lever has been superimposed on the wheel and axle to better show the comparison between them. The portion of the lever to the left of the fulcrum is equivalent to the radius R of the wheel, while the portion to the right of the fulcrum is equivalent to the radius r of the axle.

The lever arm is normally moved through only a limited distance, whereas the wheel and axle can be continuously rotated. For this reason the wheel and axle can be used in many places where it is not possible to use the lever.

Wheel and axle action as shown results in a change in direction. By applying the weight to the left-hand side of the axle, the directions of the

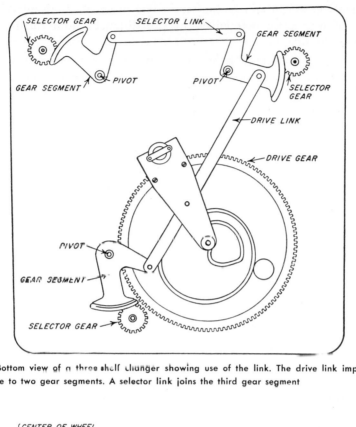

Fig. 7. Bottom view of a three shelf changer showing use of the link. The drive link imparts the cam force to two gear segments. A selector link joins the third gear segment

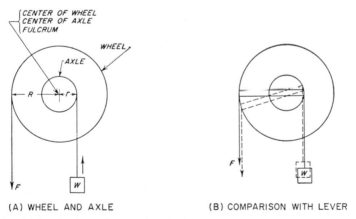

(A) WHEEL AND AXLE   (B) COMPARISON WITH LEVER

Fig. 8. The wheel and axle combination has the fulcrum at their mutual centers. It can be compared to the lever but has the advantage of complete rotation

force and the weight will be the same. The mechanical advantage of the system is once again determined by the distances from the force and weight to the fulcrum.

In many applications it is not necessary to have a complete wheel assembly because the movement is limited. For this reason, in order to save material and weight, only a portion of the assembly is used. This may be viewed in Fig. 9A. In Fig. 9B the wheel has gear teeth to assure a better grip with its mate. The principles apply equally well to both the wheel and the gear.

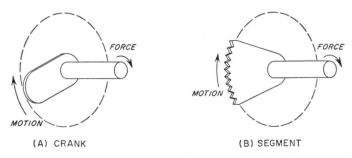

(A) CRANK   (B) SEGMENT

Fig. 9. Examples of the wheel and axle where only a portion of the wheel is required. Principle applies equally to a wheel with either friction contact or gear teeth

Where the portion of the wheel is very small, the combination is frequently termed a crank or crankshaft. Where the portion used is larger in size, it is often termed a segment.

The most common use of segments in record changers is in the mechanism which drops the records in a two-shelf or a three-shelf changer. One example was shown in Fig. 7 where a link and a segment of a wheel and axle are combined to actuate the record-dropping posts.

Gear. A gear assembly consists of two or more circular toothed wheels which mesh with each other. This is shown in Fig. 10. When gear 1 revolves in a clockwise direction, it makes gear 2 revolve in a counterclockwise direction. The teeth assure that there will be no slipping between the two. This is desired where the load on the gears is relatively large.

It is essential that the gear teeth be designed to fit together smoothly so as to avoid strain and chatter.

If the tooth of one gear does not fit between the teeth of the other properly, play will exist; this means that if one gear is held firmly, the other can be moved back and forth a small amount. This play or movement is termed backlash.

Frequently an assembly is made without the use of teeth. This might perhaps be termed a wheel assembly, but it is the same basic principle as the gear. In order to assure that no slipping occurs, this wheel assembly usually includes at least one rubber wheel so as to provide good friction. Rubber-wheel assemblies have the advantage of providing quiet movement since they do not transmit sounds as readily as the metal gears. For this reason most record changers have an idler wheel with a rubber tire.

In Fig. 10A two gears are shown, the larger of radius R and the smaller of radius r. When the larger wheel revolves through one complete revolution, the smaller wheel will rotate considerably more than one revolution. This

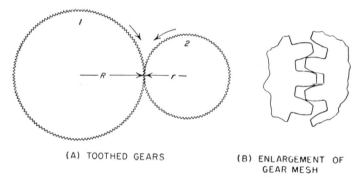

(A) TOOTHED GEARS   (B) ENLARGEMENT OF GEAR MESH

Fig. 10. When gear I moves clockwise, gear 2 will move counterclockwise. A perfect mesh between the teeth is required to prevent play called backlash

gives a mechanical advantage, just as with the wheel and axle. The speed of one wheel multiplied by its radius is equal to the speed of the other multiplied by its radius. If the larger wheel has twice the radius of the smaller wheel, one revolution of the large wheel will cause the small wheel to make two revolutions. Expressed another way, if the larger wheel has twice as many teeth as the small wheel, one revolution of the large wheel will cause the small wheel to make two revolutions. The gear or wheel which causes the rotation (or applies the force) is called the drive gear or drive wheel. The unit which receives the force is the driven element.

Idler Gears or Wheels. Any number of gears or wheels can be assembled to work together. Figure 11 shows an assembly of three wheels. If the drive wheel turns in a clockwise direction, the middle wheel will turn counterclockwise. This in turn will cause the third wheel to move in a clockwise direction. Since the wheel which performs the final movement is called the driven wheel or element, the middle wheel which is used to transmit the movement is termed the idler wheel.

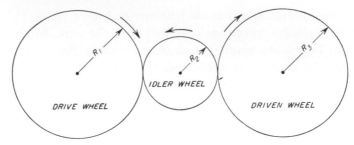

Fig. 11. An assembly of three wheels. The speed relations are the same as though the idler wheel were not present, but both the drive wheel and driven wheel rotate in the same direction

Here, if the drive wheel and the driven wheel are identical, they both rotate an equal number of times. The idler wheel merely acts like a belt between them. Idler wheels are widely used in rim-drive record changers, such as shown in Fig. 12.

The most common use of the gear in record changers is in the cycling or record-changing mechanism. The cycling cam generally has an outer toothed surface which meshes with teeth of a gear on the hub or shaft of the turntable.

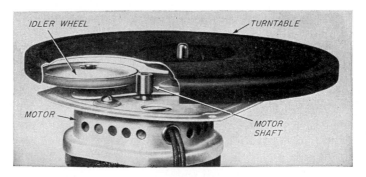

Fig. 12. The use of a wheel assembly in a record changer. The motor shaft drives the idler wheel, which in turn rotates the turntable. (General Industries photo)

Belt Drive. A belt or pulley drive consists of two wheels separated by a distance but connected by an endless belt which loops around them. This is shown in Fig. 13A. The principle is very similar to that of the gear or wheel assemblies. However, where the gear and wheel assemblies cause a change in direction of rotation, the belt drive results in both wheels turning in the same direction.

In most cases, the belt drive consists of two rubber wheels looped by a rubber belt resembling a rubber band. The rubber belt is made slightly smaller than the required size, and the stretch assures a good friction fit between the belt and the wheels.

In some cases the same technique is used with an endless chain or spring linking two gears. This is called a chain drive. The mechanical advantage and speed relationships for the belt and chain drives are identical to those for the gear and wheel assemblies. The uses for the belt and chain drive are much the same as those for the gear and wheel assemblies. Use of a belt or chain is convenient in some instances to provide linkage between the wheels or gears where they are relatively widely separated. Figure 13B shows a belt-drive arrangement for propelling the turntable.

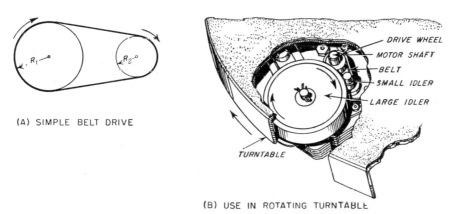

(A) SIMPLE BELT DRIVE

DRIVE WHEEL
MOTOR SHAFT
BELT
SMALL IDLER
LARGE IDLER

TURNTABLE

(B) USE IN ROTATING TURNTABLE

Fig. 13. Use of belt drive to rotate a turntable. The motor shaft acts as an axle fastened to a drive wheel, which in turn is connected to a small idler wheel by a belt. The small idler rotates the large idler which in turn rotates the turntable

Cam. A cam is defined as a rotating piece (as on a wheel) that is used for imparting a desired peculiar movement to a roller moving against its edge or to a pin free to move in a groove on its face. This movement may be more or less helter-skelter in several directions.

As an illustration of a peculiar movement desired in a record changer, consider the lateral (horizontal) motion of the pickup arm. It is desired that the pickup arm stay in a fixed lateral position while it lifts from the record, so its needle won't scratch across the record grooves. Once the pickup arm is free of the record, it must move laterally from the center of the record outward beyond the edge so that it is free of the dropping record. This arm must then move back just inside the edge of the record and remain motionless laterally there while it is lowered onto the playing surface. Motions such as this are produced by a cam.

Figure 14 illustrates a cam which is used in a record changer. The cam here serves to raise and lower the pickup arm. In Fig. 14A the pickup arm is floating free on the record because the lift rod is in the valley of the cam. As the cam rotates, it causes the lift rod to raise. The upper end of the lift rod is located to the left of the fulcrum. The pickup arm is then forced up and off the record as in Fig. 14B.

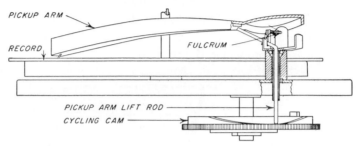

(A) PICKUP ARM IN NORMAL PLAYING POSITION

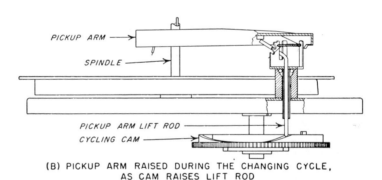

(B) PICKUP ARM RAISED DURING THE CHANGING CYCLE,
AS CAM RAISES LIFT ROD

Fig. 14. Use of a cam to raise and lower the pickup arm

If the rod were riding in the irregular groove of a cam like that shown in Fig. 15, the arm would also swing in and out at the right times to permit dropping the next record. Such actions will be discussed in more detail as the complete operations are described in other portions of the book.

Clutch. A clutch is a coupling for connecting two working parts, permitting them to be engaged or disengaged. In a record changer the only significant motion occurring while a record is playing is rotation of the turntable. The other important actions take place during the change cycle. When the record has finished playing, the turntable keeps on rotating and sets into motion various gears, levers, cams and other mechanical assemblies that serve to drop and play the next record. When the pickup arm is properly located on the next record, the motion of the changing mechanism must cease. Here then is a requirement for a clutch: to engage and disengage certain working parts.

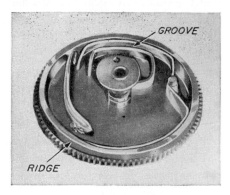

Fig. 15. The grooves of the cam provide the source of lateral motion for the pickup arm, and the beveled ridge imparts the vertical motion

In an automobile and other high-speed machines, a clutch might take quite a complicated form. In a record changer the relative speeds of the pertinent parts is not very great, and the clutch need not be so complicated.

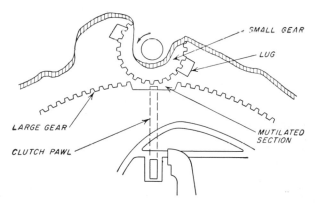

Fig. 16. A simple clutch arrangement between two gears. When the clutch pawl is up, as shown, it will be struck by one of the lugs on the small gear wheel. This causes the large gear to move sufficiently so that the gear teeth will engage

In Fig. 16 sections of two gears are illustrated. If it is desired that these gears be alternately engaged or disengaged, the arrangement may be as shown. A section of the larger gear is cut out so that the small gear may rotate independently. Under these circumstances the two gears are disengaged. Now if the large gear were moved slightly clockwise, the two gears would engage and the small drive gear would cause the other to rotate.

It will be noted that the small drive gear has two lugs which protrude at a level below the gear teeth. The large gear contains a clutch pawl also located below the level of the gear teeth. When the two gears are disengaged, this clutch pawl is pulled back toward the center of the large gear. If the clutch pawl is now pushed outward toward the small gear, one of the lugs on the small gear will strike it as the small gear rotates. This will impart a push to the large gear, allowing the teeth of the two gears to join and thus engage. When the large gear has gone through one complete revolution, the mutilated section will again appear in the position shown. If the clutch pawl has been drawn back toward the center and if the large gear has very little inertia so that its weight does not continue its rotation, the two gears will again be disengaged.

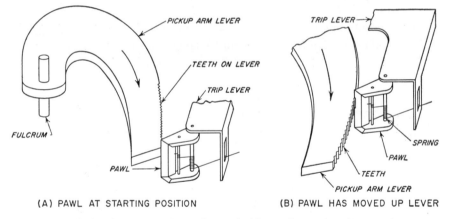

(A) PAWL AT STARTING POSITION   (B) PAWL HAS MOVED UP LEVER

Fig. 17. A ratchet combination consisting of a notched bar and a pawl working together to provide a trip mechanism

Ratchet. A ratchet consists of a notched bar with which a pawl works to prevent reversal of motion. In some cases the notched bar is actually made in the shape of a wheel. The purpose of such an arrangement is to allow motion to take place in one direction and prevent it from occurring in the opposite direction.

A ratchet combination used in one record changer is shown in Fig. 17. In Fig. 17A the combination is shown with the pawl engaging the pickup-arm lever teeth at the end. As the pickup-arm lever moves clockwise, additional teeth will move past the edge of the pawl. The pawl will engage each succeeding tooth, acting to prevent the pickup-arm lever from moving back to its original position. After a substantial motion of the lever has occurred, the relative position of the pawl and the pickup-arm lever is as shown in Fig. 17B. This illustration is taken from the actual operation of one type of trip mechanism used in record changers to start the record-changing cycle. The pickup-arm lever is connected to the pickup arm and the trip lever to the clutch. At the start of the record the relative positions are as in Fig. 17A. As the record plays, the pickup arm moves clockwise. The pickup-arm lever follows, assuming the position shown in Fig. 17B. When the needle is in the finishing groove, it first moves in toward the center of the record (clockwise) and then out again (counterclockwise). Since the pickup-arm lever follows this motion, it changes direction and moves counterclockwise also. The pawl engages a tooth and the trip lever is forced upward. This causes the clutch pawl to engage a lug, starting the change cycle.

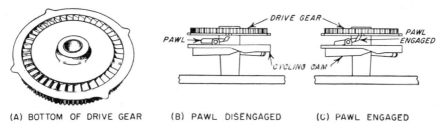

(A) BOTTOM OF DRIVE GEAR   (B) PAWL DISENGAGED   (C) PAWL ENGAGED

Fig. 18. Use of a ratchet combination to rotate the cam of a record changer. Note that the notches are cut into the flat side of the drive gear

Figure 18 illustrates another arrangement of a ratchet. Here the ratchet notches are not along the edge but are cut into the flat surface of a drive gear. The pawl in this instance is attached to the cycling cam in such a fashion that when the drive gear rotates in the desired direction, the pawl engages it, causing the cam to coincide with its rotation. This then is another illustration of the use of a ratchet. Its purpose in a record changer will be taken up later.

Friction. Friction is the resistance to relative motion between two bodies in contact. In some cases it is desirable to keep friction at a minimum. A wheel rotating on an axle may be an example of this. In other cases, such as when stopping an automobile on slippery pavement, it is desirable to obtain as much friction as is possible.

With such large use of moving parts, friction must usually be kept at a minimum in a record changer. This fact will be assumed in most instances and no particular mention will be made of it. There are cases, however, where high friction is taken advantage of in the operation of a record changer.

In general, direct metal-to-metal contact without oil or grease results in relatively high friction. If the friction is desired, these surfaces may be left relatively rough to take advantage of this fact. If friction is not desired, the surfaces are made smooth and lubricated.

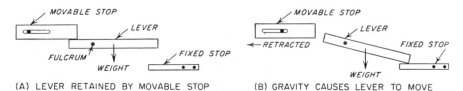

(A) LEVER RETAINED BY MOVABLE STOP   (B) GRAVITY CAUSES LEVER TO MOVE

Fig. 19. Use of gravity to obtain action. When the movable stop is retracted, the weight of the lever causes it to rotate until it strikes the fixed stop

Gravity. The effect of gravity is well known. Its action is utilized in a record changer to change the position of a particular part. The center of gravity of a piece is the point at which the weight of the piece seems to be concentrated. If the piece is pivoted at a distance from the center of gravity, it serves as a lever, with the pivot acting as the fulcrum and the weight acting at the center of gravity as force. If in Fig. 19 a piece is so used, it will remain in the position shown as long as it is held by the stop at the top. When the stop is removed, the force of gravity will cause the piece to swing about its fulcrum until it rests on the other stop. Actions similar to this are used frequently in a record changer.

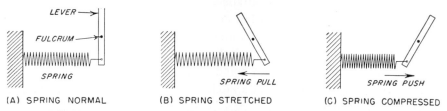

(A) SPRING NORMAL   (B) SPRING STRETCHED   (C) SPRING COMPRESSED

Fig. 20. A spring will try to return to its normal shape, thus exerting a push or a pull if stretched or compressed

Spring. A spring is a coil of wire that tends to oppose any change in its shape. Thus when stretched, it will exert a tendency to compress. If compressed, it will exert a force tending to expand. Figure 20A shows a spring in its ordinary form. If the bottom of the lever is moved to the right, the spring will pull against it, trying to return it to its original position as in Fig. 20B. On the other hand, if the lever is moved to the left as in Fig. 20C, the spring will tend to push the lever back to the original position.

The force exerted by a spring depends upon the wire size and characteristics, tightness of the coil, and other design factors. The spring is generally used to return a part to its original position after it has been moved through some action. In order to do this, it is often necessary to maintain a constant pull or push on the part, using a stop of some sort to hold it in its at-rest position. Figure 21 illustrates the use of a spring to hold the idler wheel of a motor-drive mechanism in contact with the turntable.

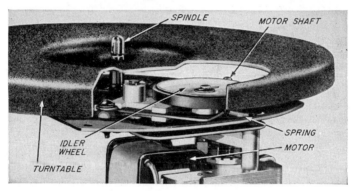

Fig. 21. Spring tension holds the idler wheel against the turntable. In this use the spring is always stretched a constant amount. (General Industries photo)

Screw and Worm. Another basic mechanical action is the screw. A screw is a device which has a thread or groove cut in a spiral fashion along its length. If the screw is inserted in a fixed piece and rotated, it will move in the direction of its axis.

Now, if instead of a surrounding matching part a gear is used whose teeth fit the thread, then we have a worm-gear combination. The screw portion is called the worm, and the matching part is called the worm wheel. Figure 22A shows a worm gear. As the shaft rotates as indicated, it will tend to advance upward. Since the shaft cannot move upward, the relative motion of the worm is upward. This causes the worm wheel to rotate about its axle as indicated. As will be noted, this arrangement changes rotation about one axis to rotation about another axis 90 degrees removed.

Inclined Plane. Another basic mechanical action is the inclined plane. If a heavy object is to be lifted from one level to another, it is often advantageous to slide it up an incline as in Fig. 22B. If a force is applied in a horizontal manner as shown, the object will be moved both horizontally and vertically on the inclined plane. Thus, a portion of the applied energy or force is changed from a horizontal direction to a vertical direction.

The amount of force whose direction is changed depends upon the angle that the incline makes with the horizontal plane. If the angle is increased, the vertical motion is increased and the horizontal motion is decreased. However, more force is now required primarily because the friction is increased by the tendency of the object to dig into the plane.

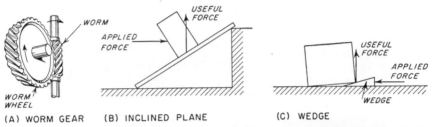

(A) WORM GEAR   (B) INCLINED PLANE   (C) WEDGE

Fig. 22. A worm gear, an inclined plane, and a wedge utilize force applied in one direction to cause motion perpendicular to it

The wedge follows a similar principle, but here the inclined plane is moved while the object is fixed in a lateral sense. This is shown in Fig. 22C. The use of the cam to operate the pickup-arm lift rod is an application of the wedge and inclined plane to the record changer. Generally, the principle is not of major importance but deserves consideration where jamming or certain other record-changer troubles occur.

QUESTIONS

1. How is the turntable rotated?
2. Describe the normal changing cycle.
3. What is a lever and how is it used?
4. How does a wheel and axle compare to a lever?
5. What are the similarities between a gear and a wheel?
6. For what purpose is a cam used in a record changer?
7. Why is a clutch necessary in a record changer?
8. What is the name of a mechanism that permits motion in one direction and prevents it in the opposite direction?
9. Is friction ever desired in a changer?
10. How can gravity be used to advantage?
11. What is the common use of a spring?
12. What is the difference between a wedge and an inclined plane?

4

Service-bench Setup

Need for Service Bench. Record-changer repairing is an important and exacting job which can easily be done by approaching it in the proper manner. It is necessary to have the right equipment and bench in order to speed up and facilitate the handling of changers.

The ideal situation would be to have a separate bench and the necessary equipment which would be used only in the repair of record players or changers. This is not always possible, and space for this work must then be provided on the same bench used for repairing radios.

When constructing a workbench where everything must be combined in one unit, provisions should be made so that a record changer can be set up and operated while you are busy on other repair work. There are many times when changers may be on test and do not have to be watched closely while they are operating. If the changer is attached to an amplifier, your ears can tell whether or not the trouble has been corrected.

Workbench. Where it is possible to have a separate bench for record-changer work, the design in Fig. 1 can be used as a guide. The working surface of the bench should be approximately 4 feet wide and about 2½ feet deep. This will give enough room on which to place the changer, a manual or service notes, and tools with which to work. There is also enough room for the radio chassis and speaker with which the changer works, should it be desired to check over-all performance after repairs have been made.

A good surface for the top of the bench is ⅛ inch pressed wood, commonly known by the trade name Tempered Masonite. The surface is extremely hard, smooth, oil- and grease-resistant, easy to clean, and rugged. The bench should be high enough so you do not have to stoop or bend while standing up to work. It is always possible to purchase a stool of the proper height for comfortable sitting at the bench.

At the front of the bench are a-c power outlets and a drawer which can be used for tools. Outlets may also be installed at the base of the rear panel. On the side of the bench are hooks over which can be hung clip leads, shielded leads, and power cords. The rear panel of the bench contains drawers in which can be placed various fittings, crystals, drive tires, or parts of any nature that are used in this particular work. Above the working area is a shelf for books, manuals, service notes, and test records.

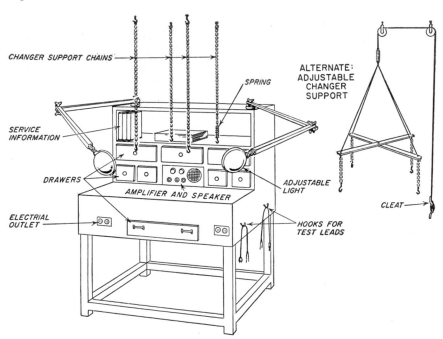

Fig. 1. A bench for repair of record changers

Changer Mount. Directly over the work surface of the bench are four chains, suspended from the ceiling. Three are of equal length, and the fourth (one of the rear chains) is about 5 inches shorter. Attached to the short chain is a 4-inch coil spring slightly heavier than a screen-door spring. Each chain should be capable of supporting at least 20 pounds. On the ends of each chain and spring are hooks for supporting the changer. These hooks are placed underneath the turned-over edge of the changer mounting or base plate. The spring provides automatic equalizing of chain lengths so the changer cannot rock on the hooks or slip off.

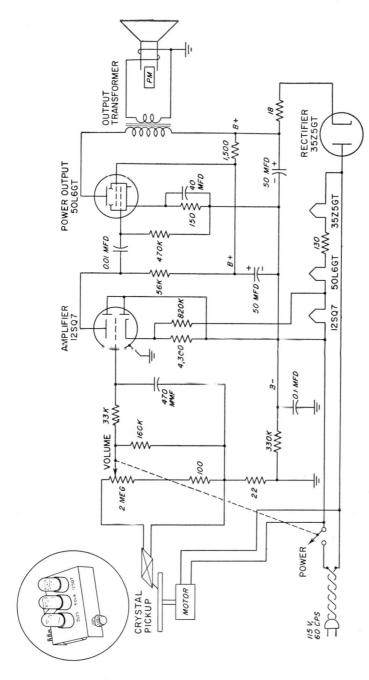

Fig. 2. The circuit of an amplifier that may be used as part of a service-bench setup

43

The chains should be cut so their lower ends are at eye level. Then the mechanism underneath the base can be readily seen and its operation observed while standing at the bench, without stooping.

For a more elaborate installation, the chains can be attached to cross arms which are mounted so they can be raised or lowered with a rope and pulley, as shown in Fig. 1. This method of support also allows the changer to be easily moved or its position altered without much effort. It will prevent many aching necks and backs.

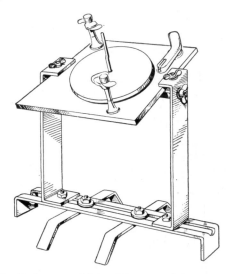

Fig. 3. A commercial bench-type record-changer rack

An amplifier and speaker are mounted on the bench for check purposes when the amplifier and speaker have not been brought into the shop. These bench units are also needed for the substitution method of isolating audio trouble. The amplifier is simple; Fig. 2 shows a typical circuit. A three-tube amplifier of this type may be purchased from most radio jobbers or wholesale mail-order houses.

Bench-type Racks. There are on the market racks and supports which are capable of holding a changer on the surface of the bench. Figure 3 shows such a holder. This type of mounting is more cumbersome, and is somewhat difficult to work around while making adjustments on the changers. It also takes some of the valuable working area away from the top of the bench.

If it is impractical to have a separate changer bench, as many of these features as possible should be incorporated on the radio-repair bench. There should be a place for everything, and everything should be kept in its place. There is nothing so discouraging as a littered bench. Better work can be done in a neat, clean atmosphere. Also, a clean, orderly bench gives a much better impression when a customer enters your shop.

Lighting. Good lighting can be obtained with two lamps, mounted on either side of the top of the rear panel of the bench. The flexible gooseneck fixture and the arm and ball-joint type of fixture are recommended. In each lamp a 100-watt bulb should be used. Lamps of this type allow the light to be directed where needed, and this is one of the essentials in doing good work. Poor light can cause eye strain which in turn creates loss of interest in the work.

Connecting Cables and Leads. Many types of connectors have been used in the line running from the record-changer motor to the source of a-c power. It is best to make up a number of power cords, each with a different fitting or connector. This saves time, eliminates the possibility of sloppy connections, and minimizes blowing of fuses. Each cord should be about 5 feet long so that there is ample length with which to work. Line cords can be bought with the plug for a regular power outlet already attached, but this may not stand up for long unless it is of industrial quality. It is best to attach your own screw-type plugs to high-quality line cord so that you can always rely on having a good source of a-c power.

Pickup Connecting Cable. Very often, upon completion of all adjustments and work on the changer mechanism, it will be desirable to check the pickup cartridge. Various manufacturers have used different methods of connecting the cartridge lead to the amplifier chassis. Some of these cables terminate in pin jacks, while others terminate in plugs.

Since your test amplifier will have the type of input jack most generally used for phonograph work, adapter cables or adapter connectors will be required. One end of each must have the same type of plug on it, as shown in Fig. 4A. The other end should have jacks to match the various plugs used on changers. One or more of the cables should have on its other end a pair of phone-tip jacks and banana jacks. Combination phone-tip and banana jacks are available. Another cable should have on its end a female microphone jack. Another should be equipped with small alligator clips.

If the shop amplifier uses another type of jack, make up an adapter for it by wiring together an RCA pin jack and a plug that fits the amplifier. Ready-built adapters of the type shown in Fig. 4B are available from radio jobbers. These come in various combinations.

There is a possibility also that a three- or four-prong plug may be encountered. In this case, the cable with the alligator clips can be used for connecting the pickup cable to the amplifier.

Since phono pickup cable is normally shielded, always use the center conductor of a test cable as the signal conductor. This practice will avoid many pitfalls in repair work.

Alligator-clip Leads. Make up several pairs of test leads by soldering small alligator clips to the ends of various lengths of flexible rubber-covered, stranded wire such as is used for test instrument leads. Good lengths are 6, 18, and 30 inches. Have equal numbers of red and black leads. The black lead is generally used for ground connections or for shielded leads. The red lead is used for connecting the inner or signal-carrying conductors of shielded cable.

These leads are useful in connecting together two units which may at the time of testing be separated from each other. Another use is for grounding the changer chassis to the radio chassis; with some changers a loud interfering hum is obtained if this is not done.

Where it is suspected that there may be an open in a cable, an alligator-clip lead can be clipped to the plug pins at each end of the suspected lead while the equipment is under test, to check whether or not the lead is open.

Tools. An important part in doing any job right is to have the proper tools. Many jobs have been butchered because an attempt has been made to repair or adjust them with improper tools. The tools required for changer work will now be described. If you are now doing service work, you will have most of these tools.

Screwdrivers. Since most record-changer repairs are made simply by turning a screw, you will need a good assortment of screwdrivers. The smallest should be about 2 inches long with a $\frac{1}{16}$-inch blade, used for removing the cartridge mounting screws and needle set screws in pickups. The heaviest can be 12 inches long with a $\frac{1}{2}$-inch blade, used for removing large mounting screws. For Phillips-type screws the two smaller sizes of screwdrivers, No. 1 and 2, will usually suffice.

Wrenches. Here the first requirement is a regular set of hollow-shaft spin-type socket wrenches which are designed for radio service work, ranging from $\frac{1}{8}$ or $\frac{3}{16}$ inch to $\frac{1}{2}$ inch in size. These wrenches are handy for use on nuts in hard-to-get-at places and are easier to use than pliers.

The set of open-end wrenches shown in Fig. 5A can be used in many places where it is impossible to use a socket wrench. The sizes range from about $\frac{7}{32}$ to $\frac{1}{2}$ inch. These wrenches can be obtained from automotive supply houses or hardware stores, where they are usually called ignition wrenches or combination box and open-end wrenches.

When using a wrench, it is important to use the proper size. Also, it is

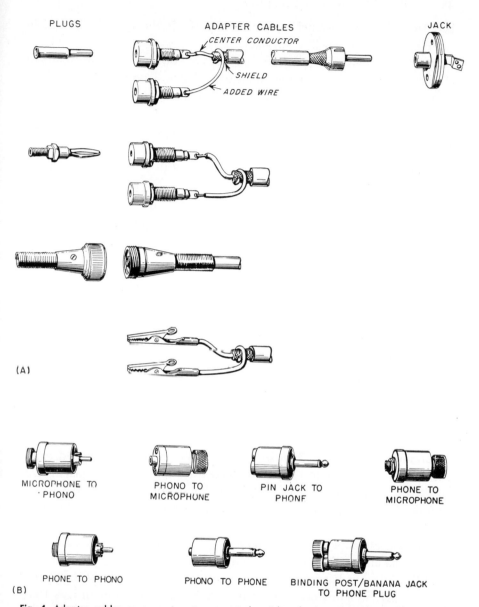

Fig. 4. Adapter cables or connectors to connect the pickup lead to the test amplifier. Cable connectors are, top to bottom, pin jacks, banana jack, microphone connector, and alligator clips each connected to a phono plug

best to pull on the wrench rather than push. If the wrench slips when pushing, damaged knuckles are likely.

Set-screw Wrenches. Collars or couplings are often fastened to shafts of changers with set screws of the Allen type. There is no way to turn these set screws except with the proper size of hexagonal wrench.

When a set screw has a hole which looks somewhat like a four-leaf clover, a Bristol wrench should be used. Kits of these wrenches, in sizes ranging from $\frac{1}{4}$ inch down, as required for service work, can be purchased from parts jobbers. Examples of these wrenches are also shown in Fig. 5.

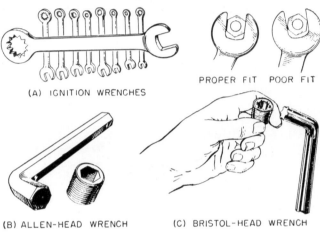

(A) IGNITION WRENCHES

PROPER FIT   POOR FIT

(B) ALLEN-HEAD WRENCH   (C) BRISTOL-HEAD WRENCH

Fig. 5. Wrenches suitable for record-changer repairing

Long-nose Pliers. The two sizes of long-nose pliers recommended are the 4- and 6-inch lengths. These are needed for removing or replacing the small coil springs, C washers, cotter pins and other small parts used in various places on record changers. It is not necessary that these pliers have cutting edges.

Duck-bill Pliers. This type of pliers is unusual in that the jaws are short and the handles rather long. The gripping surfaces of the jaws are flat, smooth, and wide. Duck-bill pliers are exceptionally useful for straightening levers of light-weight stock which have been bent. Their smooth jaws leave no marks or roughness on the surfaces.

Slip-joint or Combination Pliers. These ordinary pliers should be available because they are occasionally needed. Use them with caution, however, because they can slip and do quite a bit of damage. They usually leave burrs, scratches, or marks on metal parts, nuts, or screws used in changers.

Diagonal Pliers. The diagonal cutting pliers are useful in cutting such things as leads and cotter pins. Because of the diagonal edge, they are also useful in removing or spreading cotter pins.

Use of Pliers. Pliers should never be used to loosen or tighten nuts while doing changer work. It is difficult to feel when a nut has been tightened to the proper degree when using pliers. Because of this the nut may not be tightened enough, or too much pressure may be applied and the threads stripped. If the pliers slip off the nut, it is possible to ruin an adjacent part or knock it out of adjustment. Wrenches should always be used to tighten or remove nuts.

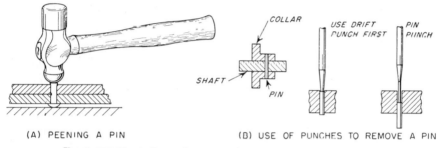

(A) PEENING A PIN   (B) USE OF PUNCHES TO REMOVE A PIN

Fig. 6. Use of a ball-peen hammer and punches to fix or remove a pin

Ball-peen Hammer. A hammer is an essential tool for working on record changers. The ordinary carpenter's hammer, with a large head on one end and claws on the other, is too heavy and too clumsy for the purpose, and a tack hammer is too light. The tool needed should be of a medium light weight. The ball-peen hammer of Fig. 6A, having about ½- to ¾-pound head, fits the requirement very well. It can be obtained in most hardware stores.

Frequently, pulleys or gears are locked to a shaft by a method using a tapered pin as the locking device. This means that a hole on the shaft is lined up with holes in the gear or pulley through which a tapered pin is driven. The flat head of the hammer is used to drive a punch for knocking out these pins.

On some changers, shafts or mounting studs are sometimes riveted into the mounting base or into some part of the underneath structure. When installing one of these studs, it is gently tapped into its hole with the flat head of the hammer. The end protruding from the other side of the base plate is then peened to lock the stud in place. This is accomplished by resting the other end of the stud on a solid object such as a bench vise and using the round head of the hammer to peen or spread out the protruding metal. Use sharp blows near the edge of the protruding piece of metal.

Drift Punches. To remove a tapered pin, it is necessary to use a drift punch or starting punch, as illustrated in Fig. 6B. The small end of the drift punch is rested upon the small end of the pin. The punch is then tapped with the flat head of the ball-peen hammer until the pin is loosened.

A pin punch can then be used to drive the pin all the way out of the hole. The pin punch has a straight shank that allows it to pass through the hole.

When installing a pin, a drift punch may be used for setting it.

Studs and rivets can also be removed by using drift and pin punches providing the peened end is first filed off or otherwise removed. Punches with ⅛- and ³⁄₃₂-inch tips are suggested. These are readily obtainable at a hardware store.

Files. Since metal is frequently encountered in repairing record changers, the file becomes a useful tool. Jamming, a frequent trouble in record-changer work, is usually caused by or results in burrs on the metallic pieces. These must be removed and made smooth.

A single-cut file has a single row of parallel teeth set at an angle across the face of the file. A double-cut file has another row of parallel teeth which cross the first, giving a crisscross appearance. This results in a lot of small diamond-shaped teeth slanting toward the tip of the file. Files are further classified according to coarseness. The common classes in order of smoothness are coarse, bastard, second-cut, and smooth. Since very smooth surfaces are frequently desired and since some rough work will at times be necessary, both bastard and smooth files are required. The shapes and sizes recommended for work on changers are as follows: 6- and 8-inch flat, 6-inch half round, 4- and 8-inch round, a 4-inch extra-slim triangular, and a 6-inch triangular.

The teeth of a file are made to cut only when the file is pushed forward. Holding the file against the work on the backstroke tends to dull the teeth. Wherever possible, the work should be held in a vise when filing. Only sufficient pressure should be used to effect a cut. Overpressure is just as bad as underpressure.

File teeth should be kept clean. This may be accomplished to a degree by occasionally bumping the tip of the file on the bench to jar the filings loose. Where clogging exists, a file card should be used to clean the file. This is a form of stiff wire brush, obtainable in hardware stores. A file loaded with chips is likely to roughen a surface which is being filed smooth; hence a clean file is essential.

Soldering Gun. The soldering gun made by the Weller Mfg. Co. or a similar type will be quite satisfactory for all soldering work on changers. These guns are fast-heating and easier to use than soldering irons.

Vise. In doing radio or changer repair work, a small vise is a necessity. The jaws should have an opening of about 2½ inches. If the jaws have rough edges, it will be necessary to use copper jaw covers to avoid scratching finished material when held. Any good hardware store can supply this item.

Lubricants. Grease and oil are used for lubricating record changers. Both must be of very high quality. One good grease having the trade name Lubriplate is sold in toothpaste-type tubes. STA-PUT is another lubricant of the same type. These greases are cream-colored in appearance, light in weight, and have excellent lubricating qualities. Most radio-parts jobbers have these or a similar product available.

Oil can be obtained from any automobile service station. Get the type known as SAE 10W motor oil. This will not gum when used on high-speed moving parts and also contains a rust inhibitor which prevents steel shafts and bearings from rusting. A pressure-squirt oil can is convenient for applying this.

Oil is used to lubricate motor bearings, pulley bearings, and turntable-spindle bearings. Grease is used on gears, sliding cams or levers, or other bearing surfaces. Oil and grease should not be used more than is absolutely necessary. Should oil or grease get on the motor-drive pulley, the rubber idler-wheel tire, the rubber friction drive, or the turntable rim, it should be removed immediately with alcohol or naptha. Oil or grease can deteriorate rubber quickly.

Test Records and Tape. Several records have been manufactured specially for checking the operation of record changers. A test record should be obtained which has the following features: a series of frequencies for making a frequency response test, an unmodulated groove for checking rumble, and a low-frequency modulated groove for checking pickup tracking. A steady tone in the 1 kc-4 kc range for checking wow may be of help.

One test record will be required for 78-rpm operation. Microgroove operation may usually be adequately checked by use of a 33⅓-rpm test record. The Dubbings D-100 12-inch vinylite test record is very good for 33⅓-rpm operation. The Clarkstan Number 2000S for 78-rpm and Number 2002S for 33⅓-rpm are also satisfactory but do not contain special tracking grooves. The Universal Frequency Record is similar to the Clarkstan but is cut for 78-rpm on one side and for 33⅓-rpm on the other.

A test tape is highly desirable for tape-recorder work. It should include the following: a series of frequencies for making a frequency response test, a steady tone in the range of 1 kc–4 kc for checking wow, a high-frequency tone for testing the azimuth alignment of the magnetic heads, a series of signals for checking signal-to-noise ratio and tape speed. Also of value is a signal to indicate maximum recording level. The Dubbings D-110 for 7½ inches per second operation is most satisfactory and is generally all that is required.

Test records and test tapes are usually available from a radio-parts jobber and are frequently carried in stock.

Value of Publications Just as with other types of service work, technical information is of value and on occasion is almost essential for repairing record changers. Such service data are available from the same three sources as television and radio service data: the manufacturer, Sams, and Rider.

Manufacturer's Service Data. Whenever a record changer is manufactured, the manufacturer prints a pamphlet or booklet which describes its operation, gives other pertinent information, and contains a parts list. The amount of service data may vary from a few sheets to perhaps 20 or 30 pages for a particular changer, depending on the manufacturer. Sometimes the manufacturer's information is of little value, but as a rule the larger manufacturers prepare admirable publications.

Specifications of the equipment are generally given in the first pages of the service data. This section may indicate the physical size of the equipment, the amount of power consumed, the voltage and frequency for which the equipment is designed, the turntable speed, the record sizes used and the record capacity, the type of pickup, and similar data. Other introductory paragraphs may indicate the general nature of the machine and the features of the mechanism. Such information includes information on the type of loading, record selection, trip mechanism, pickup, automatic shutoff, playing of both sides of the record, and intermix operation.

Manufacturer's service data on changers usually tells how to unpack the instrument. Certain portions of the equipment may be tied down or prevented from moving by use of cardboard, rubber bands, or shipping bolts. To prevent the record changer itself from bouncing around on its springs during shipment, it is customary to use temporary bolts which fasten it rigidly to the cabinet. These shipping bolts must be removed in order to allow the equipment to float freely and avoid transmission of mechanical sounds into the electrical circuit. Operating instructions are often also given, including such things as correct loading procedure, setting of the various controls, the purpose of the controls, and the sequence in which they are meant to be operated.

Main Parts. One section of a manufacturer's manual generally identifies the main parts of the record changer and tells what they do. The lesser links and parts that are actuated by the main parts may also be covered. A quick reading of this section will often serve as a useful review.

Larger manuals give a step-by-step analysis of the actions of the various parts of the record changer. This generally tells what happens from the moment the REJECT button is operated till the time when the next record has played and the cycling repeats itself. The relationship of the manual reject and the automatic trip is pointed out.

A record changer usually has several adjustments. Nearly always there is an adjustment for the indexing mechanism. Another often found is for the push-off shelf or spindle push-rod that drops the records. A section on adjustments is included in virtually every record-changer manual, regardless of how skimpy it may be in other respects.

Troubleshooting. One section of a good manual is generally devoted to troubleshooting. This gives possible sources of trouble and the remedies. When confronted by an unfamiliar design, these troubleshooting suggestions can often save you time.

Lubrication of the record changer is usually covered briefly. Free and easy operation is essential in many parts. On the other hand, there are some parts that are designed to operate with a low force, by gravity or by friction. Notes of caution about these are usually included because oil or grease can cause improper operation.

Manuals generally include one or more diagrams showing the various parts of the record changer, and sometimes also showing the change cycle.

A replacement parts list is an essential part of every manual. This list gives the reference numbers which are used in the illustrations to identify each part. When ordering replacement parts, it is essential to give this manufacturer's part number.

In some cases the manual will indicate the price of each part, so that the serviceman can send proper payment and thus expedite shipping of the part. Manufacturers or their distributors do not ordinarily like to ship COD (cash on delivery) because of the added expense and trouble involved. It is therefore best to send a check with your order to cover the price of the part plus the parcel-post or shipping charges. In addition, some manufacturers have a minimum fee of perhaps one or two dollars for each parts order because of the amount of labor and paper work involved in making up a purchase order.

Warranty. Some manufacturers publish their warranty in the service manual. The purpose of this is to acquaint the serviceman with the extent and the limitations to which they will back their product. Generally speaking, the manufacturer warrants that the material is free of defect in workmanship and material and agrees to correct any such defects which may turn up in a reasonable period of time, generally 90 days. Such service is provided by the manufacturer on an FOB factory basis except in those few instances where the manufacturer has local representation.

When a changer defect occurs during the warranty period, the dealer who made the sale is often willing to provide the labor necessary to correct the item and will return any defective parts to the manufacturer for replacement without charge. This involves bringing the changer back to the dealer and picking it up again some days or weeks later; hence it is usually far better for you to do the labor yourself.

It is customary for the manufacturer to send the replacement parts prepaid when under warranty. The dealer or serviceman then pays the shipping charges for one-way transportation to get a free replacement part under warranty.

Howard W. Sams Photofact Publications. Photofact Folder sets cover record changers as well as audio amplifiers, tuners, radios, and television sets. The service data for changers is presented in a special standard form that is planned for maximum usefulness to servicemen.

A special feature of each record-changer folder is the exploded view. This is a large drawing showing all of the parts of a record changer in their correct relative locations but spread apart so that each item is shown separately. An example is shown in Fig. 7. The chief value of these special diagrams is in determining the relative locations of visible and hidden parts and in identifying a particular part and part number. Correct identification is, of course, essential in ordering replacement parts.

To find the Photofact Folder for a particular record changer, use the PF Index. This is published every other month so as to provide an up-to-date index which tells you exactly which folder set has the desired data. Always replace the folders when done with them so they will be there the next time you look.

For those specializing in record changers, Sams also publishes handy bound volumes known as Record Changer Manuals. Each of these contains Photofact Folders for approximately 40 different changers and associated equipment, arranged alphabetically by make for easy reference. Many serv-

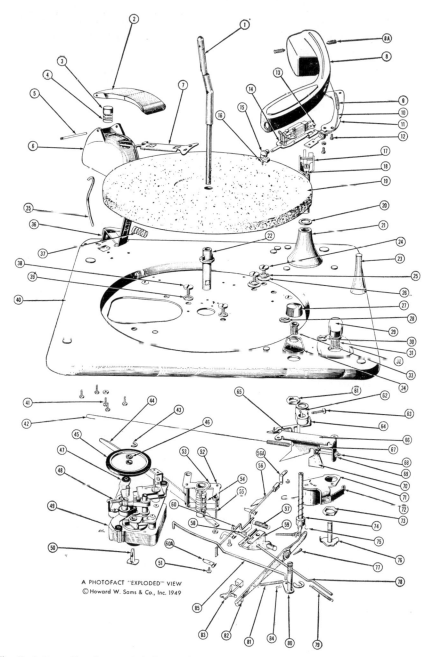

A PHOTOFACT "EXPLODED" VIEW
© Howard W. Sams & Co., Inc. 1949

Fig. 7. A Sams Photofact exploded view illustrates a record changer in accordion-like fashion. (Howard W. Sams)

55

icemen buy these for their record-changer bench even though they have the complete file of Photofact Folders. The folders and manuals are available from most parts jobbers.

Rider's Manuals. Original manufacturer's service data on record changers is included with receiver data in Rider's Manuals. Many servicemen prefer this type of data yet find it impractical to write to a manufacturer for data each time they get in a new model of changer.

If doing receiver work now, you very likely have record-changer service data already. Keep this up to date, and refer to it whenever you find yourself guessing or poking blindly into the works of a balky changer. You're not expected to remember how every single changer works; use the available literature whenever it can save you working time.

Duplication of Information. The record changers used in combination radio-phono sets are generally made by one of the large independent record-changer manufacturers. A particular model of record changer may thus be found in many different makes of sets. There may be variations such as a slightly different style of pickup arm but the mechanism will be the same. Of course, the radio manufacturer may have his own trade name in a conspicuous place instead of the name of the record-changer manufacturer.

The radio manufacturers using a particular record changer will generally publish identical or similar manuals based on the changer manufacturer's own manual but carrying the receiver manufacturer's model number. You will be able to recognize the similarity once you have glanced at a few of these manuals. Use of the same changer in different makes of sets provides you with duplicate sources of information on the changer.

QUESTIONS

1. What provisions should you include in a workbench?
2. Describe a simple suspended changer mount.
3. Why is it easier to work on a changer mounted at eye level?
4. Name four types of connectors used on record changers and amplifiers.
5. What screwdrivers should you have for changer repairs?
6. Should you push or pull on a wrench?
7. What is the difference between an Allen-head and a Bristol-head screw?
8. What four types of pliers should you have?
9. What tool should be used to tighten or remove a nut?
10. How do you peen a rivet?
11. Describe a double-cut file.
12. Where can you buy a test record or a test tape?
13. Name three sources of published record-changer service information.

5

Pickups, Needles, and Records

Mechanical Pickup. During the early days of record playing the mechanical method of reproducing sound from records was used. Today this same basic system is used in the inexpensive portable record player.

In a mechanical sound head, the needle is fastened to a needle chuck, which in turn has an arm fastened to it. The chuck is pivoted so that as the needle follows the groove, the chuck may swing back and forth. The end of the arm coming from the chuck is fastened to the center of a diaphragm. Being made of a flexible material, the diaphragm will move back and forth following the needle movement.

The frame that holds the diaphragm also supports the pivots for the chuck. This whole assembly is then fastened to a horn. Thus, as the needle follows the record groove, the vibrations are transmitted through the needle, the chuck, and the arm to the diaphragm which moves the column of air in the horn, causing audible sound. The only way to control the intensity of the sound from a mechanical pickup is to change the stiffness of the needles or to vary the opening of the throat of the horn.

Early phonograph records were recorded with the reverse of this process. A person sang or spoke into the horn, starting the train of action which resulted in the sound grooves being cut in the master record.

Crystal Pickups. The majority of modern record players and changers utilize the crystal pickup. The popularity of the crystal pickup is primarily due to the fact that it is inexpensive and has a high output. The relatively high output allows it to be used with a low-gain amplifier.

The principle on which the crystal operates is known as the piezoelectric effect. The word *piezoelectric* can be translated as *pressure-electric*. This word is applied to certain crystals such as Rochelle salt (sodium potassium tartrate), which show a mechanical strain and change shape when subjected to an electrical charge.

The converse is also true; when the crystal is stressed, a difference in potential develops between two faces of the crystal. When the crystal is stressed mechanically, charges are developed on the flat sides of the crystal. The stronger the stress, the larger the charge that is produced. A change in stress from compression to tension or from tension to compression changes the polarity of the charges on the crystal surfaces. Thus, the electrical signal produced is determined by the magnitude and direction of the applied force.

In a record player, as the needle follows the grooves of a record, it is caused to move back and forth. This movement is transmitted to the crystal through the needle holder. A small variation in the movement causes a low voltage to be produced by the crystal, while a large variation causes a large voltage to be developed by the crystal. A crystal cartridge will provide an average output of about ½ to 3 volts.

The crystal has a very high internal impedance, being in the order of a megohm or greater. As a result, it is necessary to connect it to a high-impedance input in order to get a proper energy transfer.

Frequency Response. Although the frequency response of a crystal pickup is ideally very wide, the usual commercial crystal has an abrupt cutoff in the neighborhood of 4,000 to 6,000 cps. As a result, a crystal pickup normally gives low to medium fidelity.

The lack of high-frequency response in the crystal has an advantage in that the ordinary scratch frequencies cannot be heard. Since needle scratch is a high-frequency noise and is frequently present in ordinary commercial-quality recordings, the crystal cartridge conveniently eliminates this.

Crystal Types. Crystal cartridges can be divided into two general types, those with a fixed needle and those with a replaceable needle. The fixed needle is utilized in a cartridge having low needle pressure. The greater the needle pressure, the greater is the wear on both the needle and the record. Although the weight on the needle can be measured in ounces the area of needle that touches the record is so small that the pressure per square inch can be in the thousands of pounds. Very few present-day record players use a fixed needle.

The construction of both types of crystal cartridges is shown in Fig. 1. As will be noted, the needle imparts a force to the crystal element through the torque wire or a coupling rubber. The torque wire or the coupling rubber transmits the movements of the needle to the crystal element but absorbs any extra vibrations. Since a moving part tends to keep on moving or vibrating (like a plucked violin string), this prevents the crystal from vibrating. Thus spurious peaks in the response curve are avoided.

The damping provided by the torque wire, coupling rubber, or other damping material varies according to the design, thereby changing the characteristic curves. Variations in the damping design are used to control the frequency response, output voltage, and spurious resonant peaks.

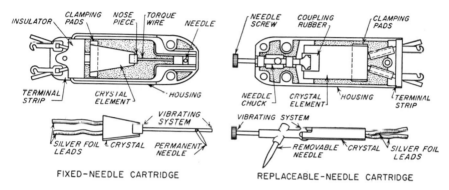

Fig. 1. A typical crystal pickup, showing basic construction details

Effect of Temperature and Humidity. A Rochelle salt crystal is affected by humidity and temperature. Maximum sensitivity is obtained at ordinary room temperatures of about 75° Fahrenheit, decreasing in either direction. Temperature limits are about − 40°F and + 120°F. If subjected to a temperature greater than 130°F, the crystal permanently loses its effect.

Because of these characteristics, a crystal pickup should be operated in a well-ventilated cabinet. It should not be stored in a warm spot such as near a radiator, nor displayed in a store window or showcase where bright sunlight or display lamps are likely to cause heating. If the crystal can be stored or operated in an area of normal temperature between 70° and 80°F, its useful life will be longer.

Caution should be used when soldering to the cartridge terminals so that heat from the soldering iron is not applied to the terminal any longer than is necessary. The terminals are usually well-tinned in manufacture. If the connecting leads are also well-tinned before joining, a minimum of heat will suffice in soldering the connection. Many crystals are now provided with plug-in connections so as to eliminate the necessity of soldering.

The most desirable relative humidity for a crystal is in the neighborhood of 50 per cent. In extremely dry climates the crystal tends to lose its natural moisture and become dehydrated. Once dehydrated, it cannot be restored.

Where the humidity and temperature are extremely high, the life of a crystal cartridge can be extended by storing it in a desiccator. A simple home-made desiccator can be made from a large-mouthed jar or container which has a top so that it can be tightly closed. Place enough desiccant such as calcium chloride or silica gel to fill the jar about half full. Take a wire screen slightly larger than the width of the jar and force it into the jar so that it forms a shelf between the desiccant and the top of the jar. Place the crystal on the screen shelf and close the jar.

The desiccant will have to be replaced at regular intervals, because it can only absorb a certain amount of moisture. To check the desiccant, place a small piece of water-soaked paper towel or blotter in the jar. If it does not dry out completely in about 1½ hours, the desiccant must be replaced.

Some desiccants can be reused after they are dried out by heating. Instructions on the package will indicate this. Desiccants can be purchased from a hardware store.

Other Crystals. Recent crystals include a number of variations to provide more desirable characteristics. One crystal, known as the PN, overcomes the shortcomings of the Rochelle salt crystal caused by high temperatures and humidity. The PN crystal is ammonium dihydrogen phosphate and can be used after immersion in boiling water. Other cartridges utilize a ceramic barium titanate crystal material which provides low needle pressure, elimination of needle talk, wider frequency response, and smaller size. This also is unaffected by humidity.

Magnetic Pickup. At one time magnetic pickups were used considerably, but with improvement of crystal types they fell into disuse. The relative inexpensiveness of the crystal type contributed considerably to the situation. With the advent of recent high-fidelity enthusiasm and new developments in magnetic pickups, they have again regained considerable prominence.

Variable-reluctance Pickup. A popular magnetic pickup is the variable-reluctance cartridge, which undoubtedly gained a share in the market due to its relatively low price. Figure 2A shows a simplified sketch of this cartridge. The pickup includes a magnet with two parallel arms, thus having two north poles. A simple cantilever, which is a single piece supported at one end, is used as the needle shank. It is placed in the air gap and the needle chuck is mounted on its free end. The shank acts like a lever which rocks back and forth between the two north poles.

This cantilever is designed so that it vibrates only at the fundamental frequency. Use of one or more small blocks of plastic material near the fixed end adds to the mass. Since it is more difficult to move a given mass at higher frequencies, this is sufficiently large so that the second harmonic is damped. Although this damps the harmonic, it presents negligible loading of the needle tip at the fundamental vibration frequency.

If the needle is forced to the left by the record groove, as in Fig. 2B, the top of the needle shank is forced to the left. The air gap between N_1 and the needle shank is now reduced and the reluctance becomes smaller. Since magnetic flux follows the path of least reluctance, it increases in the left pole piece and decreases in the right pole piece.

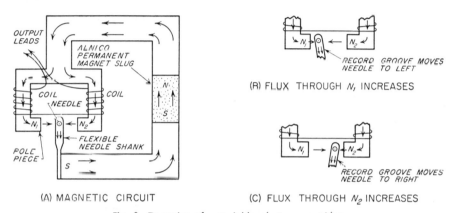

(A) MAGNETIC CIRCUIT   (C) FLUX THROUGH N_2 INCREASES

Fig. 2. Operation of a variable-reluctance cartridge

In a similar manner, if the needle is forced to the right, as in Fig. 2C, the top of the needle shank moves to the right. Now the air gap between needle shank and N_2 becomes smaller and the flux through the right-hand pole piece increases while the flux through the left-hand pole piece decreases.

Conversion of Magnetic Energy to Electric Signal. A coil is used to change the varying magnetic flux to a varying audio-signal voltage. In the variable-reluctance pickup a pair of series-connected coils are used, one over each of the parallel arms. Each of these coils contains about 2,400 turns of wire, and the pair is closely matched to assure faithful reproduction.

The flux which flows in the magnetic circuit links these coils in such a manner that the needle movement is changed to an alternating electrical current. To induce a voltage in the coils, the flux must change. The voltage is proportional to the change in flux so that the greater the change in flux the greater is the voltage developed.

When the needle moves from the center to the left, the flux flowing between N_1 and the needle shank increases, and a voltage is induced in the left-hand coil in one direction. The flux flowing between N_2 and the needle shank decreases, and a voltage of opposite polarity is induced in the right-hand coil. The coils are connected so the voltages add together.

When the needle moves to the right, the flux flowing from N_2 to the needle shank increases while the flux flowing from N_1 to the needle shank decreases. A voltage is now induced in the opposite direction. Thus, as the needle swings back and forth in the record grooves, an audio signal is generated.

Needle movement in a vertical direction changes the reluctance of the parallel circuits equally so that no output results. This means that needle scratch is very low.

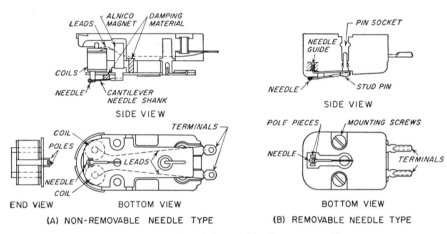

Fig. 3. Construction of the variable-reluctance cartridge

Figure 3 shows the actual pickup. The needle shank has a right-angle twist near the fixed end. This allows the needle shank to yield as much in the vertical direction as in the horizontal direction. If the pickup arm is dropped, the needle will then recede within the guard provided by the pole faces and will not be damaged.

Since the output voltage is proportional to the needle (or cantilever) velocity, the resulting reproduction is the same as that contained in the record groove as long as the needle properly follows the groove. This is another way of saying that the frequency response is flat. The actual response is virtually flat from 10,000 cps down to the point where pickup-arm resonance occurs, which is normally at about 40 cps.

The voltage output of the variable-reluctance cartridge is about 0.01 volt.

As a result, a special preamplifier is required to bring the signal up to the normal output level of a crystal cartridge. Since the pickup is flat for constant-velocity recording but a portion of the frequency spectrum is recorded with a constant-amplitude signal, equalization is required. It is normally included in the preamplifier.

The Cobra Radionic Pickup. The Cobra pickup, utilized by Zenith in many of their models, is a device that varies the output of a radio frequency oscillator. By use of detection and amplification the audio output is obtained.

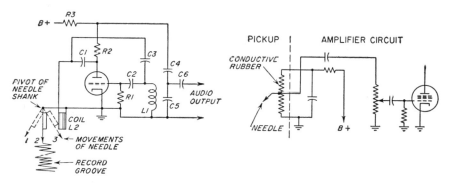

Fig. 4. A simplified diagram of the oscillator used in the Cobra pickup

Fig. 5. Method of connecting the variable-resistance cartridge to an amplifier

A simplified circuit is shown in Fig. 4. The oscillator, which operates at a frequency of 2.5 megacycles, includes a coil L2 in the plate circuit. This coil has 40 turns of No. 40 wire, whose d-c resistance is about $2\frac{1}{2}$ ohms. The needle, tipped with an osmium-iridium point, has a stainless-steel vane spot-welded to it. This vane is located in the field of the coil, and thus it affects the mutual inductance. Since mutual inductance appears as reflected resistance in a coil it affects the Q of the coil. The higher the resistance, the lower the Q, and the lower the voltage obtained across the coil.

When the needle is at rest, it is in position 2, and a constant r-f voltage is produced across the coil. As the needle follows the record variations, it moves between positions 1 and 3. When the needle is in position 1, the vane is furthest removed from the coil. This results in a low mutual inductance (or a high Q), and the voltage across the coil is a maximum. When the needle is in position 3, the vane is closest to the coil and the mutual inductance is high. This gives a low Q, and the voltage across the coil is a minimum. This variation in coil voltage serves to amplitude-modulate the

2.5-megacycle signal. The variation of the vane also changes the inductance of the coil, changing the resonant frequency of the oscillator circuit. This gives some frequency modulation, but since there is no frequency discrimination, it is not detected.

Coils L1 and L2 are part of a single tuned circuit. Any voltage variations across the plate coil L2 will also appear across the grid coil L1. This causes a shift in the average plate current, and plate detection takes place due to the curve in the plate-current–grid-voltage characteristic. The changes in average plate current appear across the plate-load resistor giving an audio voltage. As a result both the audio voltage and the r-f voltage appear at the plate of the oscillator tube.

Resistor R2 and condensers C4 and C5 filter the r-f voltage. The audio voltage is coupled through C6 to the grid of the amplifier. Plate coil L2 is located in the cartridge. The other oscillator components are mounted in an oscillator preamplifier chassis.

Variable-resistance Cartridge. A pickup which might be called a variable-resistance type has been used by Admiral in several of their models. This cartridge uses a small piece of special conductive rubber having connections at both ends and in the middle. The end connections are solidly supported, and the center connection is fastened to the needle shank. As the needle follows the variations of the record groove, it causes one side of the rubber to stretch as the other compresses, and vice versa. This changes the resistance differently in the two halves of the rubber pieces, giving an effect like that obtained when the center arm on a potentiometer is moved back and forth. The conductive rubber piece is only ¼ inch long, ⅛ inch wide, and 0.022 inch thick.

If a voltage is impressed across the two outside terminals of the rubber piece, that portion of the voltage between the needle and one end of the rubber may be taken off just as in a volume control. This voltage is d-c when the needle is at rest. When the needle is following a recorded sound, the voltage changes in accordance with the resistance variations giving an a-c voltage superimposed on the d-c. This desired a-c output is applied to the grid of the amplifier tube through a d-c blocking condenser as shown in Fig. 5. In practice a voltage of about 90 volts d-c is impressed across the cartridge.

Because of the nature of the pickup, the needle is permanently mounted and is hence not replaceable. When the needle wears out, which is rather rapidly because it generally has an osmium tip rather than sapphire, the entire cartridge must be replaced. The new cartridge plugs in easily because it uses its three-prong connectors for support. No mounting screws are needed. The plastic cover cannot be opened since repairs are not possible.

Dual-play Cartridges. Although compromise needles are made that can be used with both the standard and microgroove records, it is desirable to use separate needles (or the tandem tips) on each. As a result, several arrangements have been made so that a single cartridge can be used, with the operator selecting the proper needle.

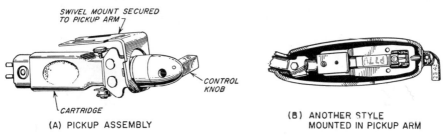

Fig. 6. Turnover cartridges having needles extending on both sides

One variety is the turnover type of cartridge shown in Fig. 6. The cartridge is designed so that the standard needle protrudes on one side and the microgroove needle protrudes on the other side. The cartridge is held in a swivel mount on the pickup arm, so the cartridge can be rotated about its lengthwise axis. The standard needle is in playing position when the control knob is in the clockwise position. The microgroove needle is in position when the control knob is in the counterclockwise position. The control knob is marked so that a replacement cartridge can be inserted properly and the user will not be confused.

Another variety of dual cartridge is the rocker type. In this case either the front or the rear of the cartridge is depressed so that either one tip or the other of the tandem needle is in the playing position. It is customary to mount the standard tip at the front (or extreme end) of the pickup arm. The customer operates a lever somewhere on the pickup arm to shift from one needle tip to the other.

A third type of dual cartridge is displayed in Fig. 7. When the knob is pushed down, the needle can be rotated 180 degrees so that the desired tip of the tandem needle is in the forward or playing position.

Needles. Many people have the impression that a needle in a modern phono pickup is good for a lifetime and need never be changed. Unfortunately, this is not true. As the needle rides in the grooves of the record there is friction, causing wear on both record and needle. Some materials of which needles are made will last longer than others, but eventually any needle will have to be replaced.

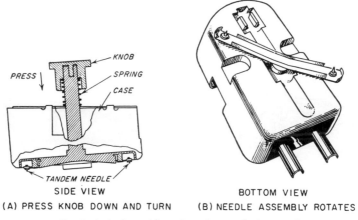

SIDE VIEW

(A) PRESS KNOB DOWN AND TURN

BOTTOM VIEW

(B) NEEDLE ASSEMBLY ROTATES

Fig. 7. A dual cartridge where the needle is rotated

Needle Wear. A worn needle can cause very poor tone quality, a hissing sound, high record scratch, and skipping of grooves. More important still, the damage done to the groove of the record by a worn needle is irreparable. It is good insurance against record wear, and will guarantee more satisfaction as far as good reproduction is concerned if the needle is replaced when it shows signs of uneven wear.

A needle can be checked with a small microscope having about 10-power magnification. A pocket microscope, magnifying glass, or jeweler's loupe may be used in the customer's home to inspect it. If worn enough so that there are flat spots as shown in Fig. 8, replacement should be suggested. Emphasize the fact that it is less expensive to replace needles or cartridges than to replace sets of records.

Figure 8 also shows the effect of a worn needle on a record groove. Notice that flat spots have been worn on the sides of the needle, causing shoulders. The worn needle touches the bottom of the groove, causing much noise and scratch to be heard. The flat surfaces have sharp cutting edges that will gouge out the record grooves. Needle wear is characterized first by loss of high frequencies, then by a buzzing sound.

Steel Needles. For mechanical phonographs, the plain steel needle is best. Some steel needles come in different types, which might be labeled soft tone, medium tone, full tone, loud tone, and extra loud tone. The loudest are the stiffest; hence they will give more scratch noise along with greater volume. The different types are made to give a control over volume because only a few mechanical phonographs have adjustable horn plugs or doors for reducing volume. Steel needles should be used for playing one side of one record only. The first part of the record wears the needle to fit the groove. By the time the record is finished, it is worn to the point where it would start to gouge the grooves. Since the mechanical pickup is so heavy, the wear on even an expensive sapphire needle would be excessive and after a few plays the needle would be worthless.

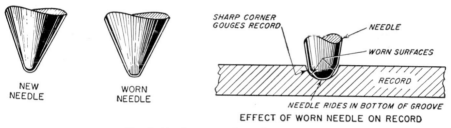

EFFECT OF WORN NEEDLE ON RECORD

Fig. 8. Needle wear and its effect on record

Chromium Needles. This type of needle is steel which has been chromium plated. It is a good type of needle for the older heavy types of magnetic pickups and for the heavier crystal pickups whose needle pressure on the record is about 5 ounces. This needle is good for somewhere between 5 and 50 plays, but it is imperative that a person be critical in using it. If a chromium needle is used which has an uneven plating, it is possible to do a tremendous amount of damage to the record surface. The reason for this is that the needle may be placed in the pickup head in such a position that a thin coating of the plating may be subjected to the greatest wear. In this case the plating would wear through rapidly and in very few playings present a sharp cutting surface to the record.

Variable-shank Needles. These needles are made by different manufacturers and come in a variety of sizes. One trade name for them is Recoton. The upper end of the needle shank is of the usual thickness, but the lower end has been thinned down quite a bit. The length of the lower end varies according to the manufacturer's design. This design was one of the early attempts to help eliminate needle talk, which is noise made by the needle as it tracks in the groove of the record.

Variable-shank needles give on the average about 10 plays with a pickup head whose needle pressure is about 3 ounces. They usually work well on changers and are usually good for playing one side of a stack of records.

Long-life Playing Needles. *As previously pointed out, there are no permanent needles.* However, there are many different types of long-playing needles on the market. Some have straight shanks, while others have bent shanks. Some use nylon between the shank and the needle point, while others use a metal spring between the shank and needle point. Many of this latter type use a hard rare metal for a point. Others use a jewel, either natural or synthetic, such as sapphire, ruby, or diamond. In this category the choice is wide. Here the serviceman may encounter customers who have very strong likes and dislikes. Most long-playing needles will give satisfactory results on modern manual record players as well as on automatic changers, provided the pressure on the needle is below about 3 ounces.

The goal in needles is to get a material that is hard and will take a good polish. These characteristics minimize friction between needle and record. The rare metal known as osmium has this quality and is satisfactory for about 50 to 200 plays. Better yet are ruby or sapphire tips; these are harder and can be polished better; hence they will give about five times the wear of osmium. Best of all though most expensive is the diamond. This is the hardest and can be polished to a much higher degree, giving a longer-lasting needle with better reproduction. It has about ten times the life of sapphire.

In figuring the cost per record played, the diamond needle is no more expensive than the others. It is often therefore considered the best buy. Needles of the jeweled type are usually used by those who value their records or desire high-fidelity reproduction; thus they should always be checked for wear with a microscope.

Needle Talk. Many things have been done to lessen needle talk in long-playing needles. They are all effective to a greater or lesser degree. Probably the best is the bent needle. An ordinary straight-shank needle vibrates and chatters, setting up a disturbance that is audible. The theory behind the bent needle shank is that the needle is broken up into smaller vibrating sections. Since the resonant frequency of a piece is inversely proportional to the length, bending places the needle resonances beyond the audible range. In this manner much needle talk has been overcome.

Selection of Needles. In suggesting needles for record players or automatic changers, it is advisable to find out who is going to use the changer. Where children are the chief users, it is best to recommend that the metal long-playing needle be used. These needles can take quite a bit of abuse without materially affecting record reproduction, whereas a jewel-tip needle can be easily chipped.

If only grownups will be handling the pickup, something better should be suggested such as a jewel needle in the medium price range, or around $2.50. In the event that the customer is a connoisseur or high-fidelity enthusiast, the very best, which is a diamond needle, should be suggested.

Pickups, player mechanisms, and records differ from one to another in a great many ways. Very often it will be found that a needle which may work well in one machine will not do as well in another type of machine. For this reason, recommend a needle that you think will serve the customer best, and ask the customer to try it on his own machine and records.

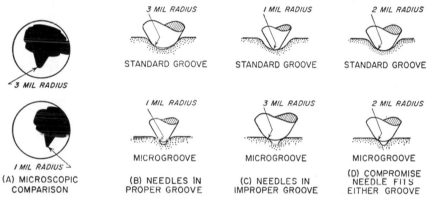

Fig. 9. Comparison of standard and LP needles. LP needle rides in bottom of standard groove and standard needle rides on top of microgroove giving poor results. Compromise needle works in both grooves

Microgroove Needles. Needles for standard 78-rpm records have a tip radius of about 0.003 inch (3 mils), as compared to 0.001 inch (1 mil) for LP or microgroove needles as shown in Fig. 9A and B. The reason for this is that the grooves of a microgroove record are not as wide or deep as in the regular record and there are many more grooves per inch.

Because of the large tip radius on a regular needle, it will not track well on a microgroove record as in Fig. 9C. Conversely, a microgroove needle would touch the bottom and fit very loosely in the groove of a standard record. A person wishing to use both types of records must then have the proper equipment. This calls for either two separate pickup arms and their respective needles, a dual-play cartridge having some method of attaching two needles so that the desired one can be used, or use of a compromise needle.

Compromise Needles. The all-purpose needle illustrated in Fig. 9D has a tip radius which is a compromise between 1 mil and 3 mils. Thus it rides high on the microgroove and low on the standard groove but works reasonably well with both. Compromise needles include 2-mil and 2.3-mil radius tip, and a 2-mil truncated cone tip having a relatively flat bottom instead of a radius.

This method is used sparingly, chiefly on inexpensive players. Since it results in an increase in distortion and surface noise, the high-frequency response of the associated amplifier is usually limited. The all-purpose needle should be used only with pickups having a needle force of not more than 12 grams. Wear on these needles is of greater consequence than with single-purpose needles because they have to work well in different size grooves.

Care of Needle. To assure long needle life, it is advantageous to use new and clean records. In addition, the record changer should have a highly compliant pickup with the correct needle pressure and a minimum of vertical and horizontal pickup-arm friction. A highly compliant pickup is one which exhibits considerable yield to the horizontal forces exerted by the varying record grooves. The higher the compliance, the less is the pressure and wear on the needle and record grooves.

Pickup Arms. The pickup arm supports the pickup cartridge so that the needle may properly follow the record grooves. Pickup arms have a wide variety of shapes for style reasons and because they are often designed to work with a particular cartridge. A cartridge-pickup-arm combination is designed to produce a wide range of frequencies at constant relative output with low distortion and little needle and record wear.

To meet these requirements, there must be very little friction in the bearings of the pickup arm. Also, the pressure of the needle on the record must be kept to a minimum consistent with proper tracking and adequate output. This necessitates balancing of the pickup arm. In addition, mechanical vibrations may possibly exist. The mechanical features that are involved have electrical equivalents and must be properly selected in design to alleviate any possible difficulties. It is impractical to design a cartridge with flat output only to have a resonance in the pickup arm. The desired result is a matched system.

Pickup-arm Characteristics. Progress in the industry is demonstrated by reduction in needle pressure. From the extreme of several ounces used in early mechanical reproducers, the needle pressure has been constantly reduced. Prior to the introduction of LP records, a needle pressure of 1 ounce plus or minus ¼ ounce was normal. In recent record changers the design is such that the same pickup arm can be used for all types of records, and the pressure is decreased to that normally used for LP records. These records require a needle pressure of roughly 8 grams plus or minus 2 grams (about ¼ ounce). Most modern changers use 6 to 8 grams pressure. It has been found that 5 grams is sufficient for proper tracking of the needle in the record groove. Vertical friction should not exceed 1 gram, and lateral friction should not exceed 2 to 3 grams. The needle pressure should not change by more than 2 grams when used with one record or a complete stack.

Substitution of Pickup Arm. To avoid undesirable pickup-arm resonances, it is safest not to make any changes in the pickup-arm assembly during servicing. Use exact or equivalent replacements of both pickup arms and cartridges. Where a pickup arm is damaged, replace it rather than try to straighten or repair it. The relatively small cost of a new arm is not of consequence when compared to the possible labor involved in making repairs and the effect on tone and needle and record wear.

Pickup-arm Support. It is necessary to support the pickup arm in a manner which will provide proper balance and minimum friction. A method is shown in Fig. 10. The pickup-arm shell is attached to a support which forms one portion of the pivot or hinge assembly. The pivot assembly is in turn attached to a vertical shaft or post which may be rotated. The pickup arm is then free to

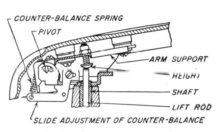

Fig. 10. A pickup-arm assembly

move both horizontally and vertically. Horizontal friction is affected primarily by the method of mounting on the vertical shaft or post. Vertical friction is determined by the pivot and by the counterbalance system.

The proper needle pressure is obtained by use of a counterbalance arrangement. This is usually a spring, counterweight, or combination thereof. To allow for production tolerances and aging of springs, an adjustment must be provided. This is arranged by allowing the counterweight to be moved or the spring tension to be changed.

Vertical movement of the pickup arm during cycling is usually produced by a lift rod that slides within the shaft or bushing. This lift rod presses against but is not generally fastened to the pickup arm. Horizontal movement of the pickup arm during the change cycle is usually obtained by rotating the pickup-arm shaft, which is a rigid part of the assembly.

Records. Although it is not the purpose of this book to discuss recording techniques, it is desirable to briefly consider the manner in which records are made in order that their properties can be better appreciated.

Cutting a Record. When a recording is made, a recorder is used to cut the impressions in a blank. The recorder is basically the same as a phonograph but has many refinements and works to very close tolerances. A blank record, mirror smooth on each face, is placed on the turntable. The turntable is much heavier than that used in record changers, thus having added rigidity to give freedom from warping and a heavier mass to give a steadier speed from the flywheel action. The turntable is driven by a high-quality motor having extremely small speed variations and high isolation from vibration.

The cutter changes the sound or electrical energy into mechanical variations. Both crystal and magnetic types are used and produce the opposite action to that previously described for pickups.

A recording stylus is used to cut the grooves in the record. It is similar to a pickup needle but must be very hard, smooth, and precisely shaped.

The cutter is driven by a feed mechanism so that as the turntable rotates the cutter is caused to move slowly across the record. For cutting transcriptions this may move inside-out (from the center to the edge), but for producing phonograph records it is caused to move outside-in.

The recorder has many adjustments, including the number of grooves per inch and the depth of cut. These are set prior to cutting a record. To cut the record, the cutter is positioned at the outer edge of the blank, and the turntable is started. The stylus will form a groove in the record, cutting out a chip or thread of material. As electrical energy is supplied to the cutter in the form of audio frequencies, the stylus is caused to move to and fro in a lateral direction, making a wobble in the groove. The variations in the wobble are the same as the audio frequencies fed to the cutter.

For standard 78-rpm records, the depth of cut is in the order of 0.002 to 0.003 inch. Microgroove records are cut to a depth of about 0.001 to 0.0013 inch. If the groove is too shallow, the needle will not follow it properly and the pickup may slide across the record. On the other hand, if the groove is cut too deep, the grooves may overlap so that there is no land between the grooves. This is known as overcutting.

The degree of polish which the stylus possesses determines the smoothness of the groove walls. The smoother the wall the less is the surface noise.

The loudness of the sound being recorded determines the extent that the stylus vibrates. Thus for louder passages the vibration is more extensive. Since a certain amount of land must be left between grooves, the number of grooves per inch is limited. It is desirable to have as many grooves as possible on the outer portion of the record. Recorders are in use that have an automatic variable pitch so that on louder passages the number of grooves is decreased and on quiet passages the number of grooves is increased. This assures the maximum number of grooves in a given space.

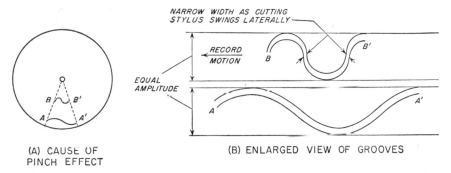

(A) CAUSE OF
PINCH EFFECT

(B) ENLARGED VIEW OF GROOVES

Fig. 11. Two grooves of the same frequency and amplitude are of different lengths at different distances from the center of the record. Width of A-A' is constant, but that of B-B' varies because of sharp swings and shape of cutting stylus. At narrow portions distortion occurs during playback

Pinch Effect. Since the turntable rotates at a constant speed, the length of groove traversed in one revolution near the outside edge is greater than the length traversed in one revolution near the inner edge. This is illustrated by Fig. 11A which shows a segment of a revolution. One cycle of a particular frequency is recorded near the outside as shown by A-A' and near the inside by B-B'. The variations of the inner groove are much sharper than those of the outer groove. Figure 11B shows an enlarged view of these variations. Because of the gentle changes in groove A-A' the width is nearly constant throughout. However, the groove B-B' has variable width due to the shape of the cutting stylus and the sharp variations. Since the width of the groove varies, when the record is played back the needle will climb or be forced up out of the groove at the narrow portions. This will result in poor tracking, a lower output, and possibly distortion due to the vertical motion. This pinch effect will occur at all frequencies but is not troublesome below 1,000 cps.

Factors Governing Pinch. For a lateral-cut record the factors affecting the pinch effect are the turntable speed, the stylus or needle tip radius, the diameter of the inside groove, and the modulation index given by the ratio of the fully modulated groove width to the unmodulated groove width. A decrease in turntable speed decreases the maximum frequency that can be recorded if the recording diameter and modulation index are constant. A decrease in the stylus or needle tip radius, on the other hand, increases the maximum frequency.

Microgroove 33⅓-rpm recordings reduce the speed by a ratio of about 2.3 to 1 over standard 78-rpm recordings, while the needle tip radius is reduced by a factor of 3 to 1. Thus, the latter more than compensates for the former. The 45-rpm speed represents an improvement in the speed ratio. The larger speed gives more output; hence the diameter of the innermost groove can be smaller for comparable distortion. Since so many variables are involved, each method uses a different fixed set of starting conditions, allowing maximum advantages to be obtained.

Record Sizes. Records for home use are classified by their diameter and are either 7, 10, or 12 inches. The standard 78-rpm records come in all three sizes, with the smaller being used principally for children's reproductions. The 33⅓-rpm LP records also come in all three sizes. The 45-rpm records, characterized by the large center hole, are made only in the 7-inch size.

All types and sizes are made of plastic, and only the standard 78-rpm records are still also made of shellac.

Troubleshooting a Mechanical Reproducer. In a record player which utilizes a mechanical head, only two portions of the assembly can cause poor sound or loss of output. These are the needle and the mechanical head. If the output level is poor, the needle should first be replaced. It is customary to secure the needle with a thumb screw so that it may be changed after each record is played.

If volume is still too low after the needle has been replaced, the head is at fault. Replacement units are available from most radio parts jobbers. One or more set screws are used to hold the head in place. Once these have been loosened, the head will slide off the end of the arm, the two having been designed to form a snug fit.

Troubleshooting a Pickup Assembly. The possible difficulties that may be encountered in a pickup assembly are low output, loss of output, intermittent output, and distortion. The components that make up an assembly are those which were previously discussed, namely, the needle, cartridge, and pickup arm. The record must also be considered since it is the source of the sound. The more common troubles are shown in Fig. 12 and discussed in the following paragraphs.

Poor Output Volume. Low output or lack of output may be due to the needle, cartridge, pickup wires, or the amplifier. Intermittent output may also be included in this category. To determine whether or not the amplifier is at fault, the input connector to the phono socket may be removed. Since the human body is somewhat insulated from ground, it picks up a stray 60-cps signal. If the finger touches the hot or high-level side of the amplifier input, this signal is introduced into the circuit. With the volume control advanced, a hum should be heard through the speaker. If the amplifier input is not readily available, the same test may be made by touching the high-level terminal of the cartridge. In the event the test is made at the cartridge terminal and no hum is obtained, the wires should be checked to determine that they are intact. A continuity check by means of an ohmmeter will verify this.

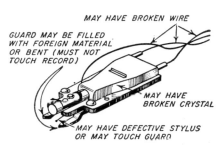

Fig. 12. Possible causes of distortion or poor output

If a hum is heard, then the needle and the cartridge remain to be checked. The needle should be inspected to determine that it has not broken, and that it is in proper position to freely contact the record. In normal trouble-shooting procedure, this will probably be the first thing checked, since it is always a good policy to first make an over-all inspection.

If there is no visible defect, the simplest procedure is to change the needle. If it is necessary to remove the cartridge in order to replace the needle, a rough check of the output may first be made by lightly rubbing the needle point with the tip of a finger. This will give a scratchy sound through the amplifier if everything is working properly and the pickup wires are connected. Another method of checking is to hold the cartridge between the fingers and play a portion of a record. If this fails to give sound from the amplifier yet a hum is heard when the hot pickup terminal is touched with the finger, the cartridge is defective and must be replaced.

Distortion. Distortion may be caused by nearly every part in the assembly. A bad record may be the cause, so try several records. A binding or defective pickup arm may also be the cause. A damaged arm should be replaced with an exact replacement part. Binding can be checked by holding the cartridge end of the pickup arm lightly in the fingers and moving it back and forth. Since the pickup arm is closely associated with the indexing mechanism, causes of binding and other pickup-arm assembly defects are discussed in a later chapter.

Distortion may also be caused by a worn or defective needle and by a defective cartridge. These items should be checked in the same way as for poor output volume. Another and more obvious cause of distortion is the needle rubbing against the guard, or lint and dirt accumulating between the needle and the guard.

Distortion in the form of a hum or an intermittent noise may be due to a loose or broken ground connection. Usually one wire is connected from the amplifier chassis to the cartridge case to serve as a common ground connection. This wire is in the form of a shield surrounding the signal wire. Magnetic and electrostatic fields set up by a-c or static voltages are intercepted by this surrounding shield and are grounded. If the ground wire is open, these stray fields are coupled into the signal wire. This stray field is usually 60 cps; hence power-line hum is heard when the ground wire is open.

Troubleshooting a Crystal Cartridge. A crystal cartridge is difficult to check other than by substitution or elimination. By the process of elimination of other possible sources of trouble, as just previously described, it is quite easy to spot a faulty crystal.

One possible check which may be of assistance is to measure the resistance of the crystal cartridge. Although this, too, does not give a definite answer, it is safe to say that if the resistance is 2 megohms or more the crystal is good. If it is 250,000 ohms or less, the crystal is bad.

As a note of caution, the application of more than a few volts to a crystal cartridge is not recommended. Voltage causes a crystal to change shape, and if excessive will break or damage it. If a dead crystal cartridge is being replaced, a check of the voltage across the leads will avoid any possibility of this. If any voltage exists, it is due to a leaky coupling condenser which must be replaced.

Servicing a Crystal Cartridge. The construction of a crystal pickup is such that no attempt should be made to repair it. There are certain defects which may occur, such as low output, distortion, fuzziness, or no output at all. If a crystal is suspected of giving trouble, it is a simple matter to substitute another and check on the performance. Should the original crystal cartridge prove defective, it should be replaced. It is not worth while trying to repair it.

Troubleshooting the Variable-resistance Pickup. The variable-resistance (not variable-reluctance) pickup cannot be repaired due to the nature of its construction. As in most cases, the simplest method of checking for a defective cartridge or needle is to replace it. The plug-in feature makes this very simple.

To check without the use of a replacement cartridge, the finger-touch test may be applied to the needle. If a hum or scratch is heard, the coupling circuit to the grid of the amplifier is satisfactory, eliminating it from consideration. In this case, the voltages across the outer terminals should be checked. Since the connectors are riveted in place, they are available from the bottom. The voltage should measure between 80 and 100 volts d-c, but depends on the external circuit. If the voltage is correct yet no sound is obtained from records, the cartridge is defective. The resistance is not critical and should measure between 100,000 ohms and 2 megohms.

In case of distortion, the coupling condensers should be checked. There will usually be two. One is connected between the center terminal of the pickup and one end of the volume control. The other is connected between the movable arm of the volume control and the grid of the first amplifier tube.

If the needle is bent, straightening can be accomplished by bending it down so that it projects about $\frac{1}{16}$ inch below the cartridge. The needle should then be pressed back several times with a flat object. The amount it springs out beyond the case is then correct.

The variable-resistance cartridge should be at room temperature when being tested, as cold will impair the output by its effect on the rubber.

Servicing a Magnetic Cartridge. Most magnetic pickups, including the variable-reluctance cartridge, must be cleaned periodically. Lint and other foreign particles on the record surface accumulate on the needle, pole pieces, and between the gaps. The needle should be removed and the cartridge cleaned by means of a soft-bristle brush. Where it is impractical to remove the needle, a piece of Scotch tape can be threaded between the pole pieces and the needle a few times. If a brush is not available, try blowing the dirt out or tickling it out with a piece of paper. Caution must be used not to disturb the pole pieces while cleaning.

It is possible to lose output because of a broken wire inside a magnetic cartridge. Replacement is best here, but in an emergency you can try to locate the break and make repairs. Since the wire is very fine and it may be necessary to scrape off the insulation before soldering, extreme care should be used. A resistance measurement can sometime be of help. A good variable-reluctance cartridge will measure about 340 ohms.

Cartridge Characteristics. Various cartridges differ widely in their output characteristics. In designing an audio system to work with a certain cartridge, the manufacturer takes into consideration the output voltage, the frequency response, and the needle pressure required to produce the first two. For these reasons it is highly desirable when replacing a crystal that either an exact duplicate be used or else one known to match the original. Another type of crystal, although new and perfectly good, may not give anywhere near the results that are desired. Only for purposes of checking should another type of crystal cartridge be used unless you get customer approval of the tone of the new cartridge.

Replacement Units. Cartridges can be obtained from a good parts jobber. Most of them are made by firms specializing in manufacturing cartridges. Most cartridge manufacturers print charts indicating stock numbers of interchangeable units. By checking the chart, a permissible replacement may be found if the exact replacement is not available. If a good percentage of work being done is on phonographs, it is a good idea to carry a small stock of the faster moving cartridges. This speeds up the repair work, and allows speedier service to the customer.

Replacing a Cartridge. Although the shapes of crystal cartridges vary considerably, practically all have identical mounting holes. It is common practice to mount the crystal by means of two screws inserted through the holes in the cartridge and fastened to the tapped holes in the pickup arm or in a supplemental plate.

To remove a crystal, it is necessary, then, to remove these two screws. Where the pickup arm does not lift sufficiently high to allow a view of the underneath side, a mirror placed on the chassis or turntable will be of assistance. Standard slotted screw heads are normally used. Where the needle is held by a set screw, it may be necessary to remove this first to provide clearance when withdrawing the cartridge from the pickup arm.

Most present-day cartridges use slip-on type terminal lugs. The pickup-arm leads are soldered to small terminal sockets which slip over the cartridge-plug tips. This eliminates the need for soldering when replacing the cartridge.

Where soldered terminal connections are made directly to the cartridge, the wires to be attached to the crystal should be cleaned and wrapped around the terminal lugs. The crystal should be placed in such a manner that the soldering iron can be applied without causing the crystal to move. The ends of the leads should be tinned and the soldering iron heated to the point where solder flows freely. It does not require much solder to hold these wires on, so that the flow of solder between the tinned terminal and the leads will probably suffice in making the joint. When soldering leads to a crystal pickup, the job should be done thoroughly but quickly. The crystal cannot stand too much heat, and it is possible to destroy its properties by holding the soldering iron on the lugs too long.

Generally a two-conductor lead is used to connect the pickup to the amplifier, but on occasion a three-conductor lead is employed. In both types, one of the leads is a braided metal cover, called a shield because it shields the other conductors from stray signals. The shield is always connected to the ground portion of the pickup and the amplifier. The case of the pickup is considered as ground.

Where a pickup has two terminals, one is usually connected to the case by a lug, making the ground terminal easily recognizable. Where three conductors are used, the two inner ones are connected to the pickup terminals and the shield is connected to the case. Figure 13 shows pickup cartridges with such connections. The various items used in mounting a cartridge are also shown in their respective positions.

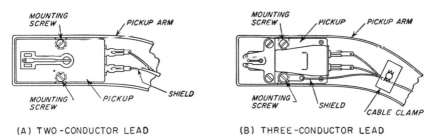

(A) TWO-CONDUCTOR LEAD   (B) THREE-CONDUCTOR LEAD

Fig. 13. Connection of lead to the pickup

In all cases caution should be used to determine the point to which the ground lug or shield is connected. It is essential that this be properly connected when replacing the cartridge so that stray pickup is not fed to the amplifier.

The procedure used to put the replacement cartridge in place is the reverse of that used to remove it. When replacing a cartridge where the ground lug is held by one of the mounting screws, it is convenient to put the other screw in place first, tightening it only enough to hold the cartridge. The ground lug can then be slipped over the other screw, which may then be put into place. Both screws can then be tightened. A short screwdriver, preferably with a spring screw holder, is handy for this.

There are some exceptions to the procedure. The Admiral variable-resistance cartridge is one. It has external connections which plug into a mating socket so that it is necessary only to push in or pull out as the case may be. This is shown in Fig. 14. In some few cases the mounting screws are inserted from the top.

A moment spent inspecting the unit is of advantage to avoid damage. It is a general rule not to use force unless sure of the technique required.

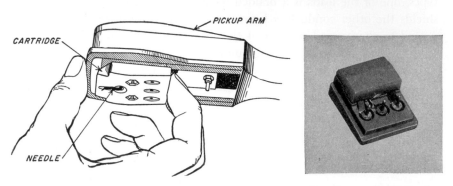

Fig. 14. The Admiral variable-resistance cartridge is removed by pulling down on the back edge. It is held in the pickup arm by its three pin connectors

Needle Replacement. The most general method of securing the needle in the cartridge is by means of a set screw. To replace the needle, it is necessary only to loosen the screw (counterclockwise) and remove the needle. If the needle sticks, it may be loosened by pulling with tweezers, prying with a knife, or pushing through from the opposite end. If the needle is pried loose with a knife, only gentle pressure should be exerted so as to avoid damaging the cartridge or breaking the needle shank.

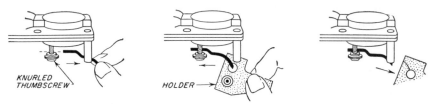

(A) REMOVING OLD NEEDLE   (B) INSERTING NEW NEEDLE   (C) REMOVING NEEDLE HOLDER

Fig. 15. The Shure Muted Stylus needle is changed by loosening the thumb screw, removing the needle, inserting the new needle as far as possible, tightening firmly, and removing the needle holder (where supplied by needle manufacturer)

In many cartridges, the needle socket goes completely through and the end of the needle shank is visible from the top when the cartridge is removed from the pickup arm. By pushing with a stiff wire, paper clip, or other suitable implement, you can readily remove a jammed needle and still exert a minimum pressure on the cartridge.

Other Needles Held by Set Screws. The Shure Muted Stylus needle, shown in Fig. 15, is specially designed to be used with the muted-stylus cartridge. Although the word stylus is defined as a tool for writing or recording, it is often loosely used in phonograph work to indicate the needle. This particular needle is held by means of a knurled thumb screw. When replacing, the needle should be inserted as far as possible. Where a cardboard tool is provided for convenience in handling the needle, it must then be removed.

One turnover cartridge, the Webster-Electric Featheride, uses two separate needles on opposite sides as in Fig. 16. The two needle shanks dovetail together and are held by a single screw. Both needles may be removed

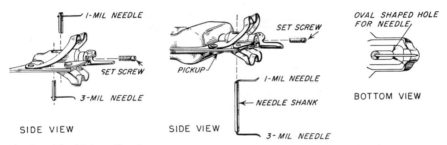

Fig. 16. The Webster-Electric F15 and F16 cartridges use separate needles inserted from opposite ends

Fig. 17. The single-shank needle for the Webster-Electric turnover cartridge is held by a set screw but must be removed and inserted with a curved motion

by loosening the single set screw. When installing new needles, the 3-mil needle must be inserted first. The 1-mil needle, colored red, is then inserted. The shanks of the two must fit together with the flat seat on the 1-mil needle facing the set screw. Once the set screw is tightened, the needles can be centered between the guards by applying lateral pressure with the finger.

The Featheride cartridge using a single shank with two needle tips is illustrated in Fig. 17. The needle is held by a set screw, but it must be removed and inserted with a curved motion. The red spot on the cartridge indicates the side for the 1-mil tip. As is usual, the needles must be centered between the guards.

Replacing Other Types of Needles. Many new and special needles have been developed in an attempt to improve performance. Some of these require special handling or special tools. At least one manufacturer, the M. A. Miller Mfg. Co. (Carillon Dynamic needles), includes such special tools with each replacement needle. Where tools of this type are not available a tweezers is usually a good all-around tool.

Friction-supported Needles. The Seeburg jukebox uses a cartridge with two needles on opposite sides in order that both sides of a record may be played without turning the record over. The needle used is shown in Fig. 18. It may be removed by inserting a knife near the shank and prying outward. The replacement needle may be inserted by use of a tool or tweezers, inserting the shank in the socket and pressing gently. If the installation tool is used, it may then be slipped off over the needle tip.

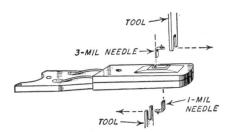

Fig. 18. The Seeburg cartridge uses two needles mounted in opposite sides of the cartridge. The shank fits in a socket by a friction fit. When a special installation tool is used, it is slipped over the tip after the needle is inserted

One type of Astatic needle (Fig. 19) has their Taper Back shank which is held in a mating, open groove. In order to replace the needle, the cartridge should be removed. The old needle should be slipped out by exerting a slight pressure away from the needle point with the thumbnail, as shown. To insert a new needle, hold it with a tweezers or a folded card and pull

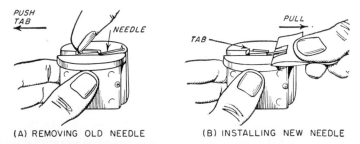

(A) REMOVING OLD NEEDLE   (B) INSTALLING NEW NEEDLE

Fig. 19. Replacement of Astatic needle having Taper Back shank. Pressure of the thumbnail on the tab will cause the needle to slide out, and the replacement needle is pulled into place by means of a folded card

so that the needle slides into place. The card may then be detached and pressure applied at the back of the needle shank to push it firmly in place. Pressure must not be applied to the playing tip of the needle.

Various types of Electro-Voice needles are used in crystal pickups having a special tapered socket that snugly fits the tapered needle shank. Figure 20 shows several needles. To remove the needle, a tweezers should be used. The replacement needle can then be inserted by holding the playing tip in a holder or tweezers and pushing firmly into place.

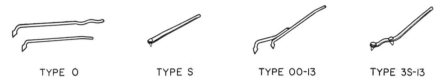

TYPE O   TYPE S   TYPE OO-I3   TYPE 3S-I3

Fig. 20. Examples of Electro-Voice friction-fit needles which must be slid in and out of cartridge when replacing

The tandem needle used by Magnavox is replaced as shown in Fig. 21. The hinge lock on the pickup arm, located underneath just forward of the pivot, must be released and the pickup arm raised. To remove the needle guard, a knife must be inserted under the eyelet at the *back* of the cartridge. Once the guard is released, the needle may be removed. To install the new needle, line up the key and slot, then push the shank all the way into the socket. If the needle does not fit snugly, it should be removed and the shank spread slightly by inserting a knife. The needle should then be

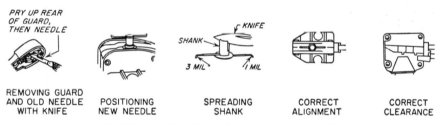

PRY UP REAR
OF GUARD,
THEN NEEDLE

SHANK

KNIFE

3 MIL   1 MIL

REMOVING GUARD
AND OLD NEEDLE   POSITIONING   SPREADING   CORRECT   CORRECT
WITH KNIFE   NEW NEEDLE   SHANK   ALIGNMENT   CLEARANCE

Fig. 21. Steps in replacing Magnavox tandem needle

positioned laterally and the needle guard replaced. Finally, bend the needle ends so that they extend about $\frac{1}{32}$ inch beyond the guard. A flat object should then be placed over each needle tip and pushed in until the object is flush with the guard. When the object is removed, the needles will spring out to the proper clearance.

One type of General Electric variable-reluctance pickup uses a friction-fit needle, as shown in Fig. 22. To remove, the cartridge must be taken out of the pickup arm. The needle may then be forced out with a wire or paper clip. The replacement needle is inserted with the fingers and, when centered between the guards, pressed firmly into place with your thumbnail.

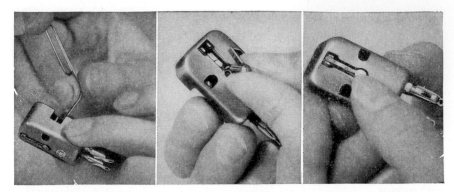

Fig. 22. Installing new needle in single-needle GE variable-reluctance pickup, after first removing pickup from pickup arm and pushing out old needle from back with paper clip (GE photo). Left—Pushing out old needle; center—inserting new needle; right—pressing in new needle

Replacing Keyed Needles. Keyed needles are also of the friction-grip variety. The Astatic type Q needle in Fig. 23 is of this style. Gently pry out the old needle with the blade of a knife. The key of the replacement needle should be aligned with the keyway of the cartridge and the needle then pressed into place. It should be lined up by using light lateral pressure so that it is in the center of the needle guard. As usual, caution should be used that pressure is not applied to the playing tip of the needle.

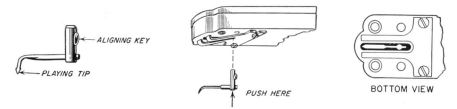

Fig. 23. Astatic type Q needle and the manner in which it is inserted in the cartridge. Pressure should not be applied to the playing tip

Replacement of the Columbia LP Microgroove needle is similar to that just described. The only difference is that both a right-hand and a left-hand key are used in various pickup models; hence the correct new needle must be ordered.

Replacement of the Philco keyed tandem needle is shown in Fig. 24. To remove the needle, the cartridge must first be taken out of the pickup arm. Hold the pickup arm securely on its rest, and push the needle selector down lightly until the lever disappears in the top of the pickup arm. The cartridge can then be removed. Remove the needle guard by inserting a knife blade under it and prying it off. Now insert the knife blade under the needle heel and gently pull the blade and needle straight out together. When the key on the new needle shank is properly aligned, press the new needle into place. Replace the needle guard with its pointed end facing toward the gold button on the cartridge case.

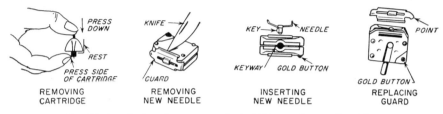

REMOVING CARTRIDGE — REMOVING NEW NEEDLE — INSERTING NEW NEEDLE — REPLACING GUARD

Fig. 24. Installation of a new needle in Philco tandem-needle pickup

Replacement of Miscellaneous Needle Styles. The Astatic type G needle has a special locking device. To replace this needle, the cartridge should be removed. The needle must be raised part way out of the socket, then rotated 90 degrees as illustrated in Fig. 25. When replacing the needle, it should be held at the right-angle position and pressed all of the way into the socket, then rotated 90 degrees to the normal playing position. Vertical pressure on the needle must be exerted only at the sharp bend.

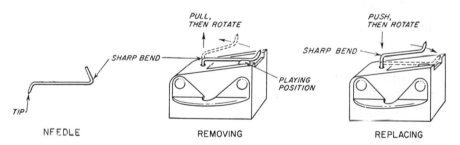

NEEDLE — REMOVING — REPLACING

Fig. 25. The Astatic type G needle uses a special twist-to-lock feature

The threaded-shank needles shown in Fig. 26 represent the usual RCA needles. Since these needles are held in place by a locking nut fastened on the upper side, the cartridge must be removed from the pickup arm. Place a mirror under the pickup arm as an aid in locating and removing the mounting screws. A screwdriver tool having a recessed screwdriver blade on one end and a hexagonal socket wrench on the other is available for this purpose from RCA distributors and most parts jobbers. The hexagonal-wrench end of the tool is then used to remove the locking nut from the end of the needle.

In replacing the needle, the reverse procedure is followed, making certain that the needle tip is centered between the guard prongs. When the cartridge is replaced in the pickup arm, the operation can be simplified by replacing the screw without the ground lug, tightening it lightly. The other screw can then be placed through the ground lug and put into place, tightening firmly. The first screw can then be tightened firmly.

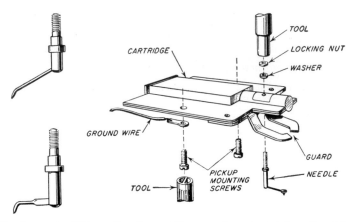

Fig. 26. To change the RCA needles, the cartridge must be extracted from the pickup arm in order to allow the locknut to be unscrewed. The needle then slips out

Servicing Pickup Arms. It is usually undesirable to attempt to repair pickup arms. Pickup-arm defects should be remedied by replacement of the entire shell with its attached parts. Adjustment of needle pressure and pickup-arm friction is, however, often necessary. The method of measuring these is by means of a scale as shown in Fig. 27. The springlike finger is placed in contact with the pickup as close to the needle as possible. The needle pressure is read directly from the calibrated scale, or better by taking the *average* of the readings obtained when the pickup arm is slowly raised and lowered.

Vertical friction is measured by moving the scale slowly upward about ½ inch and then downward to the original position. The *difference* between the two readings is the vertical friction.

To measure horizontal friction, the pickup arm must be balanced so that no weight is placed on the scale. This can be accomplished by placing a weight on the rear of the pickup arm as in Fig. 28. Where the overhang behind the hinge is small, it may be necessary to fasten a relatively long block of wood to the rear of the pickup arm. Scotch tape or masking tape is useful for this purpose. Once the pickup arm is balanced, you can move it horizontally. The needle pressure is read directly from the calibrated scale.

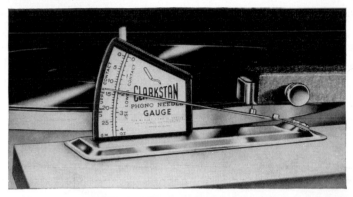

Fig. 27. A scale for measuring needle pressure. When needle is on upper button of spring-steel arm as shown, pressure is read in grams on outermost scale. For old 78-rpm cartridges needle is placed on lower button and value is read on ounce scale. (Pacific Transducer Corp. photo)

Fig. 28. Measurement of horizontal friction. Temporary weight is placed at rear end of pickup arm to balance it off turntable so needle does not touch anything. (Philco photo)

If the pickup arm has an adjustable counterweight, the needle pressure can be adjusted by moving the weight forward or backward. Moving it backward reduces needle pressure.

Where a spring or spring and counterweight are used, there is usually some means for adjusting the spring tension to change the needle pressure. Generally this is done by moving one end of the spring mount or by moving one end of the spring itself, as shown in Fig. 29. The direction of movement for reducing or increasing needle pressure can be determined easiest by trial.

If the vertical friction is too great or binding is indicated by erratic readings of the scale during test, the hinge assembly should be checked for grit, burrs, or other foreign particles. Cleaning by liberal application of carbon tetrachloride is in order. If burrs exist, the hinge should be disassembled, the burrs filed off, and the parts smoothed by rubbing thoroughly

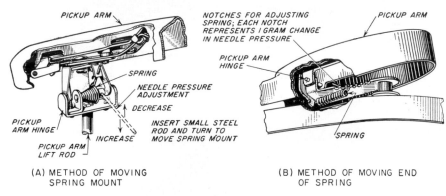

(A) METHOD OF MOVING
SPRING MOUNT

(B) METHOD OF MOVING END
OF SPRING

Fig. 29. Adjustment of needle pressure by varying the tension in the counterbalance spring

with a crocus cloth. Some record changers utilize two short-pointed pivots which fit into similarly shaped bearings. To allow for removal of the pickup arm, one pivot is actually a screw. Be sure the adjustable pivot is not so tight that it binds.

Horizontal friction may be caused by either the pickup-arm assembly or by a portion of the indexing mechanism associated with it. The pickup-arm assembly itself contains some sort of vertical shaft which fits in a bushing mounted on or in the record-changer base. This should be checked for burrs, grit, or other causes of binding. Again, washing with carbon tetrachloride is in order. Burrs may be removed by means of a light file and/or use of crocus cloth. The crocus cloth is necessary to provide a fine, smooth surface. Difficulties due to the associated indexing mechanism are taken up later.

Servicing Records. Care of records is not the serviceman's problem, but you will often be asked for advice on this subject. There is very little that can be done by the customer to repair or maintain records other than to take good care of them. However, Vinylite records get noisy after use due to accumulation of static charges.

Several compounds are available to eliminate this. One such product is Merix Anti-Static. This is applied by brushing over the record surface on one side only. Since static attracts dust, this compound also assists in keeping the surface clean. When recommending or selling a product like this, warn the customer that the dirt will be picked up by the needle on the first playing after an application. This dirt will clog the needle space, particularly on variable-reluctance pickups, unless cleaned out after every few records. It is best for the customer to play all records once after cleaning.

The best way to store records is vertically in albums. If stored horizontally, they will soon warp. For this reason records should not be left on the record player, particularly on the record shelves.

Handling. Since the needle and cartridge are most vulnerable to mishandling during transit, the pickup arm should be fastened to the center post with a heavy rubber band or with string when taking a changer to or from your shop. Sometimes it is easier to tie the pickup arm to its rest.

Records should be handled by the edges. If the grooves are touched, oily fingerprints are left which attract dust and dirt and may attack the record material. Since many customers never touch the record grooves, you should be extremely careful not to do so.

QUESTIONS

1. How does a crystal pickup work?
2. Why should a crystal cartridge be kept out of the show window?
3. Why is needle scratch low in a variable-reluctance pickup?
4. Name two types of dual-play cartridges.
5. What is the proper way of checking a needle for wear?
6. Name four jewels used as needle tips.
7. What is needle talk?
8. Describe the difference between standard, microgroove, and compromise needles.
9. Why is it desirable to have a highly compliant pickup?
10. What determines vertical and horizontal friction in a pickup arm?
11. How can you tell if poor volume is caused by the pickup or the amplifier?
12. Where will you look for trouble if you get a hum which disappears when the phono connection is disconnected from the amplifier?
13. How do you replace a crystal cartridge which has a two-conductor lead soldered to it?
14. How do you measure vertical and horizontal friction?
15. What precaution should you take when transporting a record changer?

6

Motors

Importance of Motor. Since the motor is the driving force of a record changer, its operation is vital. Good tone quality and proper reproduction cannot be obtained if the record changer is not functioning because of improper motor operation. A sustained note may waver, a voice may sound off-pitch, or music may drag or be so fast that all traces of good musicianship are lost. Naturally, other parts being worn or defective could have an effect on reproduction, but a smooth-running motor, at the proper speed, is the basis of satisfactory results.

Motors used in record players are not complicated pieces of mechanism. After a few units have been repaired, the jobs boil down to a matter of routine.

Spring-wound Motors. Motors used in the portable mechanical phonographs are of the spiral spring type. As such, all repairs are purely mechanical in nature. Where the motor is at fault, it must be removed from the case. To do so, the crank must first be taken out of the motor by turning counterclockwise, the turntable removed from the motor spindle, the screws loosened that hold the motor board in the case, and the entire assembly lifted out.

Governor. The motor in Fig. 1 has its speed controlled by a governor of the type used in mechanical motors. The governor consists of two or three weights attached to a hinged support. Each weight is mounted on a flat-strip spring which tends to keep it in close to the motor shaft.

As the speed of the motor increases, centrifugal force causes the weights to move outward. This causes the friction disc to move against the braking pad, increasing the load on the motor and tending to slow it down. As the motor slows down, the springs tend to pull the weights inward, thus decreasing the friction between the disc and the braking pad and allowing the motor to speed up. As this action continues, the motor tends to revolve at a very constant speed. A lever attached to the speed-regulating post controls the speed at which governor action occurs. This is accomplished by moving the adjusting plate that positions the braking pad. Because the governor is mounted on the end of the motor shaft, the turntable drive is geared to come off at right angles. In this case the turntable spindle rotates and moves the turntable.

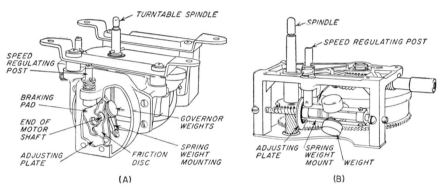

Fig. 1. A motor-drive assembly which includes a governor to regulate the speed. (A) Cutaway view of two-weight governor, (B) three-weight governor. (Howard W. Sams)

If the governor is at fault, it will not be necessary to disassemble the unit further. Trouble caused by the governor could result in a chattering, uneven speed, or noise.

When replacing a governor spring or weight, it must be exactly the same as the original part. This must be so; otherwise the balance will be disturbed and uneven speed will result. A governor is usually held in place by a small screw at either end, with the weight being attached to the spring in the same manner.

The brake plate, to which one end of the governor springs attach, must be clean and polished. Since the brake pad rubs on this plate, any foreign matter or roughness would affect smooth operation. Since the brake serves to control the speed rather than to stop the motor, only a small amount of friction is required. The brake pad should be clean and soaked with SAE 10W oil so that this condition is met.

Defective Mechanical Motor. The most likely troubles are a broken main spring and worn gears. Since few mechanical motors are used, it is difficult to obtain replacement parts. It is best to obtain a replacement motor if possible. The best source for this is the manufacturer. Look on the motor and the record player to find the name and address of the manufacturer of either. Also look for a model number as this will be necessary for the manufacturer to identify the item. When writing for the replacement motor, it is better to send too much information than too little.

Electric Motors. By far the majority of motors used are of the electric type. The reasons for this are the convenience of not having to rewind after each record and the more constant speed obtained. To better appreciate this, it might be well to set forth the desired qualities of a motor other than those established by the desire for convenience.

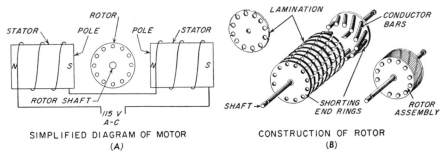

Fig. 2. An electric motor consists of a magnetic stator and a rotor which revolves on its shaft. (Howard W. Sams)

Constant speed, even under load, is a necessity to avoid variation in sound. This also requires that the turntable be driven at full speed almost immediately. The motor must be of convenient or small size and light weight. The desired long life dictates ruggedness and dependability. To produce satisfactory sound, silence and freedom from electrical interference are required.

To understand the operation of the electric motor, the magnetic theory will be briefly described. This will assist materially in attacking motor problems encountered in practice.

In an electric phonograph motor, the field or electromagnet portion remains stationary and is called the stator. The coil rotates and is called the rotor. This is sketched in Fig. 2A. Instead of using a single coil, a rotor consists of a number of copper conductors set into grooves in a laminated steel core. The ends of these conductors are shorted to each other by means of copper shorting rings at the ends, as shown in Fig. 2B. Instead of being parallel to the rotor shaft, the conductors are slightly askew. This gives a more even torque and eliminates dead spots from which the motor would not start itself.

The motors used in record changers are of the shaded-pole induction type, such as shown in Fig. 3A. The portions of the stator which are closest to the rotor are called the pole faces. The normal pole face is modified to take a shading coil as shown in Fig. 3B. The pole face is notched and a

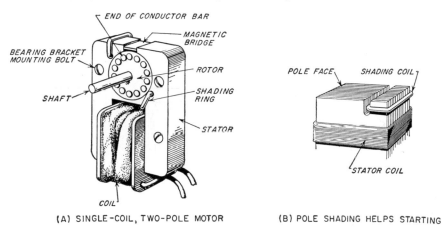

(A) SINGLE-COIL, TWO-POLE MOTOR   (B) POLE SHADING HELPS STARTING

Fig. 3. A shaded-pole induction motor is commonly used in record changers. (Howard W. Sams)

copper ring is placed so as to surround the smaller portion, usually about one third. This shading coil makes the motor self-starting. The rotor movement can be determined by looking at the shading coils because it rotates from the unshaded area toward the shaded portion as shown in Fig. 4.

Fig. 4. Rotation can be determined by location of shading rings. (Howard W. Sams)

As the load on the motor increases, the speed of rotation is decreased, but a greater rotating force or torque is developed. The motor is designed to have maximum torque near the speed at which the record changer is normally operated.

The theoretical maximum speed in a two-pole motor is 3,600 rpm and in a four-pole motor is 1,800 rpm. Since slippage is necessary, the rotor in a two-pole motor will rotate at about 3,000 to 3,500 rpm, and in a four-pole motor at about 1,300 to 1,750 rpm. The speed is determined by the designer and is relatively constant under the load variations imposed.

Construction Features. A four-pole motor has a lower speed and better power. Because of the lower speed, vibration occurs at lower frequencies where it is not as objectionable. The physical size of the rotor is larger and more easily balanced. Because of the slower speed, a larger drive pulley can be used so tolerances do not have to be so close. These extra features are more costly since the four-pole motor is more complex than the two-pole motor. For that reason it is used only in deluxe units.

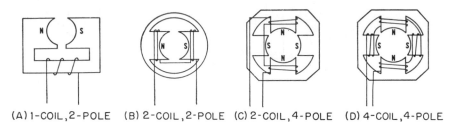

(A) 1-COIL, 2-POLE   (B) 2-COIL, 2-POLE   (C) 2-COIL, 4-POLE   (D) 4-COIL, 4-POLE

Fig. 5. Stator and coil arrangements used in phonograph motors. (Howard W. Sams)

Stators and Coils. Since the coils are wound on the stator, both must be discussed together. Figure 5 illustrates coil and stator arrangements used. The most common type of construction is the single-coil, two-pole unit shown in Fig. 3A. A magnetic bridge joins the ends of the poles. This increases the flux between the shaded portion of one pole and the unshaded portion of the other pole, providing a uniform air gap between all portions of the stator and the rotor, thus improving the performance of the motor. It also cuts down on stray magnetic fields so as to keep extraneous pickup in the cartridge to a minimum.

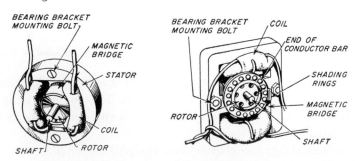

Fig. 6. Two-coil, two-pole motor (left) and a two-coil, four-pole motor (at right). (Howard W. Sams)

A two-coil, two-pole motor and a two-coil, four-pole motor are shown in Fig. 6. The latter unit uses two shading rings. In some cases three pole-shading rings are used. The additional rings give faster acceleration during starting.

Bearings. To support the rotor, bearings are mounted in the end plates of the motor frame. A motor showing the end supports is shown in Fig. 7. The assembly is exploded in Fig. 8. The bearings are of the sleeve type. They are usually of a porous, oil-impregnated combination generally considered oilless. To assure proper lubrication, an oil-saturated felt washer is often included, as in the case illustrated. In addition, some manufacturers specify oiling as a maintenance procedure.

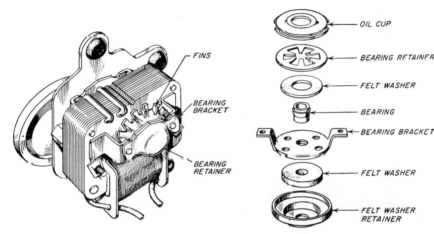

Fig. 7. The end supports mount on the stator and provide bearing support for the rotor. The fan on the rotor shaft provides ventilation. (Howard W. Sams)

Fig. 8. An exploded view of the bearing assembly. (Howard W. Sams)

The bearing retainer is a star-shaped piece into which the bearing fits in a manner which allows movement at right angles to the rotor shaft. Thus the bearing assembly is self-aligning so that the end plates may be adjusted to center the rotor in the stator opening. Where provision is made for adjustment, the screws holding the bearing bracket must be loosened. Then move the bearing assembly so the rotor is centered, and tighten the screws.

In more expensive motors ball bearings are used. This allows construction of a nature where shaft movement along its axis is reduced. Since the motor mounts with the shaft in the vertical plane, vertical movement of the rotor shaft is reduced. This is of particular advantage in wire and tape recorders because it assures level winding and avoids variations in the sound level.

Other Features. Many motors use a fan arrangement on the end of the motor shaft to provide ventilation. Figure 7 shows such an arrangement.

The shaded-pole induction motor can be stalled for long periods of time without causing undue damage. This means the motor is rarely damaged when the cycling mechanism jams.

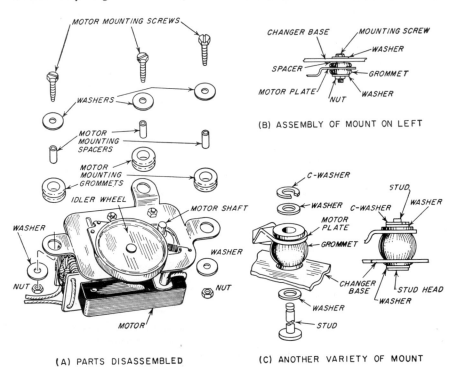

Fig. 9. The parts used to isolate the motor from the base of the record player to avoid transmission of mechanical vibrations

Mounting the Motor. Since a pickup converts small mechanical variations into electric signals that are amplified tremendously, it is essential that normal vibrations of the rotating motor do not reach the needle. This is accomplished by mechanically shock-mounting the motor. The most common method is to mount the motor to the base of the record player by means of rubber grommets. This is shown in Fig. 9. The motor brackets have relatively large holes into which are inserted the rubber grommets.

The mounting screws and any desired spacers or standoffs fit through the inside of the grommets and are secured to the changer base plate. In this manner the grommet isolates the metal pieces and absorbs the vibrations which exist. The spacers or standoffs are designed so that the nuts may be tightened on the screws and not come loose.

Motor Repairs. The foregoing discussion indicates the relatively simple construction used in record-changer motors. The sturdy mechanical features assure a minimum of trouble. As a result, the amount of work that a serviceman may carry out is definitely limited. At the same time, a little experience and the ability to recognize the proper approach can result in material savings in time.

Isolating Trouble. Where the motor does not rotate, it must first be determined that it has not been stalled by an excessive load. Rotation of the turntable by hand will determine whether or not any part of the changer mechanism is jamming.

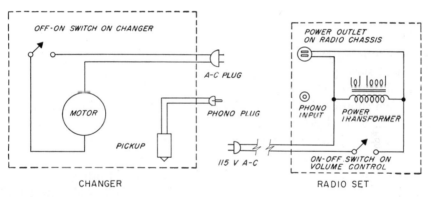

Fig. 10. The usual electrical circuit in a record changer. Sometimes the changer is connected directly to the power line and phono input without using the outlet on the radio chassis

Make sure that electricity is being applied to the motor. Be sure the trouble is not in the switch or an open lead or connection. Figure 10 shows the usual electrical circuit in a record changer. Once the difficulty has been isolated as being in the motor, a check should be made to determine whether or not the rotor is free to turn. This may be accomplished by trying to rotate the rotor with your fingers. If it rotates, the trouble is electrical in nature; otherwise it is mechanical.

Frozen Rotor. If the rotor does not move or is very stiff when turned by the fingers, the spacing between the rotor and stator should be checked to ascertain that there is clearance all the way around. If this clearance is lacking, the end plates should be loosened and tapped lightly so as to properly align the rotor.

A gumming condition can give the same results. In this case the lubricant turns to varnish and leaves a hard film on the rotor shaft or the bearing surfaces. This film may be removed with emery cloth after taking the motor apart. Use care to remove only the film. Both the shaft and the bearing should then be polished by means of a crocus cloth. The oil retainers should be washed well with carbon tetrachloride. After the washed parts have dried, they may be lubricated with a light, high-grade motor oil, such as SAE 10W. Do not use 3-in-1 oil.

Rust on the rotor or pole pieces can also cause binding. This can be located by inspection. The rust may be removed with fine emery cloth, after which the rotor should be cleaned with carbon tetrachloride and the motor reassembled.

Worn bearings may cause rubbing between the rotor and stator, or an annoying chatter. Badly worn bearings can be replaced if new ones are available, but usually the entire motor must be replaced.

Slow-running Motor. The troubles described above can cause a motor to run at slow speed. The proper repair is carried out in the same manner as would be used for a frozen rotor.

Broken shorting rings at the end of the rotor can result in a motor slowing down under load. Soldering to complete the circuit will correct this. Crimping the joint may correct the trouble temporarily, but solder is essential for a permanent repair.

Lamination Buzz. Loose laminations in a motor will often cause a mechanical buzzing sound. Tightening of the rivets or bolts will correct this, provided it is possible to take up on them sufficiently.

Magnetic bridges may also buzz. In this case they should be pressed out, bent, then replaced in exactly the same position as before.

Electrical Troubles. A motor with open stator winding will not run. Since the coils are wound on a special machine and cannot easily be rewound by hand, it is advisable to replace the entire motor.

A short in the stator windings can cause a motor to run slowly or have no pulling power. In this case the windings will probably become hot because of the heavy current drain. Where there is more than one stator coil, a measurement of the resistance would result in one reading considerably less than any other. Again, the motor should be replaced.

A short between a stator winding and the core creates a shock hazard.

In this case the motor shell and possibly the whole record changer becomes electrically hot so that it may shock a person. It may also result in continual blowing of fuses, particularly if the changer is grounded to the radio as it should be.

Dirty Motor. Where it is found that a motor has been oiled to excess and a heavy accumulation of oil, lint, dust, and dirt is on the motor, it should be taken apart and washed thoroughly with carbon tetrachloride. After the parts have dried, the bearings should be lubricated with SAE 10W motor oil and reassembled.

QUESTIONS

1. Why do governor weights move outward when a motor speeds up?
2. What are two reasons for using electric motors?
3. Describe a rotor.
4. What is the purpose of shading rings?
5. How can you tell the direction of motor rotation by looking at it?
6. What are the advantages of a four-pole motor?
7. What is the most common combination of coils and poles in a changer motor?
8. How do you align the rotor if it is off center?
9. How do you clean a motor that has frozen due to gumming of the lubricant?

7

Motor Drives

Variety of Drives. The methods used by different manufacturers to drive turntables or record changers are varied. None are complex or elaborate. Simplicity seems to be the main thought. The desired result, which is driving the turntable at the standard speeds of 78.26 rpm, 33⅓ rpm, and 45 rpm, must be the same regardless of how it is designed. Turntable speeds may be any one of these three or a combination of all. The earlier standard speed of 78.26 rpm is generally referred to simply as 78 rpm. With the exception of portions of this chapter this broader generalization will be used.

Direct Drive. In the direct-drive system, the turntable is attached directly to the motor shaft. In this case the rotor must spin at 78.26 rpm, and the design of the motor is the governing factor. Since the turntable has considerable weight, it acts as a flywheel tending to maintain constant speed. It is doubtful that such an arrangement will ever be encountered as it is seldom used.

Shaft couplings between the motor and turntable may sometimes be encountered. These will generally have some sort of rubber link to transmit the power from the motor shaft to the turntable shaft, but they will absorb vibrations and sudden speed variations. To obtain proper operation, the rubber link must be in good condition. If found to be hard or damaged, it should be replaced. A hard strip will not properly absorb vibrations but will tend to transmit them.

Gear Drive. Connection of the motor to the turntable shaft through a gear assembly has been used quite frequently, although precision machining is required in order to have no gear noise or speed variations. Figure 1 illustrates

100

an induction motor with a gear drive. A worm gear on the rotor shaft engages a pinion gear. The upper end of the pinion-gear shaft is the seat and spindle for the turntable. The worm gear can be fastened to the rotor shaft or can actually be cut as an integral part of the shaft. The worm is of steel construction. The pinion may be a fiber- or linen-base Bakelite to help reduce gear noise. There is usually a set-screw adjustment in the housing which holds the end of the rotor shaft. This prevents the worm from moving back and forth laterally; hence it removes end play. In a gear drive it is necessary to eliminate this end play because it could result in momentary changes in speed of a turntable. A change in speed results in a wow or variation in the reproduction of sound.

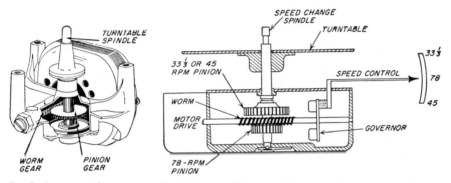

Fig. 1. A motor with a worm-gear drive

Fig. 2. A gear-drive turntable arranged to play at all three speeds. Pinions are shown in neutral position, where motor spins without driving turntable

Two- and Three-speed Gear Drive. Figure 2 illustrates a three-speed gear-drive mechanism featuring a speed-change spindle. When the spindle is in the up position, the standard 78-rpm rotation is obtained. When in the down position, either the 33⅓-rpm or 45-rpm speeds are obtained as determined by the setting of the governor control.

Rim Drive. The rim-drive method is used in practically all home-type record players of today and has proven to be most satisfactory. The drive is easy to manufacture, and the precision necessary in a gear-drive assembly is not required here. Figure 3 shows a rim-drive mechanism with its motor and the mounting plate. The end of the motor shaft is used as a drive wheel.

A larger rubber-tired wheel, known as the idler wheel, is mounted so that it presses against the motor shaft and at the same time against the turntable rim. A spring is connected to the idler arm so that constant pressure can be kept against the motor shaft and the turntable rim. The size of the idler wheel has no effect on turntable speed, but serves mainly to prevent slippage and absorb vibrations.

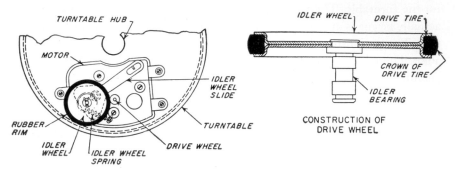

Fig. 3. A rim-drive mechanism

A tight-fitting spring or bushing may be forced over the motor shaft to change its diameter and thereby change the speed ratio, as shown in Fig. 4. The thicker the motor shaft or drive wheel, the lower is the speed ratio and the faster is the turntable rotation. By adding such a bushing or spring, a normal 60-cycle motor may often be utilized on 50-cycle current, thus compensating for the resulting slowing of motor speed at 50 cycles. Similarly, the addition of a spring to the motor shaft can change 33⅓-rpm operation to 45-rpm operation.

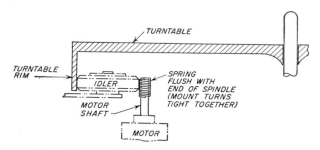

Fig. 4. A wheel-assembly drive mechanism showing a spring sleeve installed on the motor spindle. This changes the speed ratio between the motor shaft and the idler so as to allow the use of a 60-cycle motor from a 50-cycle source. (Howard W. Sams)

Dual-speed Rim Drive. Two speeds may be obtained from an arrangement such as shown in Fig. 5. Here two different drive wheels and idlers are used to do the job. By using a lever, the upper drive wheel and upper idler can be put into service, giving a speed of 33⅓ rpm. Changing the position of the lever brings the lower set into operation and gives a speed of 78 rpm.

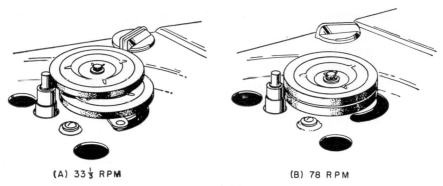

(A) 33⅓ RPM   (B) 78 RPM

Fig. 5. A two-speed drive arrangement

Three-speed Rim Drive. The three-speed arrangement of Fig. 6 is called a turret-type drive because the three idler pulleys are on a single mount. This mount is rotated from position to position by means of a speed-changing lever. When one of the idler pulleys is against the large idler wheel to give the desired speed, the motor shaft is in contact with the lower portion of that same idler pulley. The idler wheel in turn drives the turntable rim.

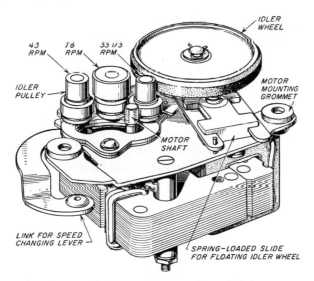

Fig. 6. A three-speed drive arrangement often called the turret type

Since each idler pulley has a different radius ratio for its upper and lower pulleys, selection of the idler pulley determines the final turntable speed.

The bottom portions of each idler pulley are identical; hence the radius of the top portion indicates the relative speed. Thus, the idler pulley with the smallest upper radius is used for 33⅓ rpm. The one with the largest upper radius is used for 78 rpm. The remaining intermediate-size pulley is used to obtain a 45-rpm speed.

Variations in Mechanical Arrangement. Although there are many other pulley and idler-wheel arrangements for motor-driven turntables, you will usually be able to figure out how they work at a glance. Only a few more examples need be considered to give the experience that builds confidence.

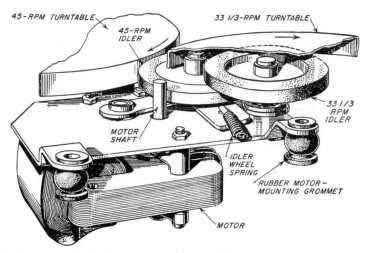

Fig. 7. A drive mechanism designed to drive one turntable at 45 rpm and another at 33⅓ rpm

Figure 7 illustrates a method of driving two turntables simultaneously, one at 33⅓ rpm and the other at 45 rpm. The motor shaft drives one idler wheel which drives one turntable at 45 rpm. A hub on this idler is used as a drive wheel to drive the other idler which simultaneously drives the other turntable at 33⅓ rpm. A single pickup arm is used to play the desired stack of 7-inch records.

Another unique arrangement is shown in Fig. 8. Here the motor shaft and idler-wheel arrangement is similar to that just described, but a single turntable is used. The ratios of wheel diameters are such that turntable speeds of 78 rpm and 33⅓ rpm are obtained by selecting the proper position of the speed control. The unique feature here is that the turntable has two rims.

For 78-rpm operation the motor shaft drives the left-hand idler wheel which engages the larger, or outside, turntable rim.

When the speed control is positioned for 33⅓ rpm, the left-hand idler wheel moves to the right. This disengages it from the rim, but still leaves it in contact with the motor shaft. A hub under the left-hand idler wheel now drives the right-hand idler wheel and this in turn engages the inside, or smaller, rim.

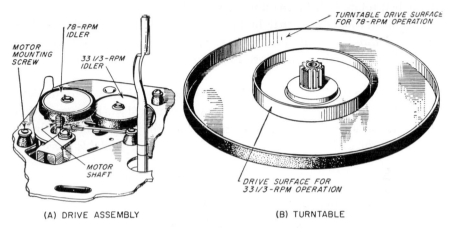

(A) DRIVE ASSEMBLY   (B) TURNTABLE

Fig. 8. A dual-speed drive system using two rims on the turntable

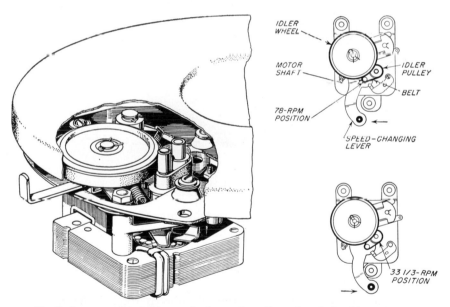

Fig. 9. A two-speed belt-drive mechanism and an illustration of the drive sequence

Belt Linkage. Another method of obtaining rim drive is to utilize a belt-linkage mechanism. The belt-drive mechanism, as it is sometimes called, is shown in Fig. 9 and consists of a drive pulley connected to another pulley by means of a rubber belt. The rubber belt is made slightly smaller than the required size and stretched to secure a good friction fit. The principles involved are the same as previously described except that both wheels linked by the belt rotate in the same direction.

The illustration shows that in the 78-rpm position the motor shaft is connected directly to the idler wheel. The motor shaft rotates the idler pulley through the belt, but since the idler pulley is disengaged, it has no effect.

To change to the 33⅓-rpm position, the idler wheel is moved to the right. The motor shaft still rotates the idler pulley by means of the belt connection. However, the idler pulley is now engaged with the idler wheel causing it to rotate at the desired new speed to give the 33⅓-rpm turntable speed.

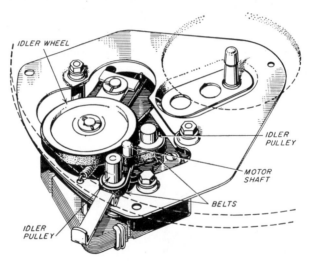

Fig. 10. A three-speed belt-drive mechanism

Belts can also be used to give a choice of three speeds, as shown in Fig. 10. In this type of drive, the idler wheel is driven directly by the motor shaft to give 78 rpm. To obtain the other speeds, the speed control lever shifts the entire idler pulley assembly much as is done in the turret-type three-speed drive.

To obtain the 33⅓-rpm speed, the assembly is rotated slightly in the counterclockwise direction. This disengages the motor shaft from the idler wheel and engages the right-hand pulley with the idler wheel. The motor shaft now transmits power through the belt to the 33⅓-rpm idler pulley. In similar fashion, the assembly is turned clockwise when the speed control is shifted to the 45-rpm position. Now the motor shaft transmits power through the other belt to the 45-rpm idler pulley which in turn drives the idler wheel.

Checking Speed with Stroboscope. If a turntable rotates but you suspect that its speed is not correct, this may be checked easily with a stroboscopic disc. Improper speed will give the wrong pitch, easily detected by musicians but often not even noticed by others. The effect of wrong speed is most evident in a spring-wound type of phonograph if the motor is allowed to run down while the record is still playing.

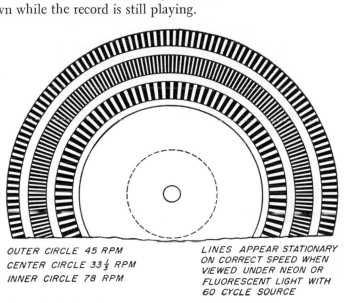

OUTER CIRCLE 45 RPM
CENTER CIRCLE 33⅓ RPM
INNER CIRCLE 78 RPM

LINES APPEAR STATIONARY
ON CORRECT SPEED WHEN
VIEWED UNDER NEON OR
FLUORESCENT LIGHT WITH
60 CYCLE SOURCE

Fig. 11. Example of stroboscopic disc used to check turntable speed and variations

If a turntable alternately slows down and speeds up, the resulting variations in the pitch are called wow. Such variations in turntable speed can also be detected by means of a stroboscopic disc like that shown in Fig. 11. These discs are usually made of paper but vary in size and in markings. Some use dots and others use short bars.

To use a stroboscopic disc, place it on the turntable and turn on the motor. Illuminate the disc with an incandescent or fluorescent light or with a 2-watt neon lamp. The dots or bars on the disc will appear to be stationary if the turntable is revolving at the correct speed. If a movement of the dots in a clockwise direction is obtained, the turntable is rotating too fast. If a counterclockwise movement is obtained, the turntable is rotating too slow.

It is well to make a test under actual playing conditions. In this manner the weight of the records and the drag of the needle are taken into consideration. Three different speed checks will give an over-all test. First, the speed should be noted with a single record on the turntable. Another check may be made with five records on the turntable, and finally a check made with ten records on the turntable. In this manner it can be determined whether or not loading the machine will cause any radical changes in motor speed or operation. Permissible speed variations depend upon the listener.

Sometimes a cyclic effect can be noted whereby the dots appear to move back and forth in an even steady rhythm. This can result from slippage, lateral movement of the motor shaft, or an uneven turntable rim. A bad meshing of gears could also give a cyclic effect. Remedies are covered near the end of this chapter. A stroboscopic disc must be illuminated at the frequency for which it was designed. As a result the discs are marked for 50-cycle or 60-cycle operation. Stroboscopic discs can generally be obtained free or at a nominal charge from makers of needles, motors, or other phonograph parts. Your local parts jobber can supply this device.

Test Records. One type of test record includes a standard steady-frequency note which will play for a considerable period of time. By listening to this through the regular phonograph sound system, any variation in speed can be detected as a change in pitch. Some test records include a series of different single frequencies which are of real help to servicemen who have never had musical training or who cannot recognize changes in tone.

Servicing Gear Drives. The gear-type drive is very satisfactory and simple, but troubles can occur. Some of the more typical difficulties include worn pinion gears and worn bearings. In either case the gear or bearings must be replaced. Dried or caked lubrication on the gears is another source of difficulty and should be washed off with carbon tetrachloride. A fresh application of a light, high-quality grease should then be applied to the worm and pinion gears. Excellent greases to use for this purpose are those bearing the trade name of STA-PUT or Lubriplate.

A varnish deposit on the shaft or bearings is another cause of difficulty. This results from the use of poor oil on the gear shaft, which should be removed by means of a fine emery cloth. The shaft and bearing should then be polished with a crocus cloth. During reassembly a few drops of a very light top-grade motor oil should be used. SAE 10W is a high-grade lubricant for this purpose and can be purchased from most automobile service stations.

Servicing Rim-drive Mechanisms. Figures 12 and 13 illustrate several possible defects in a rim-drive system. Idler-wheel difficulties include worn bearings that cause the wheel to wobble, defective tires that are either hard and glazed or soft from oil or grease, and tires having indentations that cause a thumping during rotation. In all cases the entire idler wheel should be replaced. No attempt should be made to repair the idler wheel because of the inexpensiveness of the item and the fact that more satisfactory results are obtained with a new wheel.

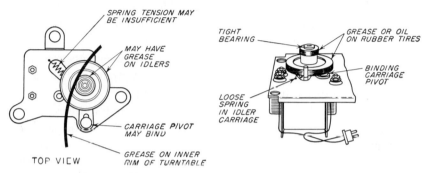

Fig. 12. Wow or slow turntable speed may be due to the drive mechanism defects illustrated here. The motor, spindle, and turntable are also sources of these troubles

Indentation of the idler-wheel tire is generally caused by a stalling of the turntable while the motor continues to run. In this event it is advisable to check the turntable operation thoroughly so that the problem does not recur.

The motor shaft, idler pulleys, idler wheels, and turntable rim should be checked for grease, oil, dirt, lint, or any other foreign matter. Alcohol is a good cleaning agent. Carbon tetrachloride should not be used on rubber as it is a solvent. These surfaces should be kept clean at all times. Slippage is due to oil or grease being present on any of the drive units.

A wow or rumble in reproduction will be caused by a turntable rim that is

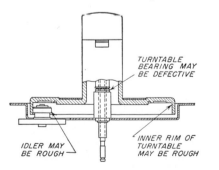

Fig. 13. Illustration of drive mechanisms that may cause rumble. Note that turntable defects can also cause this trouble

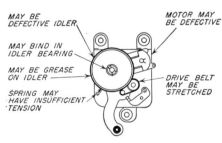

Fig. 14. In a drive mechanism that utilizes a belt drive, the belt is an additional source of wow or slow turntable speed

dented or out of round. Since it is almost impossible to hammer a turntable to its original shape, it should be replaced.

In servicing the rim-drive mechanisms, caution should be taken when lubricating the idler wheel. A drop of light motor oil, SAE 10W, is enough. In the event that there are felt washers which go on the idler shaft, the oil can be applied to those washers. As previously indicated, if any oil gets on the idler-wheel tire or turntable rim, it should be washed off immediately with alcohol.

The same type of difficulties apply to belt-drive arrangements except that the rubber belt is now an added item to consider. A stretched belt may be a cause of wow in such a system, as shown in Fig. 14.

General Service Hints. In repairing or adjusting motor drives, it is essential to keep in mind the necessity of doing a thorough job. The parts must be clean and free from excess oil. It is perhaps better to lubricate too little than too much. It is a good thing to remember that oil has a very bad effect on rubber. Never hesitate to clean any of the parts involved with alcohol.

Parts that show signs of wear or age should be replaced. The result will be a smoother-running job, which will be evidenced when the stroboscopic disc is used to check the speed. Be sure the motor is floating and free from any surrounding objects.

QUESTIONS

1. Name the three normal turntable speeds.
2. What is the common type of turntable drive mechanism?
3. Describe a three-speed rim drive.
4. What is the difference between the direct rim drive and a belt-linkage rim drive?
5. How do you use a stroboscope disc?
6. What method other than the stroboscope disc can you use for checking turntable speed?
7. If a thump is heard when the turntable rotates, how would you fix it?
8. What is the effect of oil on a rubber idler wheel?

8

Tripping Mechanisms

Power Drive to Change Records. In a record player, the motor serves only to drive the turntable. In a record changer, however, the motor also performs the task of changing the records.

If the turntable is fastened to the record spindle, a gear can be placed on the spindle for delivering power to the record-changing mechanism. In practice it is often desirable to keep the spindle stationary, so that it does not rotate with the turntable. In this case the gear is put on the hub of the turntable, and a hole is placed through it so the spindle fits inside yet remains independent. A turntable with a hub gear is shown in Fig. 1. Since

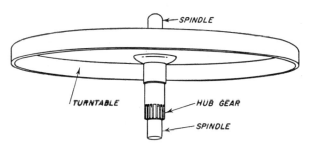

Fig. 1. A turntable with a hub gear. The spindle fits freely inside the hub so that the turntable will rotate independently of it

this hub gear is usually smaller than the gear it drives, it is often referred to as a pinion gear.

The customary means of operating the changing mechanism is to use a drive gear which may or may not have a cam mechanism built into it. This drive gear meshes with the hub gear of the turntable.

Requirement for Trip Mechanism. Since the changing mechanism is used during only a portion of the operation, there must be some sort of clutch arrangement whereby the gears or wheels can be engaged or disengaged while a record is being played. It is for this purpose that the tripping mechanism has been designed. When the record is finished playing, a tripping mechanism must engage the clutch to start the changing cycle which in turn removes the pickup arm from the record, drops another record into position on the turntable, brings the pickup arm back, and sets it down in the starting groove of the record. This chapter will tell how these clutch and tripping mechanisms work, how they can get out of order, and how they are fixed.

Mutilated-clutch Mechanism. One of the simple methods of disengaging the gears of the changing mechanism is to cut away or mutilate a section of the larger drive gear. Now the hub gear can rotate without contacting the drive gear.

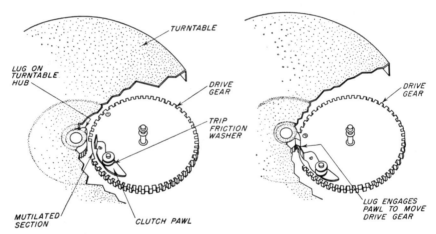

Fig. 2. A simple clutch arrangement where the drive gear has a mutilated section and a lever is used as a clutch

In order to operate the drive gear during the changing cycle, it is then necessary to provide a means of meshing the two gears. If a projection is put above the hub gear in such a manner that it will contact another projection on the top of the drive gear, as in Fig. 2, a means of meshing the gears is provided. The drive gear has a mutilated section for disengaging the gears between cycles. A movable lever called a pawl is mounted on the drive gear. To engage the gears, the pawl on the drive gear is pushed outward by a part of the tripping mechanism. Now when the offset on the hub gear comes around again, it catches on the pawl. This turns the drive gear far enough so that the teeth of the hub gear and the drive gear mesh. As the turntable rotates, the drive gear is caused to go through one revolution. If the pawl on the drive gear is now drawn back toward the center, the drive gear will rotate to the point where the mutilated section is again opposite the hub gear. The two gears are now out of mesh or disengaged, and rotation of the drive gear is stopped.

If the load on the drive gear is sufficiently heavy, it will not coast past the mutilated section. If the load is light, it may be necessary to provide a means of stopping the drive gear in the proper position. This may be accomplished by some sort of detent action. One method is illustrated in Fig. 3 where a roller on the end of a spring-loaded lever fits into a notch cut in the edge of a protrusion on the drive gear.

Gravity-type Clutch Mechanism. Another possible arrangement of gears is to place one above the other and provide some means of connecting the two. Figure 4 shows such an arrangement where two gears are placed one above the other on the same axle. The lower gear has a freely pivoted

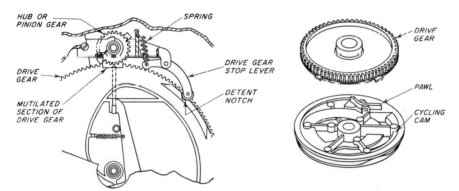

HUB OR PINION GEAR — SPRING — DRIVE GEAR — DRIVE GEAR STOP LEVER — DETENT NOTCH — MUTILATED SECTION OF DRIVE GEAR — DRIVE GEAR — PAWL — CYCLING CAM

Fig. 3. A drive gear for the changing mechanism which uses a detent action to assure that it stops in the proper place after completing the cycle

Fig. 4. An over-and-under type of drive using a gravity-type pawl to engage the two gears. Right end of pawl is heaviest

pawl rigidly fastened to it in such a manner that one end is heavier than the other. Thus the heavy end normally drops and the opposite end rises. The light end of the pawl is shaped so that it will fit into any one of the teeth cut in the lower face of the upper gear.

When the pawl is in its free position, the two gears are locked and rotate together. Another part of the changing mechanism is used to hold the light end of the pawl away from the upper gear when they are to be disengaged. This principle is used in some mechanisms as a drive feature.

Actuating Mechanisms. The actuating or tripping mechanisms which are used to operate the clutch assembly consist of three types. These types are the position trip, the eccentric trip, and the velocity trip.

The position trip operates when the pickup arm has reached a specified distance from the center of the record. Usually this occurs at about 1⅞ inches out from the center of the record.

The eccentric trip is actuated by the eccentric movement of the pickup arm when it is in the fast-finishing grooves at the inside of a record. When the needle enters the fast-finishing grooves, the pickup arm moves quickly toward the center of the record, then outward again for a small portion, then in again. The eccentric trip utilizes the change in motion from an inward direction to an outward direction.

The velocity trip works on the basis that when the record is playing, the pickup arm moves slowly toward the center of the record, but when the record is completed, the pickup arm moves rapidly inward due to the fast-finishing grooves. The velocity trip utilizes this rapid movement to actuate the clutch mechanism.

Variations and Combinations. Almost any possible combination of the clutch and actuating mechanisms may be used in record changers. However, once you know how each type of clutch and each type of trip works by itself, you will be able to figure out and repair any of the combinations, no matter how new they may look at first glance.

Some newer models of record changers use switches and electric solenoids to operate various mechanisms. The solenoid is a positive device which eliminates the possibility of uncertain action. Both switches and solenoids initiate tripping in the same way as is done by the reject button on changers. A switch can be incorporated in any of the trips that will now be taken up.

Position Trip. The position trip was frequently used in the early changers, but because of its limitations it is seldom used today. Some manufacturers used the position trip in conjunction with the eccentric trip on the same changer.

One example of the position trip which initiates recycling when the pickup arm is about 1⅞ inches from the center of the record will be considered here.

Position-trip Mechanism. Power from the motor is delivered to the rim of the turntable by means of a conventional idler-wheel rim drive. The

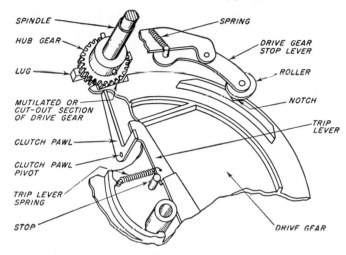

Fig. 5. In the neutral position of the trip lever it holds the clutch pawl above the lugs on the hub gear, so the lugs do not hit it as they turn during the playing of a record

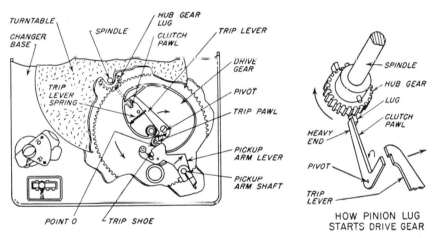

Fig. 6. When the trip lever releases the clutch pawl, the heavy end falls, allowing it to contact one of the hub-gear lugs and start the change cycle

record spindle, which rotates with the turntable, has at its lower end a hub gear that serves to transfer power to the changing mechanism when the pickup arm reaches the tripping position at the end of a record.

The neutral or record-playing position of the trip system is shown in Fig. 5. The hub gear has two lugs which are directly opposite each other. The drive gear has about half a dozen teeth left out directly opposite the hub gear when the drive gear is in its neutral position. In neutral the trip lever holds the clutch pawl above the lugs on the hub gear, so that these lugs cannot hit anything as the hub gear rotates with the turntable. When the pickup arm moves toward the center of the record, the pickup-arm lever shown in Fig. 6 moves also. The pickup arm is clamped to the upper end of a shaft and the pickup-arm lever is clamped to the lower end. The shaft thus acts as a pivot. As the needle reaches a point about 1⅞ inches from the center of the record, the trip shoe on the pickup-arm lever hits the trip lever at point O. This forces the lower end of the trip lever clockwise. The other end of the trip lever also moves clockwise out of position so that there is now nothing on the lower end of the clutch pawl. The weight of the upper end of the clutch pawl now makes this end drop down against a stop. This is just far enough so that one of the lugs of the rotating hub gear comes in contact with the pawl.

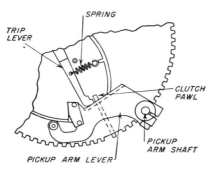

Fig. 7. The edge of the pickup-arm lever resets the clutch pawl

When the hub-gear lug hits the projecting clutch pawl on the drive gear, it moves the drive gear enough to allow the teeth of the hub gear and the drive gear to engage. This starts the change cycle. One complete revolution of the drive gear gives an entire change cycle.

During this revolution the clutch pawl and trip lever are reset automatically, so that as the drive gear returns to the neutral position, the lugs on the hub gear will not engage the clutch pawl. As the drive gear rotates, the trip lever is returned to its rest position by the pull of the trip-lever spring. The heavy end of the clutch pawl is still hanging down. The light end of this pawl is hence hanging forward toward the outer edge of the drive gear. When the drive gear approaches the halfway mark in its cycle, this light end contacts the flat edge of the pickup-arm lever, as in Fig. 7. This pushes against the clutch pawl forcing it back so that the trip lever catches it.

Upon completion of the cycle a lever and roller assembly drops into a notch in the drive gear to prevent it from coasting past neutral, as shown in Fig. 5.

When the control knob of this mechanism is set to REJECT, the control slide, shown in Fig. 8, is pulled to the left. This shifts the connecting link in such a manner that the manual reject slide is pushed upward. The reject contact, which is a lip on the manual reject slide, pushes a stud on the trip lever causing it to rotate clockwise. This releases the clutch pawl and the changer cycles. The control-slide spring returns the linkage to its rest position as soon as the control knob is released.

Manual Play. It is customary to provide a control knob position allowing a record changer to be set in a MANUAL play position. In this position the record changer acts like a record player, and will not change records automatically. This is done by providing a means of keeping the clutch from actuating.

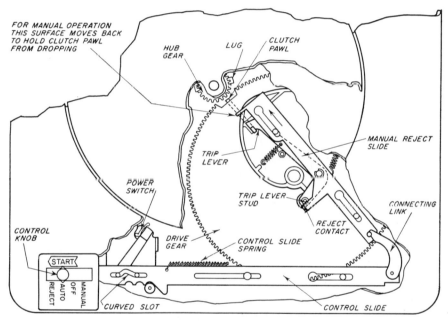

Fig. 8. A reject mechanism for the position trip. The reject contact pushes the trip-lever stud, moving the trip lever clockwise

In Fig. 8 operation of the control knob to the manual position moves the linkage, so that the manual reject slide moves down. A tab at the upper end of the manual reject slide catches the clutch pawl. When a record has finished playing and the trip lever is caused to move clockwise away from the clutch pawl, the tab on the manual reject slide keeps the clutch pawl from dropping. Hence, the record changer will not cycle.

Limitations of Position Trip. This is perhaps the simplest of the various tripping mechanisms, but it has its limitations. The mechanism will trip when the needle is at a point 1⅞ inches from the center of the record. If playing an older record that has a short recording and no eccentric finishing groove, the needle will never reach a point 1⅞ inches from the center of the record. This means that the mechanism will not trip for that record. On the other hand, if playing a longer recording which has been cut in closer to the center than the 1⅞ inches trip point, the mechanism will trip before the recording has been finished.

Eccentric Trip. The key to the eccentric trip is the operation of a ratchet-type mechanism. The eccentric trip works on the basis that as the pickup arm moves outward in the eccentric finishing grooves, the trip mechanism is actuated.

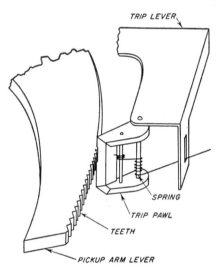

TRIP LEVER

SPRING

TRIP PAWL

TEETH

PICKUP ARM LEVER

Fig. 9. An illustration of the eccentric trip. The pickup-arm lever can move downward freely, but reversing the movement will cause the trip lever to move upward

Thus, it is desired to have a mechanism which does not function as the pickup arm moves toward the center of the record but works in a positive manner as the pickup arm reverses its direction. A mechanism which provides this type of action is illustrated in Fig. 9. This mechanism consists of a pickup-arm lever with teeth along a portion of one edge. A trip pawl is hinged or pivoted on a trip lever in such a manner that it is in contact with one tooth of the pickup-arm lever. A light spring action assures that the pawl is in contact with the pickup-arm lever at all times.

As the lever is caused to move in a clockwise or downward direction, while the trip lever remains stationary, the pawl moves from one tooth in to the next. The further the pickup-arm lever moves, the further the pawl is from the lower end of the lever. Because of the very light spring action, the pawl exerts practically no force so that the pickup-arm lever is not retarded by it.

When the pickup-arm lever reverses its direction, as the pickup arm reverses in the eccentric finishing grooves, the sharp edge of the pawl catches in a tooth and cannot slip out. As a result, the pawl and trip lever will be forced in an upward direction if provisions have been made so that they can move.

Eccentric-trip Mechanism. The pickup arm is rigidly attached to the pickup-arm lever. When the pickup arm moves toward the center of the record, the pickup-arm lever moves in a downward direction and is not retarded by the pawl. However, as the pickup arm begins its oscillatory motion when it reaches the eccentric groove, the backward motion causes the pickup-arm lever to move upward, thus pushing the trip lever. This trips the clutch that starts the changing cycle. Since there is no question about the action of this mechanism when the pickup arm reverses direction, it is often called a positive-type trip.

Operation of Eccentric Trip. By addition of an auxiliary trip shoe, as in Fig. 10, the record changer described for position trip will have an eccentric trip as well. This insures that both old and new records will trip the changer, regardless of whether they have eccentric finishing grooves.

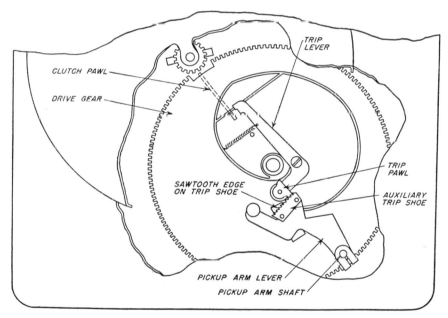

Fig. 10. The addition of a saw-toothed edge to combine with the trip pawl forms a ratchet and provides an eccentric trip

As the pickup arm follows the record grooves toward the center of the record, the pickup-arm lever moves in a clockwise direction. The trip shoe, which has a saw-tooth edge, contacts the trip pawl after a portion of the record has been played. The point at which the two pieces first made contact is about midway in the playing of the record. There is very little friction between the trip shoe and the pawl as the pickup arm moves toward the center of the record. As a result, there is practically no loading effect on the pickup arm, and it is allowed to move freely.

The ratchet-type mesh between the trip shoe and the trip pawl is such that if the pickup-arm lever moves toward the outside of the record, the trip pawl and trip shoe are rigidly connected. This makes the pickup arm move the trip lever, releasing the clutch pawl. The pawl then drops by gravity and starts the change cycle in exactly the same way as it does for the position trip.

Variations in Eccentric Trip. Another example of the eccentric or positive-type trip mechanism is shown in Fig. 11. This changer also demonstrates a unique difference in the drive arrangement.

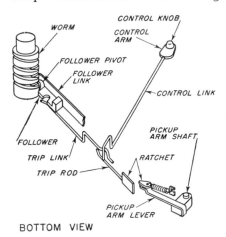

Fig. 11. A positive or eccentric trip which includes use of a worm drive gear

The hub gear on the turntable shaft of this changer has a spiral groove rather than the more common pinion gear. A follower is shaped so that it rides in the groove. As the turntable rotates, the follower moves up and down in the endless spiral groove. Six turntable revolutions produce one up-and-down cycle of the follower. The follower is arranged so that it engages with the worm only during the change cycle.

The control knob is linked to a control arm which in turn is fastened to a control link. When the control knob is moved to the REJECT position, as illustrated, the control link pushes the trip rod counterclockwise away from the follower. The follower is pivoted off center so that its heavy end falls. As a result, the follower tilts counterclockwise and engages the spiral groove or worm.

If the record changer is in operation, the pickup arm causes the positive trip to work by means of the ratchet action between the pickup-arm lever and a flat plate on the trip rod. The eccentric motion of the pickup arm as it follows the finishing groove of the record causes the pickup-arm lever to pivot the trip rod in a clockwise direction. The pivoting action of the trip rod causes the trip link to turn. As in the case of manual rejection, the rotation of the trip link moves it away from the follower, allowing it to contact the worm gear. The follower then transmits the power to the record-changing mechanism through the follower link.

The change cycle lasts for the time it takes the follower to move downward to the bottom end (the upper portion in the diagram) and then back up to the other extreme. As the follower moves up toward the record at the end of the cycle, it moves off the worm gear and is latched by the trip link which has been returned to its rest (clockwise) position.

Other Combination Position and Eccentric Trips. Many changers use a combination of the eccentric and position trip. Combining the two types of trips does not make the mechanism more complicated because proper location of the trip piece is all that is necessary to add the position-trip feature to the eccentric trip.

In one such arrangement the pickup arm is rigidly fastened to a pickup-arm shaft and pickup-arm lever, shown in Fig. 12, which follow the movement of the arm across a record. At one end of the pickup-arm lever is a trip shoe which acts as part of a ratchet. This trip shoe engages the trip pawl after the needle has covered the major portion of the record, as shown in Fig. 13.

When the needle moves back out in the eccentric groove at the end of a record, the trip pawl catches on the trip shoe and is pushed to the right. The fulcrum of the trip lever is at the bottom; hence the lever moves slightly to the right in a clockwise direction when the tip of the trip pawl is moved to the right. This motion closes the trip switch contact at the extreme right-hand edge of the lever energizing the solenoid.

The solenoid in turn pulls the end of the clutch-release arm. This causes the clutch-release arm to rotate clockwise. The upper right end of the clutch-release arm moves away from the clutch pawl. The pawl spring can therefore pull the clutch pawl in a counterclockwise direction so that the tab at the right end of the clutch pawl engages the turntable drive wheel. The turntable drive wheel rotates with the turntable. The clutch pawl is fastened to the drive sprocket by its pivot; hence this action causes the drive sprocket to rotate with the turntable drive wheel. The drive sprocket is meshed with the idler sprocket, which in turn drives the changing mechanism through the drive chain.

The position-trip portion of the mechanism does not depend on the eccentric groove at the end of the record to activate it. When the needle is approximately $1\frac{7}{8}$ inches from the center of the spindle, the position-trip adjustment screw contacts the lip of the trip lever. Further movement of the pickup-arm lever causes the trip lever to move sufficiently far so that the switch makes contact. This action depends upon the proper shaping and positioning of the parts and does not require anything extra except the adjustment screw.

The illustrations show the clutch-release arm in a simplified form. It is actually separated above the pivot, forming two pieces. When the pickup-arm lever moves clockwise during the change cycle, the trip switch is opened and the spring on the lower half of the clutch-release arm pulls it back to the position shown in Fig. 12. The upper half remains away from the clutch pawl.

Not shown in this diagram is a timing sprocket driven by the drive chain. The timing sprocket controls the pickup-arm cycling and is located near the pickup-arm shaft. A reset stud on the timing sprocket contacts an extension of the top half of the clutch-release arm, and moves it so that it again contacts the clutch pawl. This disengages the clutch pawl.

Defective Position Trip. If the trip shoe is incorrectly set, the mechanism may trip too early or not at all. Where the trip shoe is adjustable, the screws holding it should be loosened. Then adjust it so that when the needle is 1⅞ inches from the center of the record, the trip shoe pushes the trip lever sufficiently to actuate the clutch mechanism. Some mechanisms have an adjustment screw for this purpose, as is the case of Fig. 12.

If the trip shoe must be moved more than a fraction of an inch, the trouble is likely to be elsewhere. If the trip lever looks normal, it is likely that the pickup-arm lever has slipped in relation to the pickup arm. Locate the point of slipping by trying to gently move the pickup arm laterally while the pickup-arm lever is held steady. Pay particular attention to the points where the pickup-arm shaft is attached to the pickup arm and to the pickup-arm lever. Loosen the pickup-arm lever on the pickup-arm shaft. A screw is usually used for this purpose. Set its position in respect to the pickup arm so that the trip will actuate when the needle is 1⅞ inches from the center of the record. Tighten the pickup-arm lever to the pickup-arm shaft. Be sure that the connection has been tightened at the point that gave trouble.

Defective Eccentric Trip. A broken or rounded tooth on the trip shoe, a bent or rounded edge on the trip pawl, or a broken or weak pawl spring will cause failure to trip in an eccentric mechanism. Light filing to reshape the metal piece will assure a good ratchet action. Improper spring action can be corrected by replacement, covered in detail later in this chapter.

Continuous Cycling. Binding parts or a weak spring are likely causes of continuous cycling. Binding is usually a result of burrs or dirt and must be

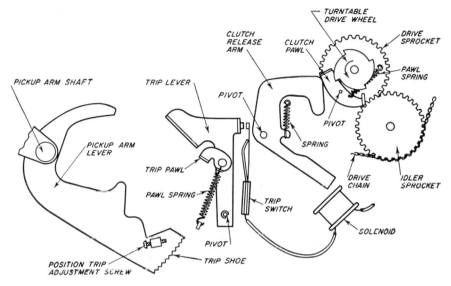

Fig. 12. A combination of the eccentric and position trip

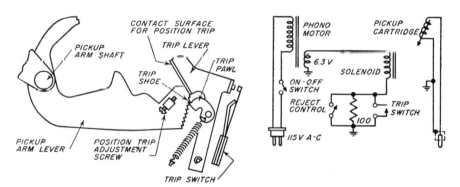

Fig. 13. The pickup-arm lever rotates giving ratchet action between the trip shoe and trip pawl for eccentric pickup. Position trip will occur if the adjustment screw pushes the turned-up edge of the trip lever sufficiently to operate the switch

Fig. 14. The electrical circuit of the record changer in Fig. 12 shows the hookup of the solenoid. The 6.3 volts is obtained from a winding on the motor

corrected by removal of the fault. A burr can be removed by filing, polishing with a crocus cloth, and then cleaning with carbon tetrachloride. Dirt can usually be removed by a liberal application of carbon tetrachloride.

In Fig. 5 continuous cycling may be caused by binding of the clutch pawl because of a burr on either it or the trip lever, dirt in the pivot or the hole through which the clutch pawl protrudes, or a weak trip-lever spring. The changer will also recycle if the roller does not stop the mutilated section of the drive gear opposite the hub gear. A binding drive-gear stop lever or a weak spring are possible sources of this trouble. If the control slide of this changer binds (Fig. 8) so that the spring cannot bring it back to the automatic position after it has been made to reject, the trip lever will be held in the trip position. In this case the slide should be lubricated after the cause of the binding has been removed.

The mechanism shown in Fig. 12 will trip continuously if it has a weak spring holding the clutch-release arm or if there is a defect in the switch. A short would be evidenced by a continual operation of the solenoid so that the clutch-release arm is constantly attracted.

In any trip trouble in this changer the electrical circuit should be checked to see that the switch and solenoid operate properly and that the proper voltage is applied to the circuit. A diagram of the electrical circuit is shown in Fig. 14. A quick check of the operation can be made by manually closing the switch contacts to see if the solenoid attracts the clutch-release arm, and then releasing it to see if the clutch-release arm is released.

Velocity Trip. The velocity trip derives its name from the fact that the trip mechanism reacts to the rapid inward motion of the pickup arm as it follows the eccentric groove in the center of the record. This trip is unique in that a record changer which utilizes it can be used to play records from the inside out. This is necessary for manually playing many home-type recordings.

The key principle of the velocity trip is a friction coupling somewhere in the trip mechanism. The usual velocity-trip mechanism uses a pickup-arm lever fastened to the shaft of the pickup arm. Thus, as the pickup arm moves to the center of the record, the pickup-arm lever moves inward. This action is transmitted to a pawl or other coupling device which links the two gears when the change cycle is to begin. Because of the friction connection, small movement is taken up during the playing of the record so that as the pickup arm moves slowly inward, no action takes place. However, when the pickup arm moves rapidly inward while in the eccentric finishing groove, the friction connection is subjected to a sufficiently sudden force that the clutch is actuated.

Velocity-trip Mechanism. First it will be shown how the power is transmitted from the motor to the drive gear. Then the tripping mechanism will be discussed to show how the power is applied to the cycling cam so that the entire change cycle is completed.

Figure 15 is a cutaway view of a record changer with the turntable and base mounting plate removed. For the purpose of this discussion it must be assumed that the turntable is in place on the spindle because the hub under the turntable is a gear which engages the large idler gear.

Power from the motor shaft is transmitted through the rubber-tired idler wheel to the rim of the turntable. The hub gear under the turntable is

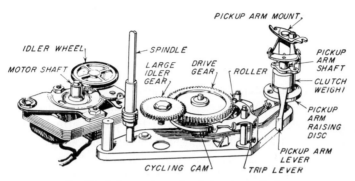

Fig. 15. A frequently used velocity-trip mechanism

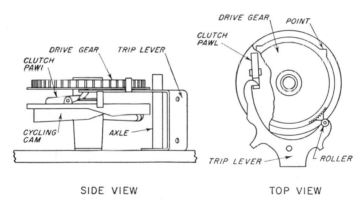

SIDE VIEW   TOP VIEW

Fig. 16. The velocity-trip assembly keeps the pawl from engaging the drive gear until the needle enters the finishing groove

meshed with the large idler gear, which in turn has a gear on its hub located underneath it. This small idler gear is meshed with the drive gear. Since these parts are always in contact or meshed with each other, the drive gear is revolving as long as the motor is running.

The drive gear is mounted directly above the cycling cam and on the same stud, as shown in Fig. 16. On the top surface of the cycling cam there is a clutch pawl. This is a pivoted piece weighted slightly more at one end than at the other. Directly above this clutch pawl, and cut into the bottom of the drive gear, is a series of notches. Each notch is shaped so that the tip of the clutch pawl can seat in it.

The clutch pawl is kept from entering one of these notches by the hook that is on the end of the trip-lever assembly. The moment this hook is knocked out of the way, the clutch pawl is free to move. Since it is pivoted, the heavy end will drop down while the light end rises. The light end engages one of the notches underneath the drive gear and in this manner provides the link for power to be transferred to the cycling cam.

Operation of Velocity Trip. By referring once again to Fig. 15, the action of the tripping mechanism can be followed as it is discussed. The pickup-arm shaft has a disc fastened to it by means of set screws. This pickup-arm raising disc is used to raise the pickup arm during the changing cycle. The pickup-arm lever rests on the shoulder of this pickup-arm raising disc and is held in place by the clutch weight. This weight and the friction between pieces is sufficient so that the pickup-arm lever will follow the movement of the pickup arm. If the pickup-arm lever is held so that this friction is overcome, it will slip in relation to the pickup-arm shaft.

As the pickup enters the grooves of the record and starts to play, it will move toward the center of the record, causing the pickup-arm lever to follow. When approximately two-thirds of the record has been played, the pickup-arm lever will come into contact with the trip lever.

As long as the movement of the pickup arm toward the center of the record is less than $\frac{1}{8}$ inch in $\frac{1}{2}$ revolution of the turntable, it will not move the trip lever sufficiently to release the clutch pawl. The reason for this is that the drive gear has four points evenly spaced around the edge which serve to prevent it from tripping. The small inward movement given to the trip lever by the pickup-arm lever as the regular grooves of the record are played is compensated for by these points which push the trip lever back. Thus the trip lever holds the clutch pawl in the rest position. Since the pickup-arm lever is dependent on friction for its movement, it will not continue to move in but will remain in contact with the trip lever. However, when the pickup arm enters the eccentric groove, its movement is rapid, and the trip lever is given a sufficiently large and quick inward push so that it releases the clutch pawl. The clutch pawl engages the drive gear, causing the changer to go through its cycle.

As the cycling cam goes through its cycle, the trip lever is moved back to its normal position by the points of the drive gear. When the clutch pawl completes one revolution, the hook on the trip lever disengages the clutch pawl from the drive gear so that the cycling cam stops. The pickup-arm lever is returned to its proper starting position during the cycle.

Since the pickup-arm lever is just held in place by the friction of the clutch weight, no undue side pressure is placed upon the needle in the groove of the record.

Manual operation of the reject mechanism is initiated by pushing the control knob to the REJECT position. As shown in Fig. 17 this moves the reject lever clockwise so as to pull the hook on the trip lever away from the clutch pawl. The mechanism trips in the same manner as just explained. A flat spring on the reject lever causes it to return to its rest position when the control knob is released.

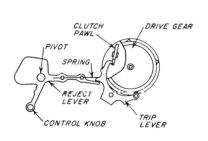

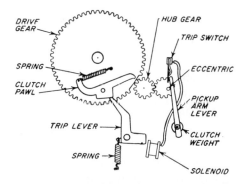

Fig. 17. Movement of the control knob to the left causes the reject lever to move clockwise pulling the velocity-trip assembly away from the pawl, thus actuating the trip. The flat spring causes the reject lever to return to its rest position

Fig. 18. A velocity-trip mechanism using a solenoid for activating the clutch. A rotating eccentric keeps the trip lever from actuating the trip switch while the record is playing

Variation in Velocity Trip. A variation of the velocity trip utilizes a solenoid action. As the turntable rotates, the hub gear does not contact the drive gear because of a segment which is cut away.

When the solenoid is activated, it attracts the trip-lever assembly. This assembly is an odd-shaped lever with the fulcrum in the center, as shown in Fig. 18. As the right-hand portion of the trip-lever assembly is attracted to the solenoid, the upper portion moves in a clockwise direction. This releases the clutch pawl.

The left-hand end of this clutch pawl is held by a spring which exerts a force in a clockwise direction. As the trip lever is activated, it allows the clutch pawl to move. Thus the pawl is caused to move in a clockwise direction due to the spring tension. This pawl then moves sufficiently far to engage the hub gear of the turntable as it rotates.

Since the clutch pawl is rigidly fastened to the drive gear, the hub gear imparts a motion to it, causing the drive gear to commence rotating. This action is sufficient to carry the drive gear to the point where the drive-gear teeth engage those on the hub gear. Thus the drive gear is rotated through its entire revolution. As the drive gear rotates, the changing cycle takes place and the pickup-arm lever moves away from the trip switch. Hence the trip action is released.

In operation, as the pickup arm moves toward the center of the record, the pickup-arm lever and clutch weight move continually toward the center of the changer, or in a counterclockwise direction. The pickup-arm lever comes into position to contact the trip switch after about two-thirds of the record has played. This switch completes the circuit through the solenoid.

To avoid premature tripping, the pickup-arm lever is kept away from the switch until the pickup has reached the fast-finishing grooves. A gear is mounted so that it is driven by the hub gear. A stud is mounted off center on this gear so it describes an eccentric motion as it is driven. Once each revolution the eccentric action tends to push the pickup-arm lever back to normal position.

Since the pickup-arm lever is driven only through the friction of the weight, the pickup-arm lever slips each time the eccentric wipes it. However, during the fast-finishing grooves the pickup-arm lever moves in rapidly enough so that it trips the switch before the eccentric can complete its revolution and push it back. The pickup-arm lever contacts the trip switch. This grounds the electrical circuit, completing it and activating the solenoid.

Once the trip has been activated and the drive gear revolves through its revolution, the pickup arm returns to the beginning of the next record and the switch opens. The solenoid then releases the trip lever, allowing it to return to its rest position.

As the drive gear completes the cycle, the trip lever contacts the clutch pawl, keeping it in its normal or counterclockwise position. When the open segment of the drive gear comes opposite the hub gear of the turntable assembly, there is no further meshing action. Because of the relatively heavy loading on the drive gear, it will stop almost immediately, thus completing the cycle.

Resetting of Pickup-arm Lever. The pickup-arm lever is pushed back (clockwise as viewed from below) in respect to the pickup arm as the last part of the record is played. Hence, to reset it for use when the next record is played, it must be pushed ahead. As the pickup arm moves to the outside during the change cycle, the pickup-arm lever moves with it. About two-thirds of the way the pickup-arm lever strikes a stud which keeps it from traveling further. Since the pickup-arm lever follows the pickup arm only because of friction, the pickup-arm lever slips on the pickup-arm shaft and is reset to its proper position.

Another Velocity-trip Assembly. Another variation of the velocity trip uses a pawl assembly with a friction connection. In this rim-drive mechanism the power is transmitted from the hub gear to the drive gear and then to the cycling slide, shown in Fig. 19. The cycling slide in turn controls

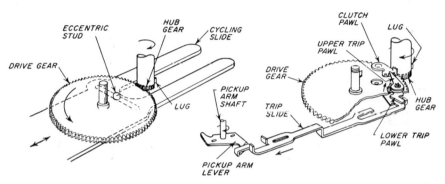

Fig. 19. An eccentric stud linking the drive gear and cycling slide changes rotary motion to a lateral motion

Fig. 20. Another variation of the velocity trip has the friction connection in the trip-pawl assembly. The trip slide fits between the drive gear and the cycling slide

the various cycling functions. The drive gear has an eccentric stud fastened to its underside which fits into a slot in the cycling slide. As the drive gear rotates, it changes the rotary motion into a sliding to-and-fro motion of the cycling slide.

The drive gear has a segment cut away so that as the turntable rotates, the hub gear is disengaged. On the top of the drive gear is a clutch pawl, which is intended to contact the lug on the hub gear.

As the pickup works its way toward the center of the record, it causes the pickup-arm lever, shown in Fig. 20, to rotate because of the rigid connection through the pickup-arm shaft. In the diagram this lever rotates in a clockwise direction. It is attached to a trip slide which is located between the drive gear and the cycling slide which is not shown. The rotation of the pickup-arm lever causes the trip slide to move to the left and pulls the lower trip pawl in a clockwise direction.

The lower trip pawl is connected to the upper trip pawl by a spring-loaded shaft and washer arrangement so that there is a snug but not a solid fit. This provides a friction connection between the two. The upper trip pawl moves the clutch pawl, forcing it toward the turntable shaft.

When a record is being played, the pickup arm moves slowly toward the center of the record, and the clutch pawl moves slowly toward the hub gear. Once per revolution of the record, the lug on the turntable shaft strikes the clutch pawl, forcing it back. The friction connection in the trip-pawl assembly takes care of this variation by allowing a slippage each time the upper trip pawl is forced back.

When the pickup reaches the fast-finishing grooves, the clutch pawl is forced rapidly toward the turntable shaft. Now when the lug comes around, it firmly contacts the clutch pawl. This imparts a rotary motion to the drive gear of sufficient force to carry it to the point where the hub gear meshes with the drive gear.

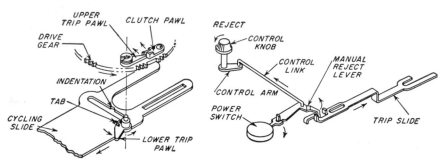

Fig. 21. A tab on the cycling slide contacts the lower trip pawl near the end of the change cycle, causing the trip assembly to return to its neutral or disengaged position

Fig. 22. Operation of the control knob causes the trip slide to actuate the trip as in the automatic case

As the drive gear completes its rotation, a small tab on the cycling slide contacts the lower trip pawl in such a manner that the upper trip pawl and the clutch pawl are forced counterclockwise into their normal rest position. This is shown in Fig. 21. This action avoids the recurrence of the trip since the clutch pawl will not contact the lug on the hub gear. The eccentric stud which slides in the slot of the cycling slide drops into a small indentation as the drive gear completes its revolution. This stops the motion of the drive gear at the point where the hub gear is opposite the mutilated section of the drive gear.

To trip this changer manually, it is necessary to turn a control knob. This in turn actuates a rod-and-lever system that pulls the trip slide, tripping the mechanism. The arrangement is illustrated in Fig. 22. The power switch is also connected to the manual reject lever so that the control knob switches it on when turned to the REJECT position.

Similar Velocity Trip. A similar friction-pawl assembly is used in another variation of the velocity trip, shown in Fig. 23. This changer has a circular pickup-arm lever which is fastened to the pickup-arm shaft. As the pickup arm comes near the end of a record, a stud on this lever contacts the trip slide. The opposite end of the trip slide contacts the lower trip pawl. The lower trip pawl is located on the bottom of the drive gear, and the upper trip pawl is located on the top. They are connected by means of a friction connection, as in the changer just previously described.

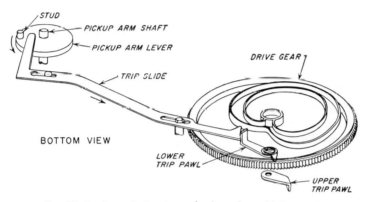

Fig. 23. Another velocity-trip mechanism using a friction pawl

As the pickup arm moves closer toward the spindle, the trip slide is made to slide so that it moves the lower trip pawl, causing it to slowly rotate. Because of the spring-washer tension in the friction connection, the upper trip pawl is caused to rotate. While the record is playing, this pawl is forced back by the wiping motion of the lug on the hub gear, and the friction connection takes up the slippage. When the pickup arm reaches the finishing grooves, the trip pawl is moved rapidly inward so that the sharp point at the end engages the lug on the hub gear, causing the drive gear to start the change cycle.

The two friction-pawl velocity-trip mechanisms just discussed are very similar in operation. Both were described in order to better illustrate the difference in appearance of various linkages and mechanical arrangements.

Failure of Velocity Trip to Actuate. A possible cause of failure to trip in a velocity-trip mechanism is a weak or oily friction connection. All friction connections must be clean and dry. A weak friction connection may be caused by weak spring loading. The double-pawl connection is of this type. Some changers use a spring to provide the friction loading of the pickup-arm lever instead of the clutch weight as described. Sometimes a felt washer is used between the clutch weight and the pickup-arm lever. If this is worn, it becomes slippery. Too much friction may cause the record changer to trip prematurely.

A bent trip lever can cause trouble because it does not contact the part it is supposed to actuate. Where this is a part of the friction assembly, it is usually made of light material which will bend easily. It should be bent carefully back into place by use of a duck-bill pliers.

Burrs on contacting parts may cause improper action of the trip mechanism. For example, a burr on the clutch pawl or the trip lever of an over-and-under gear assembly (Fig. 16) will not allow the pieces to separate. Removal of the burr by filing, polishing, and cleaning is necessary.

Binding at the pivot is another source of trouble. In a part such as the trip lever of Fig. 16 a bent part could cause friction between the axle and the two pivot holes. To correct this, gently bend the assembly, using duck-bill pliers.

Continuous Cycling. Continuous cycling of the velocity-trip mechanism shown in Fig. 15 may be caused by a bent trip lever allowing the clutch pawl to constantly engage the drive gear. If this part is bent, it may also rub against the drive gear causing a chattering. It should be straightened by use of a duck-bill pliers.

A binding reject lever is another cause of continuous cycling. When the record changer is manually tripped, the reject lever moves so that the wire pushes against the lip of the trip lever, releasing the hook from the clutch pawl and allowing it to engage the drive gear. The straight spring returns the reject lever to its normal position.

In the event that the reject lever binds, the spring will continually bear against the lip, keeping the hook of the trip lever from contacting the clutch pawl. This would result in a continuous cycling of the mechanism.

Binding may be caused by the control knob catching in the slot of the base-plate assembly. In this case enough clearance should be filed in the slot to allow the knob freedom of movement. Caution should be used not to remove too much. File a little, then try the reject lever until the proper freedom has been obtained. Binding in the pivot is another possible source of this trouble. Cleaning with carbon tetrachloride is then necessary.

Still another cause of continued cycling is a damaged roller on the trip lever. Should this roller be broken, the hook on the end of the trip lever cannot contact the clutch pawl and disengage it from the drive gear. This is due to the fact that the reset points will not return the trip lever to its normal position. To remedy this, the trip lever must be replaced if a roller is used. Some changers use a bumper instead of a roller. This usually is damaged by having a groove worn in it, but may be replaced without changing or removing the assembly.

In the mechanism of Fig. 18 continued or premature cycling can be caused by a weak clutch-pawl spring or binding of the clutch pawl. Use of a clutch-pawl spring that gives too much pull could also cause this.

Proper action of this type changer requires proper setting of the trip switch. To adjust this, the turntable should be rotated until the eccentric is in its maximum right-hand position. The trip lever and the trip switch should be separated about $\frac{1}{16}$ inch. If this needs adjustment, the support for the copper-bronze strip shown in Fig. 24 should be bent.

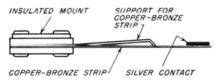

Fig. 24. A trip switch can be adjusted by bending the support for the copper-bronze strip.

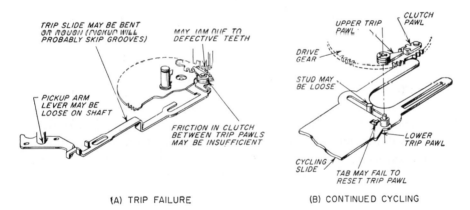

(A) TRIP FAILURE   (B) CONTINUED CYCLING

Fig. 25. Possible causes of trouble in a velocity-trip mechanism

The possible causes of continued cycling in the mechanism of Figs. 20–22 are most likely to be a loose stud or bent tab, as illustrated in Fig. 25. The stud stops the drive gear so that the mutilated section is opposite the hub gear. If the stud is loose, the drive gear may not be stopped and the two gears will mesh again, causing the cycle to repeat. A bent tab may not reset the trip and clutch pawl, allowing the clutch pawl to contact the lug on the turntable hub and thus causing recycling.

Repairing Trip Mechanisms. Difficulties in the trip mechanism evidence themselves by a failure of the mechanism to start the change cycle or by starting to cycle too soon. Among the more general causes of trip difficulty are improper adjustments, binding in release or friction components, defective springs, bent parts, and defective electrical parts.

When the trip mechanism is suspected of causing trouble and previous experience has not indicated a likely clue, a check should be made first of the more obvious and available points. Lack of an eccentric or lead-in groove, excess wear, or foreign matter in the grooves are possible record defects that will cause failure of trip action. A defective center hole in a record may cause the normal groove to revolve in an eccentric manner, causing the trip to actuate prematurely.

The mechanisms previously discussed form an arrangement resembling a Y. One arm is the pickup-arm lever, and the other is the manual control slide or link. Both join at some point and move the leg which consists of the trip slide and pawl assembly. This feature can be used to isolate any trouble. In order for the trip to function on most record changers, the control knob must be set in the AUTOMATIC position. Play a record until the needle enters the finishing groove. If the record changer does not trip, operate the REJECT button. If the mechanism fails to trip either way, the difficulty is probably in the leg of the Y—the trip slide or pawl. Turn off the record changer, adjust the control knob to the REJECT position, and watch the mechanism as the turntable is rotated by hand. Pay special attention to the leg of the Y.

If operation of the control knob to the REJECT position causes the trip to function, but the changer does not trip automatically upon completion of a record, the difficulty probably lies in the arm of the Y containing the pickup-arm lever.

If the changer trips automatically at the end of a record, but the REJECT feature does not work, look for difficulty in the arm of the Y containing the control slide or link.

Springs. Missing and weakened springs are frequent causes of trouble. A variety of springs are used. Some of these are illustrated in Fig. 26.

Springs cannot usually be repaired, and are so inexpensive that it is not worth while trying to do so.

Spring washers are used in sandwich-type assemblies to create an outward pressure. The double-pawl assembly in a velocity-trip mechanism uses this feature. In critical applications such as this an exact replacement is recommended.

Coil springs are by far the most common. Various lengths and diameters are used. For a given size tension varies somewhat, depending upon the material used. Coil springs have a hook or loop on each end so that the ends may be fastened over studs, tabs, or notches or may be inserted in a hole. Assortments of coil springs can be purchased from a radio-parts jobber. Trial and error is frequently a convenient method of selecting a replacement. By feeling the tension of the defective spring, it is usually possible to select a suitable replacement on the basis of both tension and size. When installed, the spring should not be stretched more than a fraction of its length or the strain will cause early weakening or failure. It is sometimes possible to tailor a spring by trimming an oversize one. Cut with a pair of diagonal pliers and re-form the end. When removing

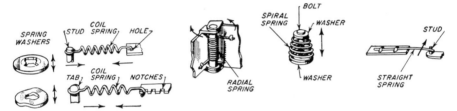

Fig. 26. Various types of springs used in record changers and methods of holding them

coil springs, it is easier to begin with an end fastened around a stub or tab than with an end inserted in a hole. The end can usually be slipped over the end of the stud or tab. To remove a coil spring from a hole, it is necessary to swing the end while pulling so as to guide the curved hook out. To do this, the spring may have to be stretched an extraordinary amount. A long-nose pliers is recommended for this task. When installing a spring, the reverse procedure is best so that the more difficult end is inserted first.

Radial springs are used occasionally to provide spring action between parts with a common pivot. Here the diameter is usually of importance since it must frequently be placed over the pivot. The tension of a radial spring is relatively weak. Tension may sometimes be adjusted by twisting the spring so as to add one or more turns before installing it. This will decrease the diameter of the spring as well. The ends are frequently held in place by inserting them in cutouts.

Spiral springs are not often encountered except for vibration mounting of the changer in its cabinet. Here the spiral spring is compressed slightly by the weight of the changer. These seldom become defective because of their relatively large size.

A straight spring is not often used but will be seen at times. It consists of a straight length of spring steel or material of similar characteristics. As with other springs, when it is bent it will tend to return to its usual shape. It is customarily held in place by cutouts or tabs.

Replacement springs can be ordered from record-changer distributors. Wherever possible it is best to obtain the part number from a service manual. If this is not possible, the defective spring should be used as a comparison. Once you have repaired a few record changers, you can accumulate an assortment of springs of the type you use or encounter most often.

A broken or weak spring will not return a record-changer part to its rest position. Careful inspection for such defects should be made before an extensive repair is started. If a spring is suspected, the part to which it is attached can often be moved by pushing lightly with the finger. It should return to place if the spring is good. Also look to see that both ends of the spring are properly anchored. Experience can be gained by carefully feeling the tension of springs in a properly operating record changer.

Binding. Record-changer parts must move freely. Any tendency to bind is a possible cause of trouble. Inspection of the binding parts will show where the trouble exists.

In a pivoted part binding may be caused by accumulation of dirt and other foreign particles. If the part is bent near the pivot point, it may squeeze the shaft. Cleaning and straightening are possible solutions.

Burred sections of pawls or other mating parts will cause undue friction. These burrs must be removed by filing. Where the part is a thin metal piece, hold it with a pair of duck-bill pliers when filing so that it is not bent. Clean off any accumulation of filings, then polish with a crocus cloth if necessary, and finally clean. Lubrication should be applied where, and only where, required.

Cleaning of metal parts is best accomplished by thoroughly washing with carbon tetrachloride. Be careful not to breathe much of the fumes from this as an excess is dangerous.

Some defects due to binding may react in different manners. For example, an actuating pawl that is stuck may cause repeated cycling or may create too much friction to be actuated by the trip lever.

Gravity-type levers and pawls should operate freely when released. The pivot is a loose fit so that there is practically no friction. Sticking may be caused by dirt, grease, lint, or other foreign matter and may be remedied by cleaning with carbon tetrachloride. Usually no lubricant is used. This is especially true if the lever or pawl is part of a friction connection such as used in a velocity-trip mechanism.

Lubrication. Generally, all changers are completely oiled and lubricated when they leave the factory. This treatment is good for about a year of service. In the event that a changer is operated where extreme heat or dust conditions exist, they should be oiled or lubricated more frequently as required.

No lubrication is generally required on the different parts of the tripping assembly. Unless the manufacturer's instructions specifically indicate lubrication of portions of the tripping mechanism, no lubrication should be attempted.

Sliding surfaces may generally be lubricated safely using a light application of Lubriplate or STA-PUT. Gear teeth may be similarly treated. The most important places to keep free of lubrication are the clutch weight, trip lever, and pawl. Should lubrication be present between the bearing surfaces of these units, the friction could be lessened to a degree where it is quite possible that the trip would not operate properly.

QUESTIONS

1. How does the motor drive the changing mechanism?
2. Why is a clutch necessary in a record changer?
3. Describe a mutilated-clutch mechanism.
4. How does a gravity-type clutch mechanism work?
5. What are the three types of trip-actuating mechanism?
6. How does the position trip work?
7. Why is a combination of the position and the eccentric trip used?
8. What is the basis of the eccentric trip?
9. What is the key principle of the velocity trip?
10. What defects would cause continuous cycling of a velocity trip?
11. How do you select a replacement coil spring?
12. How would you correct a binding condition?

9

Record-dropping Mechanisms

Types of Dropping Mechanisms. After a record changer has been loaded with the records to be played, it is necessary that one record at a time be allowed to drop to the turntable. This has been accomplished in various ways. The more commonly used methods will be studied in an effort to become acquainted with the general workings of these mechanisms.

There are in general use today three popular ways of doing this job. They are as follows: (1) slicer type using two- or three-shelf support; (2) pusher type, using shelf-and-spindle support; (3) spindle type, using only the spindle to support the records. Examples of these three methods will be thoroughly discussed, giving a complete account of the action, the possible causes of failure to work properly, and the necessary repairs or adjustments to put them back into correct operation.

Slicer-type Two-shelf Support. For a long time the most often used method of selecting records was the use of rotating blades which cut in between the bottom record and the one on top of it, allowing the bottom record to slide down the spindle onto the turntable. A good design of this type will work well. Figure 1 is a view of this type of changer, showing it loaded with a stack of records with another one on the turntable in playing position. There are two record shelves supporting the unplayed stack of records. The spindle protrudes through this stack, keeping each record centered on the shelves. At the same time the spindle serves as a guide for the record when it is dropping to the turntable, and acts in its usual capacity to center the record on the turntable.

Slicer-type Operation of Selector Arms. Figure 2 is a top view of one of the record-selector posts, which is an assembly including an arm with a blade and a shelf. The normal position of the arm is just slightly clockwise of that shown so that the selector blade is about ⅛ inch out from the edge of the bottom record. In the position shown, the selector arm has just started to

Fig. 1. A two-shelf slicer-type changer will play ten 12-inch records or twelve 10-inch records without overloading. The selector-post assemblies support the record stack and automatically drop the bottom record to the turntable during the change cycle

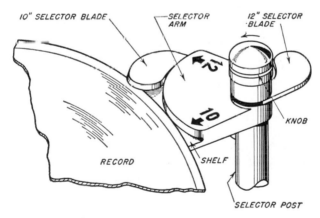

Fig. 2. The selector arm of a slicer-type changer starting a change cycle. To play 12-inch records, the knob on the selector post must be pulled up and rotated counterclockwise so the 12-arrow is pointing toward the record

do its work of separating the bottom record from the stack. The selector arm is rotating in a counterclockwise direction. Since there are two selector posts, this same action is repeated simultaneously on the opposite side of the stack of records.

Assume that there are more records on top of the one shown. As the selector arms rotate, the selector blades move in and knife between the bottom record of the stack and the one on top of it. The blades support the records remaining in the stack. As the selector shelves turn, they move out of the way, and the bottom record which rests on them drops to the turntable.

After the record has dropped, the cam, which is activating the selector arms, reverses the direction of rotation of the arms and brings them back to their normal position. The records drop onto the shelves and the selector

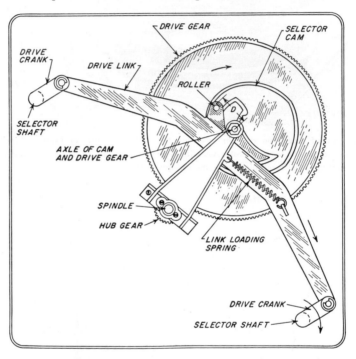

Fig. 3. The activating portion of a two-shelf slicer-type dropping mechanism

blades move to the side out of the way. The selector posts are then ready to repeat this performance at the conclusion of the playing of the record that has just been dropped.

Slicer-type Two-shelf Mechanism. Since there are two selector arms, they must be coupled together so that they are synchronized and will do exactly the same thing at the same time. Figure 3 is a bottom view of the changer showing how this is accomplished. Each selector arm is fastened to a selector shaft which goes through the supporting post and bushing to the bottom side of the chassis. A drive crank is fastened to the bottom end of each of these selector shafts, and in turn, these drive cranks are coupled to each other with a drive link.

A small arm protrudes from one side of the drive link near the center. Fastened to this arm is a roller which is in contact with the selector cam. The selector cam is part of the drive gear. As the drive gear rotates, the selector cam forces the drive link to move the selector posts through the record-dropping cycle. The link loading spring shown fastened between the drive link and part of the frame of the changer keeps the roller in contact with the selector cam and brings the selector arms back into their normal position with the selector blades clear of the remaining records.

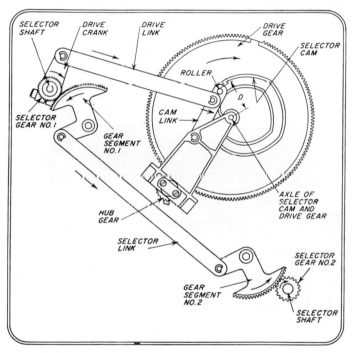

Fig. 4. A two-shelf slicer-type dropping mechanism with separate links between the selector shafts and the selector cam

During the change cycle the drive gear is rotating in a clockwise direction as indicated. Since the distance D from the center of the drive gear to the point of contact between the roller and the selector cam is decreasing, the link is moving toward the lower right. This causes the crank to move clockwise as viewed from the bottom or counterclockwise as viewed from the top. When the mechanism reaches the point where the distance

D begins to increase, the link will move in the opposite direction and the selector arms will reverse direction.

Two-shelf Variations. Another two-shelf changer is shown in Fig. 4. The principle of action is the same as that just described, but the mechanical layout is different. In this case the cam link is pivoted at one end, while the other end follows the selector-cam groove. As the drive gear rotates, the cam link changes this rotary motion to a back-and-forth movement.

In the instant shown, the cam link is moving to the right since the distance D from the cam axle to the roller is decreasing. The cam link and drive link transmit this motion to the drive crank which causes selector gear 1 to rotate in a clockwise direction. In order to couple this to selector gear 2, two gear segments and a selector link are used.

Fig. 5. A three-shelf slicer-type mechanism. (Howard W. Sams photo)

Selector gear 1 causes gear segment 1 to rotate in a counterclockwise direction. This odd-shaped segment of a gear has a stud to which the selector link is attached. As the gear segment rotates, it causes the selector link to move, which in turn rotates gear segment 2 in a counterclockwise direction. Since it meshes with selector gear 2, the latter rotates in a clockwise direction. Thus the two selector arms move outward at the same time.

Slicer-type Three-shelf. With a two-shelf changer records are supported at two opposite points and can tip sideways if their center holes are oversize. A third shelf helps to hold the records more rigidly and overcomes this drawback. The principle of operation is the same in both cases. Figure 5 shows a three-shelf changer, and Fig. 6 is a sketch of the bottom view.

This mechanism resembles a combination of the two-shelf changers described. The drive link imparts the selector-cam action to two drive cranks which rotate the gear segments. One of these gear segments is linked in turn to the third.

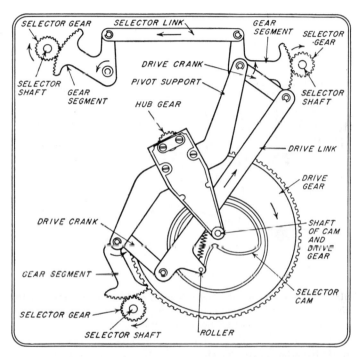

Fig. 6. The activating portion of a three-shelf slicer-type changing mechanism

Slicer-type Intermix Action. An intermix slicer-type changer can be used with a stack of 10-inch records, or a stack of 12-inch records, or a stack of 10- and 12-inch records intermixed.

Where the stack consists of records of a single diameter, the action is the same as that of the two-post changer previously described. This also holds true if one record is followed by another of the same size. When two adjacent records are of different sizes, there are two possible situations; one where a 10-inch record is beneath a 12-inch record and another where a 12-inch record is beneath a 10-inch record.

When a 12-inch record is below a 10-inch record, the problem is not so difficult. In this case the selector blades contact the edge of the 12-inch record and then tilt or slide upwards as they rotate so as to clear the added thickness of the 12-inch record. When they have swung in to the edge of the 10-inch record, the edges pass under it, holding the stack, while the 12-inch record on the bottom drops to the turntable.

When a 10-inch record is below a 12-inch record, the situation is more difficult due to the fact that the 10-inch record is thinner than the 12-inch record. To overcome this, the selector arm is equipped with a lifter shoe and a lifter plunger as shown in Fig. 7. When the 10-inch record is on the

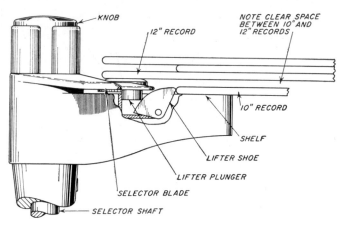

Fig. 7. The intermix mechanism in a slicer-type changer. As the selector rotates, the 10-inch record forces the lifter shoe back. This in turn raises the lifter plunger which lifts the record stack so that the selector blade can enter between the two records shown

record shelf, its edge contacts the lifter shoe as the selector arms rotate, forcing the lifter shoe back to the left. This raises the lifter plunger, which is a sliding button. The lifter plunger raises the 12-inch record just above it, along with the remainder of the stack, so that the selector blades enter into a clear space between the 10- and the 12-inch records. The 10-inch record is then dropped onto the turntable as the selector arms rotate further.

Other Slicer-type Changers. Although the action of the slicer is the same in all changers of this type, many variations in physical appearance exist. Figure 8 is a view of a two-post changer that has one fixed record shelf and one selector post. Another variation, illustrated in Fig. 9, has one fixed record shelf and two separator posts. A fixed record shelf stabilizes the stack of records without the added cost of the link and separator mechanism.

Servicing the Slicer-type Changers. Wear, abuse, incorrect handling, or misinformed tinkering can cause poor, erratic, or nonoperation of this changer mechanism. An effort will be made to cover troubles which might appear from any of these causes.

Slicer-type Jamming. It is possible that the selector blades may jam

Fig. 8. A slicer-type changer with one fixed shelf and a selector shelf adjacent to the pickup arm

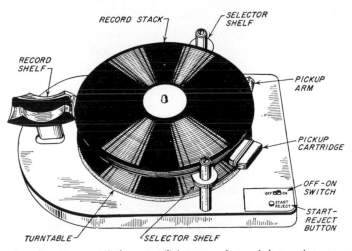

Fig. 9. Another slicer-type record changer utilizing two selector shelves and a separate record shelf to keep the records balanced

against the edge of the record under several circumstances. To relieve this jamming, turn off the motor and rotate the turntable counterclockwise by hand until the record has been released.

Jamming can be caused by having the selector arms set for the wrong size of record. In this case the jam must be cleared as just described, and the record removed while the selector arms are positioned correctly for the size record used.

Badly warped records can cause jamming when the selector blade cannot rise above the edge of the record. The warp in the record throws the top surface of the record edge beyond the limit of the rise of the selector blade. Records of this nature should be played manually.

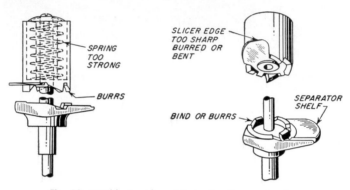

Fig. 10. Possible trouble points in the slicer mechanism

Very thick records may also cause the selector arms to jam against the edge of the record. Once again manual operation is necessary. Usually records with these defects can be spotted quite readily, and the difference between these and good records easily pointed out to the customer.

Slicer Type—Defective Selector Blade. Possible troubles are shown in Fig. 10. The leading edge of the selector blade must be smoothly rounded and well polished. If the blade is blunt or irregular, it will jam against the edge of the record instead of rising and slicing between the bottom two records. The remedy for this is to buff the edge of the blade until it is rounded and then polish it with crocus cloth. The edge must be smooth and well polished. The selector blade must also be free in its mounting, having an up-and-down movement, and be able to return to normal position by its own weight if a spring is not used. Excess spring tension is also a possible cause of jamming.

Foreign material lodged in between the blade and the record shelf may keep the blade from moving either up or down. This foreign material should be removed with a thin tool. In many cases it is convenient to disassemble the selector mechanism for a thorough cleaning.

Slicer Type—Fixing Bent Selector Blades. If the selector blades are bent up or down, jamming may result. To adjust this, put on a 10-inch record of average thickness (0.074 inch) and rotate the turntable manually clockwise until the selector blade contacts the record. The blade must rise after it first contacts the edge of the record. This rising cam action results whenever pressure is applied to the leading edge of the selector blade.

It is desirable to have records available that are of average thickness, thinner than average, and thicker than average. If a micrometer is not available, a simple method of selecting these records can be used with reasonable results. Select ten 10-inch records, stack them, and measure the total thickness with a ruler. Since the records will likely be warped a little, squeeze the records together at the edge where the measurement is made. Since the average record thickness is 0.074 inch, the stack should measure very close to ¾ inch. If it does, the average of the 10 records is proper. By inspection select records of small, average, and great thickness. If the stack thickness is greater than ¾ inch, the average is on the thick side, and if less than ¾ inch, the average is on the thin side. Use this knowledge in selecting the desired records, or else select another group of 10 records and try again.

A bent blade may be adjusted by bending very slightly to the correct position using pliers with tape-lined jaws, or duck-bill pliers. The height to which blades are set must be *less* than the smallest record thickness. Otherwise, the blade will attempt to change two records at a time because of the cam action which *always* operates in an *up direction*. To check this, try the action with both a thin and a thick record at the bottom of the stack.

When necessary, the same adjustment should be made on the 12-inch selector blades, using a 12-inch record (approximately 0.090 inch thick; 10 records of average thickness should measure about 14½/16 of an inch). In most cases the blades are given a slight downward tilt of about 0.02 inch (⅓ of 1/16 inch) in order to work properly with slightly warped records. This can be roughly determined by use of a straight edge to aid in estimating. Do not try to adjust this tilt unless absolutely sure that it is necessary. If adjustment becomes too troublesome, replace the blade.

Slicer Type—Record Drops on One Side Only. A record having a large center hole is apt to shift its position so that more of it will be resting on one shelf than on the opposite shelf. This would cause the short side to drop very quickly, allowing the opposite selector blade to cut underneath the record. This leaves the record hung up on one shelf instead of dropping. Such a record should be played only manually since it is usually not worth while to repair the center hole.

A record with a broken edge may also hang up on one shelf if the broken part is at the other shelf. If the record is not too badly damaged, it can be placed on the supporting shelves so that the blades will not be near this damage.

A record with broken edges will be handled perfectly by a spindle-type changer. If the customer has a great many chipped records, you have an opportunity to sell and install a new changer of this type.

A bent spindle keeps the records off center so that one side drops first and the other hangs up. Straightening a spindle is a ticklish operation and should not be attempted, but rather the spindle should be replaced.

Do not attempt to straighten a spindle by laying it on a flat piece of metal and pounding it with a hammer or placing it in a vise and straightening it by hitting the free end of the spindle. This will only result in a rough and uneven job. It is far better to replace it.

If the selector-arm post is bent, one side of the record may always drop first. This is a rare condition but could occur if the entire changer is dropped. Usually the post itself is not bent but rather the chassis base to which it is fastened. Repair can be accomplished by placing the changer base plate in a vise in such a manner that the selector post may be bent back into position without buckling the changer base plate. The jaws of the vise must be smooth or padded with some smooth material so that there are no marks left on the surface of the base plate. Some changers use a white-metal support which is easily broken and cannot be repaired, so it is well to inspect the changer before starting repairs of this nature.

Slicer Type—Selector-shaft Binding. Binding of the selector shaft would be noticed as a back-and-forth movement of the entire selector arm and post assembly. There would also be a marked decrease in the speed of the turntable, indicating that an extra load is being placed upon the motor. The cure for this is to remove the shafting from the changer posts, following the manufacturer's instructions or studying the assembly to determine how they are fastened. A lot of pressure may have to be exerted on the shaft to remove it because of the binding effect, but first be sure that the shaft fastenings have all been removed or loosened.

Binding is usually caused by drying and caking of lubrication. To remedy this, the shaft and the hole in the post should be washed with carbon tetrachloride. The shaft should then be polished with crocus cloth, and the hole in the post inspected to make certain that the entire surface is thoroughly clean. One approach is to roll up a very fine emery cloth to fit the post hole and clean it in this manner. Before assembling, test the shaft in the hole. If it seems free enough, remove again and apply a thin coating of Lubriplate before reassembling.

Another result of binding is sticking of the selector blade. The blade is then not able to get out from under the stack of records as it is returning to its normal position. Cleaning the shaft should cure this trouble also.

Slicer Type—Cam Spring Missing. If the spring holding the cam link in contact with the drive-gear cam is missing, the selector arm may not return to its normal position. Replace this with a comparable spring. Try several, of different lengths, thickness, and stiffness. Too weak a spring will not pull the slicer blades back out of the way. Too strong a spring applies too much pressure between the roller or stud on the link arm, loading the drive gear excessively and slowing down the changer.

Slicer Type—Crankshaft Binding. The selector shaft is made of a metal alloy which may have a tendency to swell with age. If this condition happens, it causes binding between the top portion of the selector shaft and the selector-post sleeve.

To fix this, remove the selector shaft and file down the top of it to increase the clearance between the top of the selector shaft and the selector-post sleeve. After filing, be sure to remove all burrs or particles of metal so that they cannot cause any further trouble.

Slicer Type—Lubrication. The slicer type of mechanism requires a minimum of lubrication. Any excess should be immediately wiped off. A thin coat of Lubriplate or STA-PUT should be applied to the selector cam so that the roller on the arm of the drive link will move with as little friction as possible. The teeth of the selector gears and gear segments should likewise be lubricated with Lubriplate or STA-PUT. A drop of SAE 10W oil should be used at the points where the drive links and drive cranks are connected together and also where the gear segment and selector link are connected. Also, a couple of drops of SAE 10W oil can be placed on the record-selector shafts where they enter their supporting posts. No lubrication should be used on any part of the record-selector blades.

Pusher Type. A later development in the handling of a stack of records is known as the pusher-type changer, which is shown in Fig. 11. Actually, the pusher shelf and the spindle are used for support of the stack of records.

When using this particular changer, it is necessary that the stack of records be all 10-inch or all 12-inch, as it is not an intermix changer. The adjustment for size is simple, as shown in Fig. 12. On the record-selector post the support shelf on one side of the post extends farther from the center of the supporting shaft than does the other side. This distance determines the 10- or 12-inch position. When the short side is facing the spindle, the distance from the spindle to the shelf is greater, and the changer will play 12-inch records. When the long side is facing the spindle as in the illustration, the distance from the spindle to the shelf is shorter as required for the 10-inch size. To select the proper shelf for the record size being played, the post must be rotated by hand.

Fig. 11. A pusher or shelf-and-spindle type of record support. A pushing motion by the shelf causes the bottom record to drop down the spindle. (Westinghouse photo)

A record stabilizer is used to keep the stack of records lying flat on the record-selector shelf. It is located on top of the record-selector post and is pivoted so that it may be moved to either side of the record-selector post. After the records have been loaded on the selector shelf and spindle, the record stabilizer is pulled over onto the top record of the stack.

Two important features control the release of a single record at a time from the stack. First, each side of the record selector post has two steps on it. When the changer is loaded, the bottom record of the stack will be resting on the bottom step. The rest of the stack will be resting above this. The height between these steps is slightly less than the average thickness of the 10-inch records.

Second, the spindle assembly, shown in Fig. 13, has a latch which is suspended from the top portion of the spindle. Just below it there is a shelf on the spindle. The clearance between the bottom edge of the latch and the top of the shelf is just slightly more than the average thickness of 12-inch records. The latch will not move horizontally but will move vertically. When records are removed from the turntable after being played, the upward pressure pushes the latch up into the head of the spindle, allowing the records to come off. These two points should be kept in mind because in the following description of the action which causes the dropping of the records, it will be shown how they tie together.

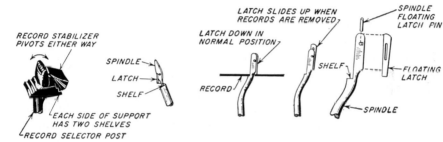

Fig. 12. The support shelf on one side of the post of this changer extends farther from the center than does the other side. The position shown is for 10-inch records. When reversed, the support holds the 12-inch records

Fig. 13. Spindle assembly used in pusher-type change mechanism. The latch plays a prominent part in separating the bottom record from the stack

Pusher Type—Dropping Mechanism. The remaining parts used for the dropping of the records can be seen in Fig. 14. The record-selector post is attached to an L-shaped lever, which is held in place by a pivot on the chassis. This lever is called the rocker arm. The rocker-arm spring, being fastened to the rocker arm on the right side of the pivot in the view shown, always maintains a constant upward pull on this side of the arm. On the left side of the pivot, that part of the rocker arm at the base of the curve limits the upward motion of the right side of the arm because it strikes the chassis.

In the illustration the cycling cam is shown as having a shelf, against the underside of which the roller on the right side of the rocker arm is pressing. As shown, it would mean that the mechanism would be starting to release the next record onto the turntable. In the neutral playing position, the cycling cam would be stopped at a place where there is no protruding shelf on its side, and the right side of the rocker arm would be slightly higher.

Pusher Type—Change Cycle. Assume that the change mechanism is about to be tripped so that the change cycle will start. In this type of changer the spindle is rigidly fixed and does not rotate. The bottom record of the stack is resting on the bottom step of the record-selector shelf and the shelf on the spindle. The remaining records are stacked in order above this record and resting on it.

When the record that is on the turntable has finished playing, and the mechanism has been tripped, the pickup arm is immediately raised from the surface of the record and swung out beyond the edge of the record so that it is clear and will not be struck as the next record falls into position. This movement is accomplished by rotation of the cycling cam, which starts to move as soon as the trip mechanism is activated. This takes only a part of the rotation of the cycling cam.

The next thing to happen, as the cycling cam continues to rotate, is that the overhanging shelf of the cam contacts the roller on the right side of the rocker arm and pushes it down. This makes the other end of the rocker arm move up, like a teeter-totter. The upward motion serves to move the record-selector post upward as well as in toward the spindle. As this happens, the riser at the back of the bottom record-selector shelf pushes the bottom record clear of the shelf on the spindle. The record then drops down the spindle shaft onto the turntable. As it drops, the slope in the spindle pulls the record clear of the record-selector shelf.

The reason the record immediately above does not fall is that it has been blocked by the latch protruding down from the head of the spindle. The latch does not let the record move horizontally as the bottom one did.

While the bottom record is dropping down the spindle, the upper record-selector shelf moves under the next record without bringing any pressure to bear on its edge. This record has now dropped down on the spindle platform but will stay there because it is not being pushed horizontally.

The rocker arm is kept depressed until the record has dropped to the turntable and the pickup arm is brought into playing position on the record. As the cycling cam ends its cycle, the rocker arm follows the overhanging shelf as its height is reduced to nothing, and thus goes back to its normal position. The record-selector post moves away from the spindle and slightly downward to return to normal. The bottom record then falls a bit more and rests on the bottom shelf of the record-selector post.

The distance between the step on the selector shelf and the back end of the spindle shelf is just enough for either 10- or 12-inch records, depending on which side of the selector post is facing the spindle.

Adjustment for Record Size. The setting of the record-selector post determines the size of the records being played. Selection is accomplished by rotating the record-selector post a half turn. The parts used here are the selector-shaft spring, selector-lever stop, and selector-lever collar. The selector-lever stop is fastened to the rocker arm and has a hole in it so that the selector shaft can go through it. It will also be noted that it is V-shaped. The selector-shaft spring is placed on the selector shaft above the selector-lever

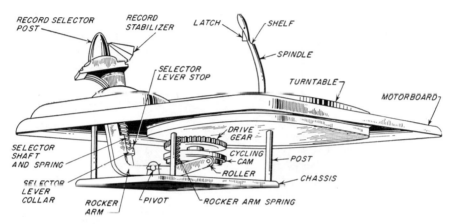

Fig. 14. The various parts of the dropping mechanism of a pusher-type changer

stop. The selector-lever collar is placed on the selector shaft immediately below the selector-lever stop. This also has a V cut in it so that it fits together with the selector-lever stop. The selector-lever stop is flexible so that it can move up and down, and the selector-shaft spring is compressed so that it holds the selector-lever stop and the selector-lever collar firmly together when the V's are matched. This forms the lock position determining whether 10- or 12-inch records are being played. Normal hand pressure is sufficient to disengage the two when it is desired to rotate the selector shaft.

Pusher Type—Variations. Another push-off type of record changer, shown in Fig. 15, uses a combination sliding and rotating action of the cycling slide and selector assembly.

During the change cycle, the drive cam engages the knurled hub, which is rotating as a result of the turntable motion. The cam shaft is mounted on the cycling slide, which in turn is mounted so that it can slide on the guide rails. Since the drive cam is eccentric (the axle is mounted off center), the distance from the drive-cam shaft to the knurled hub varies as the drive cam rotates. This changes the position of the cycling slide so that as the drive cam rotates, the cycling slide slides back and forth on the guide rails.

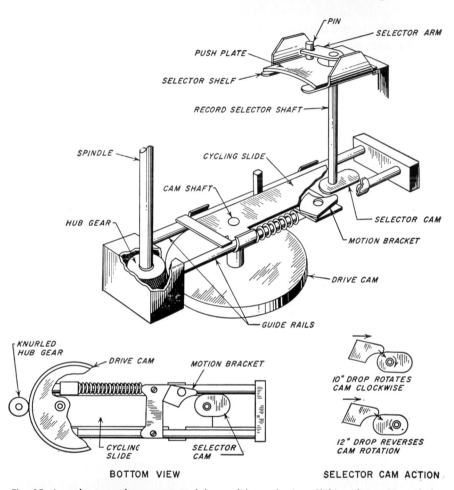

Fig. 15. A pusher-type changer actuated by a slide mechanism. Shifting the position of the motion bracket with respect to the fulcrum of the selector cam uniquely reverses the rotation of the selector shaft when it is reversed to change record size

In Fig. 15 the cycling slide is closest to the spindle, which is the neutral position. After the pickup arm has been raised off the record and caused to move out beyond the edge, the dropping action takes place. As the drive cam rotates, the cycling slide is pushed away from the spindle. The motion bracket on the cycling slide comes into contact with the selector cam. As the cycling slide moves further away from the spindle, the pressure of the motion bracket causes the selector cam to rotate. This in turn rotates the selector arm which is on the upper end of the same shaft.

A slot in the end of the selector arm loosely engages a pin which is rigidly fastened to the push plate. The selector cam thus forces the push plate to move toward the spindle, forcing the bottom record from the spindle shelf. As the drive cam continues to rotate, the cycling slide begins to move back toward the spindle, reversing the action.

The selection of 10- or 12-inch playing position is made by rotating the record-selector assembly. As it is turned, the selector arm rotates the shaft and the selector cam so that the entire assembly is rotated. The action of the selector cam, shaft, and selector arm is now in the opposite direction, but since the push plate has been reversed, it moves in the same manner as before.

Pusher Type—Servicing Problems. Although the pusher-type mechanism is not so likely to damage records by jamming them between the moving parts, the spacing between the shelf and the spindle is quite critical. Problems will also result from abuse, wear, and incorrect operation. The following paragraphs indicate some of the more common problems and the methods for correcting them.

Pusher Type—Drops More Than One Record. The latch in the head of the spindle assembly is normally spaced so only one record at a time can slide between the bottom of the latch and the platform of the spindle. The latch has an elongated hole permitting upward movement so that it can slip into a recess in the spindle head when records are being removed from the stack.

If foreign matter accumulates in the recess, the latch is apt to stick, allowing more than one record at a time to be pushed onto the platform of the spindle. This foreign matter will have to be removed with a thin sharp tool, such as a scriber or a very thin-bladed knife. Washing with carbon tetrachloride will assist in cleaning. This part of the mechanism should not be lubricated.

To avoid scratching the records or damaging their center holes, the top of the spindle shaft and the shelf on it must be free from burrs and rough edges. The edge of the record shelf must be smooth also and only slightly rounded. The bottom edge of the latch should not be rounded.

Another cause for more than one record dropping at a time could be unusually thin records. This is not too likely but can happen and should then be explained to the customer. The unbreakable plastic 78-rpm records are most likely to cause this trouble. Three alternative remedies are possible: (1) the records can be played manually; (2) the records can be discarded or at least set aside for possible future use; (3) you can make certain that the records adjacent to the very thin record are of average size.

Pusher Type—Record Drops on Pickup Arm. In the rocker-arm arrangement the initial movement of the drive cam at the start of the change cycle causes the record-selector post to move toward the spindle about $\frac{3}{32}$ inch. The post stays in this position until the pickup arm is out of the way. The record-selector post then moves toward the spindle again, causing the bottom record to drop into playing position.

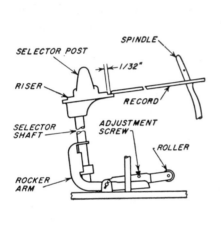

Fig. 16. Adjustment of the screw changes the relative position of the selector post and the spindle

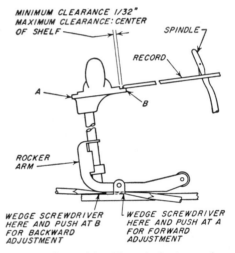

Fig. 17. The models with a single-piece rocker arm require bending the arm to adjust the relative spacing between the selector post and the spindle. The spacings shown are for the neutral or playing position

If for some reason the record-selector post has been bent back away from the spindle far enough so that the bottom record catches the edge of the selector-post shelf, the initial movement of the record-selector post drops the record on the pickup arm.

The correction for this condition is to bring the record-selector post nearer to the spindle. To accomplish this, the changer mechanism must be in the rest position. Look for a rocker-arm adjustment screw, as shown in Fig. 16, that will change the distance between the spindle and the selector post. If the changer has this screw, experiment with it until you know which way to turn it, then adjust it until a standard-size record rests at least halfway over the record-selector-post shelf when placed on the spindle shelf.

Where this adjustment screw is not available, a screwdriver must be wedged between the rocker arm and the base just to the right of the rocker-arm pivot, as shown in Fig. 17. The record-selector post should then be pressed with the heel of the hand to force it toward the spindle, using a standard-size record as before to indicate when enough correction has been made.

It is recommended that the distance between the edge of the record and the step of the record-selector post be held to $\frac{1}{32}$ inch so that records with rough or sharply beveled edges will not catch on the outer edge of the record-selector post. A standard-size record must be used in making this adjustment. A standard 10-inch record measures $9\frac{7}{8}$ inches $\pm$ $\frac{1}{32}$ inch diameter. A standard 12-inch record measures $11\frac{7}{8}$ inches $\pm$ $\frac{1}{32}$ inch diameter.

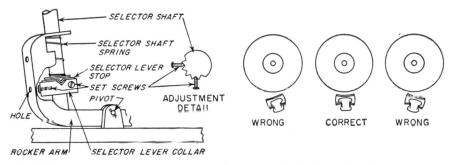

Fig. 18. Adjustment of the angle of the push-off post is made by alternately tightening one set screw while the other is loosened and vice versa

Pusher Type—Shelf-and-spindle Misalignment. Another possible cause of improper dropping with the rocker-arm arrangement is improper angle of the push-off post. The curve of the shelf should match the curve of the record, as shown in Fig. 18.

If the angle is incorrect, put a 10-inch record on the shelves as an adjusting guide. Locate the two set screws that control the position of the push-off post, and get the proper wrenches or screwdrivers for them (several Webster-Chicago changers require two No. 8 Bristol wrenches for these). Alternately adjust the screws so as to loosen one and tighten the other, and vice versa, until the angle is correct. Because of the V grooves in the selector shaft the shaft will rotate with this adjustment. Both set screws must be tightened after the correct setting has been made.

Improper dropping may also be caused by a bent spindle. It is desirable to replace the spindle rather than trying to realign it. Since some changers use the spindle to control the automatic shutoff after the last record has been played, be sure that this feature is not impaired when checking the spindle.

Pusher Type—Record Fails to Drop. This may result from the fact that the record-selector post is bent or positioned away from the spindle enough so that the lateral forward movement of the selector post does not push the record off the platform of the spindle. Once again this may be caused by a bent or misadjusted record-selector post or by a bent spindle. In either case the adjustment for this will be the same as for the correction of a record dropping on the pickup arm, as just previously described.

For the rocker-arm type of changer, a record will not drop if the record-selector post has been bent in toward the spindle too far by mishandling. The bottom record of the stack then rests on the top shelf of the record-selector post instead of the bottom shelf. Then as the record-selector post is moved in toward the spindle during the change cycle, there is nothing to push the bottom record off the spindle platform. The remedy for this condition is moving the record-selector post away from the spindle. Where the adjustment screw is available as in Fig. 16, it should be adjusted until a standard-size record rests on the bottom shelf at least $\frac{1}{32}$ inch away from the step. When this adjustment screw is not available, the rocker arm must be bent as in Fig. 17. With the changer in its rest position, push the record-selector post out with the heel of the hand. This should be done gradually, checking the adjustment at intervals.

Pusher Type—Adjustment of Push-off Cam. Several conditions can cause failure to drop or other dropping irregularities in the slide-actuated mechanism. Uneven edges, burrs between the record support and the push-off plate, a loose push-off arm, or a loose or improperly set cam may cause such a condition. These points are indicated in Fig. 19.

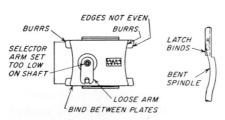

Fig. 19. Possible causes of improper dropping in the slide-actuated pusher mechanism

Proper setting of the push-off arm and cam is necessary. First make sure the mechanism has finished its changing cycle. If the record-selector post is in the 12-inch position, the long side of the cam should face the spindle. If the selector post is in the 10-inch position, the short side should face the spindle. The selector cam should be checked to assure that its axis is parallel to the guide rails. The selector arm should then be in place over the shaft, engaging the push-plate pin near the top edge.

To check the setting, press the control knob to the REJECT position, and rotate the turntable slowly by hand. Make sure that the push plate does not reach its limit before the motion bracket has reached the end of its outward travel. If it does, move the selector arm away from its 90-degree setting just enough to correct the condition, then make sure the changer operates properly on both 10- and 12-inch records.

Pusher Type—Lubrication. There are three places where lubrication might be required on the rocker-arm mechanism. On the selector-lever stop a small

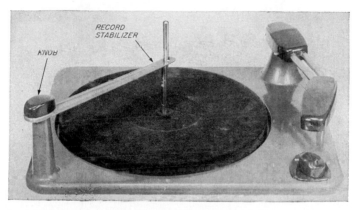

Fig. 20. A spindle-type record changer utilizes a long record stabilizer to keep the record stack level. (Howard W. Sams and V-M Corp.)

amount of Lubriplate or STA-PUT should be applied between it and the selector-lever collar. A drop of SAE 10W oil should be applied to each bearing surface of the rocker-arm-pivot shaft. Lubriplate should be applied to that portion of the cycling that comes in contact with the roller on the end of the rocker-arm assembly. Again overlubrication is to be avoided and any excess wiped off.

In the sliding assembly Lubriplate or STA-PUT should be lightly applied to the guide rails. SAE 10W oil should be applied to the shaft of the drive cam.

Spindle Type. Many of the newer record changers use only the spindle to support records. Usually some means is employed to keep the stack of records level. The example shown in Fig. 20 is of the intermix type and will play automatically up to ten 12-inch, twelve 10-inch, or 10 intermixed records.

The unit is jamproof and shuts off automatically at the completion of the last record.

To load this changer, pull the knob of the record stabilizer straight up and then swing it out of the way. Place the records on the shelf of the spindle,

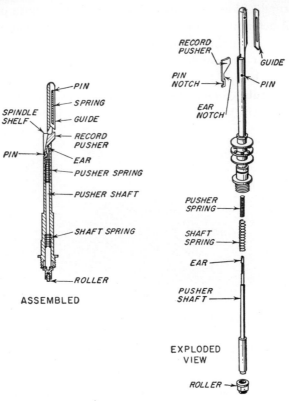

Fig. 21. A drop-type spindle mechanism. The record pusher moves up into the center hole of the record and then swings around so as to force the record off the shelf. (A PHOTOFACT "EXPLODED" VIEW © Howard W. Sams & Co., Inc.)

steadying them with one hand until the record stabilizer is swung back and replaced over the spindle. Gentle downward pressure on the record stabilizer knob is then applied to set the records parallel with the turntable. The control knob is now turned clockwise to the REJECT position and released. The changer will now play the entire stack. On completion of the last record, it will return the pickup arm to the rest post and shut off automatically. The selecting and dropping of the records is all taken care of by the spindle.

Spindle Type—Spindle Mechanism. On spindle-type changers, the spindle does not turn with the turntable. The records on the shelf, waiting to be dropped, do not turn either. Figure 21 illustrates two such spindles as they would look if removed intact from the changer, and it shows the parts that would normally be hidden inside the spindles.

In Fig. 22 is shown an underneath view of the changer, with the spindle roller just protruding out beyond the spindle housing. On the end of the lift arm, near the spindle roller, is the inclined cam surface on which the spindle roller rides and which forces the spindle pusher assembly to move during the change cycle. This lift arm is activated by the cam on the drive gear as this gear is going through its revolution to complete a change cycle.

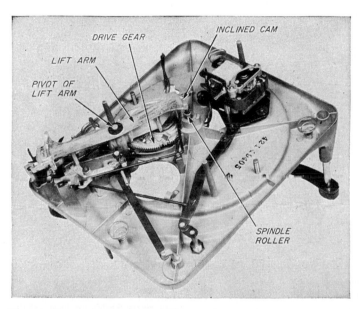

Fig. 22. The activating mechanism in a spindle-type changer. The lift arm rotates clockwise so that the inclined surface of the cam forces the spindle roller (and pusher shaft) into the spindle. (GE photo)

When the cam at the end of the lift arm sweeps across the spindle roller, it pushes upward and raises the pusher shaft of the spindle the required distance. An ear on the end of the pusher shaft fits into a notch in the bottom half of the record pusher and holds the pusher against the edge of the slot on the inside of the spindle.

When the pusher shaft raises, the pusher moves straight up and enters the center hole of the record. The pin notch in the bottom of the record pusher now reaches the pin in the spindle. As the pusher shaft continues to raise, the pusher pivots counterclockwise around the pin so that its upper end moves outward forcing the record off the shelf. The portion of the pusher extending above the shelf of the spindle is slightly less than the thickness of a record.

The guide, which is held down by a spindle guide spring inside the spindle, prevents more than one record at a time from being dropped. When records are removed from the turntable, the guide moves straight up allowing free movement of the spindle.

After a record has been dropped, the heart-shaped groove in the bottom of the cam on the drive gear reverses the movement of the lift arm and returns the spindle to its original position.

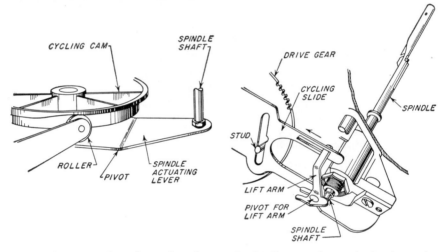

Fig. 23. The cam overhang forces the roller to move the lever, which in turn actuates the spindle drop by pushing the spindle shaft up

Fig. 24. The actuating mechanism in another spindle-drop changer. The rotary gear motion is converted to a sliding motion. The slide in turn moves the lift-arm lever, which raises the pusher shaft

Spindle Type—Spindle Activation. Many manufacturers have record changers that use this push-up type spindle support. The spindle construction and operation is very nearly the same in all of them. The differences are primarily in the method of activating the pusher shaft.

Use of a lever arrangement between the cycling cam and the spindle is shown in Fig. 23. In this case the overhang on the cycling cam varies in height as it rotates with the drive gear. This change in level is imparted to the roller, which is located on the end of the set-down lever closest to the spindle. Since the fulcrum of the set-down lever is in the middle, the right end moves down pushing against the left end of the spindle-actuating lever. Hence the right end of the spindle-actuating lever raises the pusher shaft into the spindle shaft.

Another way to raise the pusher shaft inside the spindle is illustrated in Fig. 24. A cycling slide is moved back and forth by a stud on the drive gear. A lift arm is inserted through a slot in one end of the slide in such a manner that it is not engaged during part of the cycle but is actuated at the time that record change is desired. As the slide pulls the lift arm to the left, the opposite end of the lever pushes the pusher shaft upward actuating the record drop.

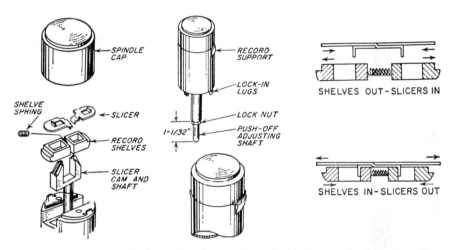

Fig. 25. The 45-rpm spindle designed to be interchanged with the normal spindle in a three-speed changer. The record stack is supported on the spindle by the record shelves

Spindle Type—Dropping 45-rpm Records. The 45-rpm record is different from those made for other speeds in that the center hole is considerably larger. Originally this record and a special 45-rpm changer were designed simultaneously. Because of the rather radical departure from conventional design a separate chapter is devoted to the 45-rpm changer.

Many record changers have provisions for playing 45-rpm records as well as the 78-rpm and 33⅓-rpm variety. One way of handling the 45-rpm records is to place an insert (called a spider) in the large center hole of each 45-rpm record. These inserts have a conventional-size center hole that fits over the conventional spindle. These inserts are reasonably priced and satisfactory but are generally not favored by the public because of their makeshift nature.

Spindle Type—Interchangeable Spindles. Another approach is to use interchangeable spindles, one of which is for the 45-rpm records. One such 45-rpm spindle is shown in Fig. 25. This fits on the changer in place of the regular spindle. Two lock-in lugs drop into holes in the turntable to make the spindle turn with the turntable just as it does on all 45-rpm changers. The record stack is held by the record shelves located on either side of the spindle.

The slicer cam and shaft has two ears with beveled sides which fit through the record shelves and the slicers. The slicers fit on top of the record shelves. Each slicer has a lip which bends down into the hole in the record shelf. During the change cycle the slicer cam and shaft is pushed upward. The holes in the record shelves are larger than in the slicer so that the beveled edges on the ears of the shaft force the slicers outward. These slicers slip into the space between the bottom two records.

The slicers are attached to the respective opposite shelves. This means that the shelves are pulled in as the slicers are pushed out. When the shelves are withdrawn, the bottom record drops to the turntable. The slicers now support the rest of the record stack. When the shaft drops, the slicers and shelves are returned to their original position by a spring compressed between the two shelves. The record stack drops from the slicers to the record shelves. All this is done while everything is rotating—turntable, spindle, and the entire load of records.

Spindle Type—Eccentric Spindle. An earlier type of spindle support uses a cam or eccentric in the spindle, as shown in Fig. 26. This spindle assembly consists of a hollow spindle through which is placed a shaft. This shaft is fastened at the lower end to a pinion gear and at the top to an eccentric. Above the eccentric is a fixed spindle cap.

When a stack of records is placed on the spindle, the bottom one rests on the eccentric. When the eccentric is in line with the cap, the records will drop slightly; the bottom one will now rest on the shelf provided by the spindle proper, and the eccentric will be located in its center hole. Now as the eccentric rotates back to its original position, it causes the bottom record to move with it, and when it is in line with the spindle, the bottom record will drop. The remainder of the stack will be resting on the eccentric and the cycle is complete.

Figure 26 also shows a common method of actuating this type of drop. The feed-sector lever has a gear sector at one end and a fulcrum at the other. In between is attached another lever which has a cam roller at the other end. The feed lever is held taut against the cycling cam by the record feed spring. As the cycling cam rotates, the feed-sector lever is moved to and fro about the fulcrum. The gear sector matches the pinion gear on the spindle, causing the spindle to rotate. It is only necessary to have 180-degree rotation of the eccentric since it can return along its original path rather than com-

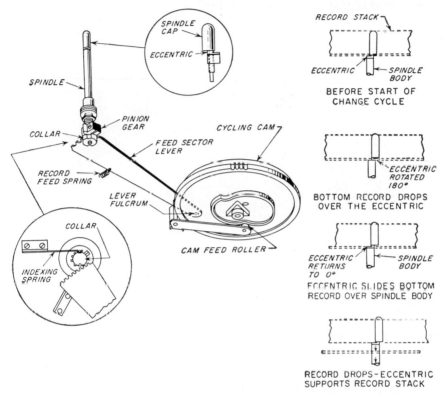

Fig. 26. A spindle-type drop mechanism using an eccentric to select the bottom record from the stack

plete the 360-degree rotation. An indexing spring assures that the eccentric will stop in the proper position for dropping the record. Figure 27 shows a record changer using an eccentric spindle plus a record shelf.

Another actuating mechanism for the eccentric spindle utilizes a crank-type drive. Figure 28 illustrates this, showing that the drive gear actuates a link shaped like a question mark, which in turn rotates a crank fastened to the spindle shaft.

Spindle Type—Servicing Problems. Since the spindle-type mechanism has only a single support and much of the drop mechanism is confined within the spindle where it is not exposed, it is likely to cause less difficulty than the other types. On the other hand, a portion of this mechanism is not visible, so any difficulty that exists may be hard to locate.

Although the spindle-drop mechanisms will operate relatively well with warped records, poor center holes will cause considerable difficulty. Such records must be played manually or discarded.

Fig. 27. A record changer with an eccentric-type spindle drop. (Westinghouse photo)

Spindle Type—Record Does Not Drop. If the spindle pusher shaft is broken, records may not drop. In this case, the pusher-shaft assembly will have to be replaced.

The record pusher may not be moving far enough forward to eject a record. Any screws that hold the lift arm, lever, or other associated mechanism should be checked to see that they are tightened all the way. The shaft spring in the spindle housing should be checked if possible, to see that it compresses slightly when the shaft nears the end of its excursion into the spindle.

If the roller spring is compressed and the pusher does not move forward far enough to eject a record, the spindle should be replaced. It may be necessary to loosen a set screw in the spindle housing of the base plate to remove it from some machines. Do not use pressure to remove the spindle; if it sticks, check again to make sure that all mounting screws have been removed.

If the pusher rises outside of the spindle body, it will not allow a record to drop. The pusher shaft must then be checked to see that it is not bent. A bent pusher shaft will cause the pusher to raise the record instead of pushing it off the spindle ledge.

One spindle-type mechanism has an adjustment nut at the bottom of the spindle assembly, as illustrated in Fig. 29. If the push-off finger does not drop the record, it may be set by stacking with 12-inch records to a height of 1 inch. If the bottom record is not dropped when the changer is energized and the REJECT button operated, the adjusting nut should be turned one quarter of a revolution in a counterclockwise direction. This makes the pusher shaft longer. This operation should be continued in steps until the record is pushed off. When the adjustment is completed, check to make certain that the shaft is not too long as this will cause the changer to stall in its cycle. When the changer is in normal rest position, there should be very little play in the actuating lever.

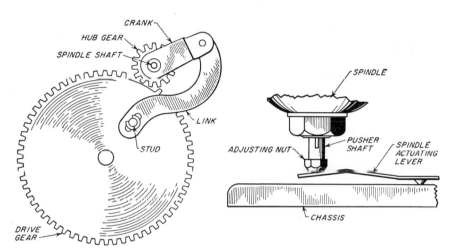

Fig. 28. A changer mechanism with a "question-mark" link to turn a crank and activate the eccentric spindle drop

Fig. 29. A spindle-type drop which provides an adjustment nut to change the effective length of the pusher shaft

Spindle Type—Two Records Drop at Once. If the spindle guide is not fully down, two records may drop at once. If the guide is bent, it may be straightened by gently bending in the reverse direction with a pair of pliers. Should binding occur, it should be eased as gently as possible. If foreign matter is lodged in the spindle assembly, it may be removed with a thin tool such as a speaker shim. The guide will normally raise slightly during the drop but should return to place of its own accord.

Where the record stabilizer is binding on the spindle, the latter should be checked to see that it is straight. If the spindle is found to be bent, it is better to replace it than to try to correct the condition. The record stabilizer arm must be square with the spindle and must slide freely down the spindle without assistance. If it appears to be out of square, it may be bent gently with the fingers in the desired direction.

If the record stabilizer shaft binds in the shaft post on the base plate, two records may drop at once. For this trouble, remove the shaft and clean both the shaft and the shaft post thoroughly with very fine emery cloth, then wash with carbon tetrachloride. After lubricating the shaft with a thin film of Lubriplate or STA-PUT, it may be reassembled.

Spindle Type—Adjustment of 45-rpm Spindle. The adjustment of the push-off shaft in the type of 45-rpm spindle shown in Fig. 25 is correct when the distance between the end of the shaft and the top of the locknut is $1\frac{1}{32}$ inches. To check this setting, place the spindle on the changer and watch the slicer blades when pressing the spindle down for locking in place. If no movement of the blades is noted, the spindle will probably operate properly.

If the slicers start to move out of the spindle when it is pressed down, adjustment is needed. Take out the spindle and loosen the locknut, then screw in the push-off adjusting shaft about one turn. After tightening the locknut, insert the spindle and check again. The procedure should be repeated until no movement of the slicers is noted.

Spindle Type—Lubrication. With the spindle-drop mechanism very little lubrication will be required. The spindle bearing requires a few drops of SAE 10W oil. Other moving parts should be given a light application of Lubriplate or STA-PUT.

All sliding portions of changers are normally lubricated with Lubriplate or STA-PUT No. 512.

Record Defects. There are several types of record defects which can cause difficulty in operation of the dropping mechanism in slicer and pusher changers. Undersize records may cause two records to drop simultaneously. Oversize records may result in failure to drop. Warped records may not drop, may drop improperly, or may cause jamming. Likewise, improper location of the center hole or excessive wear in this portion may cause premature or uneven dropping, jamming of the mechanism, or simultaneous dropping of two or more records. These defects can be determined by inspection of the records. Since there is no remedy for them, the records should be discarded for automatic playing. In most cases these records can be played manually. However, where the center hole is greatly enlarged, the record may be off center on the turntable and cause distortion.

The only record defect that may affect spindle-type changers is an enlarged center hole. This can either make records drop prematurely or fail to drop.

Record Squeal. If the stack of records squeals due to friction between the center holes and the spindle, it can be eliminated by applying a small amount of wax to the spindle.

Summary. The various methods of dropping records have been discussed in detail. With this information you can now tackle any problem involving the changing of records, regardless of the method used. Most dropping problems will be the fault of the records, but regardless of the reason you can make the necessary repairs to return the equipment to its proper condition.

QUESTIONS

1. What are the three methods of dropping the bottom record of a stack onto the turntable?
2. How does a slicer-type changer separate the bottom record from the rest of the stack?
3. How does a slicer-type intermix changer compensate for the smaller thickness of the 10-inch record?
4. What record defects are likely to cause improper dropping in a slicer-type changer?
5. How does the spindle help in selecting the bottom record of a stack on a pusher-type changer?
6. How do you adjust a pusher-type non-intermix changer for different record sizes?
7. How do you lubricate a pusher-type changer?
8. What record defects are likely to cause improper dropping in a pusher-type changer?
9. Describe how the record pusher is caused to operate in a spindle-type drop mechanism.
10. What record defects are likely to cause improper dropping in a spindle-type drop mechanism?
11. Why do the 45-rpm slicers come out of the spindle when the record shelves retract?
12. How can you eliminate record squeal?

10

Cycling the Pickup Arm

Pickup-arm Cycling. This chapter deals with the mechanisms used in record changers to move the pickup arm out of the way after playing of a record is finished so that the next record in the stack can drop. Return of the pickup arm to the beginning of the next record, known as indexing, is another important part of this operation.

A large percentage of the troubles encountered in changer repair work can be fixed simply by making adjustments to the indexing section. The reason for this is that the pickup arm, being entirely exposed, has the greatest chance of being mishandled by the person operating the unit. The parts that are connected with it, although they may be underneath the mounting plate, are subjected to this same abuse.

Operation of Changers. Changers can be divided into two types according to the way they operate after playing a stack of records. In one type the pickup arm will move to the side of the changer and stop on its rest post. The motor may or may not stop, depending upon design. This automatic-shutoff type does not give too much trouble from mishandling because it has usually completed the cycle and shut off before the operator has had a chance to do anything about it.

In the second type the changer repeats the last record until it has been shut off. This type of changer is apt to be more troublesome. One of the reasons for this is that the user, after hearing the last record repeated three or four times, decides that something should be done about it. Upon approaching the machine, he grabs the pickup arm, which is usually part way through the record. When the arm is picked up, the machine is unwittingly tripped by the erratic movement. Almost immediately a movement of the pickup arm is felt. The reaction, due to surprise, is often to grab and hold. This places a terrific strain on all of the mechanism involved. The result is bending of levers, moving of set-screw positions, or possibly breaking some of the parts.

Shutting Off Changer during the Change Cycle. Another mistake that operators frequently make is to shut the changer off in the middle of a change cycle. When the cycle has been approximately half completed, the pickup arm will be in a raised position at the side of the changer base. If the motor is turned off at this point, cams, gears, and levers are left in their engaged positions. The next person using the changer may attempt to bring the pickup arm manually into playing position before turning on the motor. Again the pickup arm and its associated parts are subjected to a force which could bend some of the parts or change the indexing adjustment.

The correct time to change records or shut off one of these changers is when the pickup arm has complete freedom of movement. This condition generally exists only during playing of the first third of a record. Suppose that the last record has been played through once and the pickup arm has again started to play this record. As long as the pickup arm has moved no more than a third of the way across the record, it is safe to pick up the arm, swing it out, and place it on its rest. This can be done because the trip lever attached to the pickup arm has not yet engaged the tripping mechanism. Until the trip lever engages the trip mechanism, the pickup arm has complete freedom of movement.

If more than a third of the record has been played, it is possible that the trip mechanism may be engaged. In this case, it is necessary to push the REJECT button and allow the changer to go through its change cycle. This brings the pickup arm into playing position on the first grooves on the outside of the record. Now the pickup arm may be removed and placed in its rest position.

Requirements of Indexing Mechanism. Whether the pickup arm will set down to play a 7-, 10-, or 12-inch record is determined by manually setting a lever in the correct position for the size of record being played. On an intermix changer which plays 7-, 10-, and 12-inch records in one loading, the set-down position is determined by the records themselves.

When the pickup arm is lowered to start playing a record, the ideal position for it to land is in the space between the edge and the first groove of the record. Here the needle will engage what is known as the starting groove, which brings it quickly into the regular playing grooves. If the needle lands too far in, some of the first grooves will not be played. If the needle comes down too far out, it will miss the record entirely. Either one of these troubles will call for an adjustment.

If the pickup arm does not rise high enough to clear the pile of records during the change cycle, the needle will drag across the surface of the top record and scratch it. On the other hand, the pickup arm may rise too high, rubbing on the underside of the records still remaining to be played. Either of these conditions calls for an adjustment of the height-control parts.

Types of Pickup-arm Cycling Mechanisms. Pickup-arm cycling mechanisms may be classified according to the activating portion. Hence we may have (1) a combination type where both the vertical and horizontal motions of the pickup arm during the change cycle are activated by the same source or (2) an independent type where different portions of the mechanism cause the vertical and horizontal motions to take place.

The basic operation can further be applied to a non-intermix changer, an intermix changer, or to both. Thus there are six possible types: (1) combination; (2) combination non-intermix; (3) combination intermix; (4) independent; (5) independent non-intermix; (6) independent intermix.

In the following paragraphs the various indexing mechanisms will be discussed one by one. In addition to the workings of each type, the method of repair, adjustment, and lubrication will be discussed. Upon completion of this you will know how to completely repair 90 per cent of the record changers that you will encounter.

Combination Non-intermix—Indexing. The record changer shown in Fig. 1 is typical of those having an easily accessible indexing adjustment. This is a screw that is reached by inserting a small screwdriver in a hole in the top of the pickup arm, near the rear. The illustration shows a side view of the changer, showing the parts involved and their positions with respect to each other. It is of the combination cycling type—the vertical and horizontal movements of the pickup arm are both obtained from the same mechanism. The pickup-arm shaft protrudes down through the base plate into the chassis assembly. Attached to this shaft on the underside of the base plate is the pickup-arm raising disc. During the change cycle this disc is pushed up by the pickup-arm raising lever. The pickup-arm raising lever is in turn moved by the cycling cam because a stud at the other end of this pickup-arm raising lever rides on a track on the cycling cam, as shown in Fig. 2.

Assume that the needle of the pickup arm is just about to enter the eccentric trip groove of the record being played. As the playing of the record has progressed, a V-shaped cut in the pickup-arm raising disc has been rotating (clockwise as viewed from the top) and approaching the beveled edge of the pickup-arm raising lever. The cutout never does quite reach the beveled edge even when the needle is in the eccentric groove of the record.

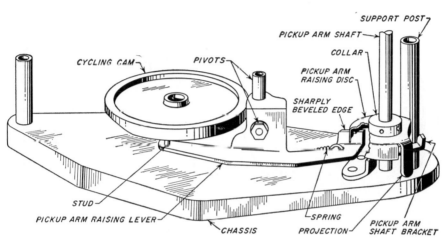

Fig. 1. A right-side view of a combination set-down changer shows the relationship of the pickup arm to the parts that determine its movements

When the mechanism is tripped, the cycling cam starts to rotate and applies a downward pressure to the stud end of the pickup-arm raising lever. Since the fulcrum is in the middle, this causes the other end of the lever to push up the pickup-arm raising disc. This in turn raises the pickup-arm shaft, thereby lifting the needle from the surface of the record.

Immediately following this, the track in the cycling cam causes the stud end of the pickup-arm raising lever to move in toward the center of the cam. In so doing, the opposite end of the pickup-arm raising lever swings out. As there is a lot of friction between the beveled edge of the pickup-arm raising lever and the pickup-arm raising disc, the disc is moved. This swings the pickup arm out away from the spindle. The pickup arm swings out until the projection on the pickup-arm raising disc contacts the pickup-arm shaft bracket. The bracket keeps the pickup-arm raising disc from rotating further. The beveled edge of the pickup-arm raising lever continues to move, slipping along the pickup-arm raising disc until it slides into the V cut on the pickup-arm raising disc.

The track of the cycling cam is cut so that the pickup-arm raising lever is held in this position until a record drops on the turntable. After this has happened, the track then reverses the movement of the pickup-arm raising lever. Since the beveled edge and the V in the pickup-arm raising disc are

1—2 PICKUP LIFTS FROM RECORD
2—3 PICKUP MOVES OUT BEYOND EDGE
      OF RECORD
3—4 PICKUP MOVES IN TO INDEX POINT
4—5 PICKUP SETS DOWN

OUTSIDE OF GROOVE FOR 10" RECORDS
INSIDE OF GROOVE FOR 12" RECORDS

Fig. 2. The groove in the cam determines the motion of the pickup arm

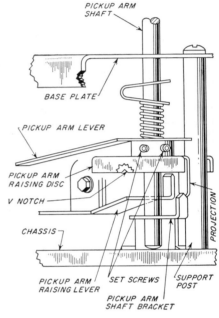

Fig. 3. When the pickup arm is moved over its rest post, the projection on the raising disc fits in the groove between the support post and the pickup-arm shaft bracket

now engaged, the entire assembly (including the pickup arm) will swing in a distance determined by the track in the cycling cam. This distance corresponds to the correct set-down position so that the needle is over the lead-in groove of the record.

At this point the pressure exerted at the stud end of the pickup-arm raising lever is relieved, and the entire assembly of the pickup arm, pickup-arm shaft, and the pickup-arm raising disc is lowered. This causes the needle to set down in the starting groove of the record.

In the neutral position after set-down, there is sufficient clearance between the beveled edge of the pickup-arm raising lever and the bottom edge of the pickup-arm raising disc so that there is no binding between these two parts. The needle therefore rides freely in the grooves of the record.

Combination Non-intermix—Rest Position. When the pickup arm is lifted and moved to the rest post of the changer, the projection on the pickup-arm raising disc touches the outer edge of the pickup-arm shaft bracket. At this position the pickup arm is not yet on the rest post. A little more pressure must be exerted outward in order to make the lip rise up over the bevel on the pickup-arm shaft bracket and seat itself between this bracket and the support post adjacent to it. When the lip is in this groove, as shown in Fig. 3, the pickup arm is locked in position on its rest post.

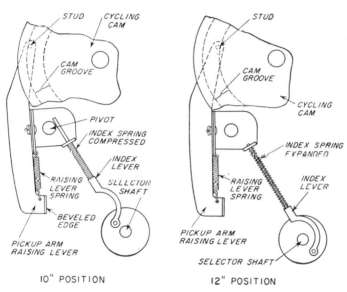

Fig. 4. The pressure or lack of pressure applied by the index spring determines which side of the cam groove the raising-lever stud will follow. Spring tension is adjusted by the setting of the selector post and shaft

Combination Non-intermix—Change of Set-down for Different Record Sizes. With a non-intermix changer, the record-selector post must be preadjusted by the operator for the size of the record. This automatically moves a lever which changes the index-spring tension applied to the pickup-arm raising lever causing it to follow either the inside or the outside of the track that is on the underneath side of the cycling cam. Both sides of the track on the cycling cam control the movement of the pickup-arm raising lever in a similar manner. The only difference is in the distance out from the spindle at which the needle sets down in the starting groove of the record being played.

When the selector post is in the 12-inch position, the pickup-arm raising lever is released from the index-spring action, as shown in Fig. 4. The weight of the pickup assembly has sufficient load so that it drags. When the stud comes to the widened portion of the cycling-cam groove, the stud is in and the pickup is out. The cycling cam moves the stud outward, and the pickup arm moves inward. Because of the drag the stud follows the inside of the cycling-cam groove so that when the pickup arm sits down it is out to the 12-inch position.

When the selector post is turned to the 10-inch position, the index lever moves toward the pickup-arm raising lever, causing the index spring to compress and place a force against the pickup-arm raising lever. This force keeps the stud as far out as possible. When the cycling cam moves so that the stud enters the wide portion of the groove, the index spring makes the stud follow the outer edge. This makes the pickup arm move to the inner or 10-inch set-down position.

Combination Intermix Cycling—Indexing. In one typical intermix changer the basic cycling mechanism is similar to the non-intermix type just studied. The record-selector post has a step in it, however. When a 10-inch record is on the bottom of the stack, it rests on the lower surface with its edge adjacent to the riser so that it can be pushed. On each side of the selector post, as shown in Fig. 5, are metal pieces which together form another step. When a 12-inch record is on the bottom of the stack, it rests on this step. The riser sections of these pieces are adjacent to the record edge, so the record may readily be pushed off the spindle. These metal pieces are pivoted so that they are raised when a 10-inch record is on the bottom. The weight of a 12-inch record forces them down when it is on the bottom of the stack.

One of these metal pieces has a long arm extending below it. On the end is a hook. This piece is called the record-selector lever. The hook catches under a surface on the index lever when the selector lever is in the up position (10-inch record on the bottom). When the selector post moves inward during the change cycle, the selector lever pulls up on the index lever. Since the index lever is pivoted on the upper right, it rotates clockwise, compressing the index compression spring. This causes the stud on the pickup-arm raising lever to follow the outside edge of the cam groove.

When a 12-inch record is on the bottom, the top of the record-selector lever is forced downward, causing the hook to rotate away from the index lever. As a result, there is no spring pushing against the pickup-arm raising lever, and the stud follows the inner edge of the cam groove.

Combination Intermix—Indexing of a Three-speed Changer. In a three-speed record changer using the basic mechanism just studied, the record-selector post has a third position to provide support for 7-inch records. To provide proper record set-down, the pickup-arm raising disc has a projection on the lower side on the portion closest to the selector post. Under this is a right-angled 10-inch set-down lever, pivoted at its bend so it can rotate

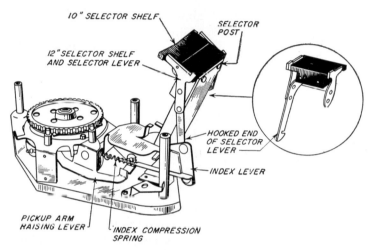

10" SELECTOR SHELF

SELECTOR POST

12" SELECTOR SHELF AND SELECTOR LEVER

HOOKED END OF SELECTOR LEVER

INDEX LEVER

PICKUP ARM RAISING LEVER

INDEX COMPRESSION SPRING

Fig. 5. Selection of 10-inch or 12-inch indexing is controlled by the 12-inch shelf and index lever

horizontally. On the outside end of this 10-inch set-down lever, just under the projection on the raising disc, is a hook designed to catch the projection when the pickup arm is just above the 10-inch set-down point. A tension spring normally holds the hook away from the raising disc projection.

The cycling cam is cut so that the pickup arm sets down for either 12- or 7-inch records, depending on whether the stud follows the inside or outside edge of the cam groove. The setting of an index spring controls the stud, just as with the model previously discussed. When the selector post is in the 10-inch position, the index spring is compressed the same as when it is in the 7-inch position.

The stud follows the outer edge of the cam groove in both the 7- and 10-inch positions. However, when the selector post is set for the 10-inch position, the selector-lever collar is in a position such that an added projection is facing the spindle. As the selector post moves in to push the record off the spindle during the change cycle, this projection pushes against a set-down actuating lever added to the rocker-arm assembly. Figure 6 shows this. This set-down actuating lever in turn pushes against the inside end of the 10-inch set-down lever, causing it to rotate slightly. This moves the hooked outer end into position to catch the projection on the raising disc, stopping the pickup-arm movement just above the proper 10-inch set-down point, as illustrated.

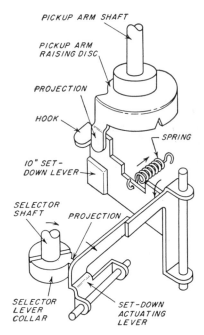

PICKUP ARM SHAFT

PICKUP ARM RAISING DISC

PROJECTION

HOOK

SPRING

10" SET-DOWN LEVER

SELECTOR SHAFT   PROJECTION

SELECTOR LEVER COLLAR   SET-DOWN ACTUATING LEVER

Fig. 6. A three-speed combination set-down changer using a special lever arrangement to hook the end of the pickup-arm raising disc when the pickup arm is properly indexed for 10-inch records. The spring keeps the hook disengaged from the raising disc projection except when the projection on the selector-lever collar contacts the actuating lever

Combination Cycling—Spindle-type Drop. Another form of indexing is used in changers where the center spindle supports the records. In one model, an indexing finger is mounted with the record stabilizer on concentric shafts, as illustrated in Fig. 7. The index finger is spring-loaded so that its end tends to rotate toward the spindle. In use, the tip of the index finger contacts the edge of the record stack. On the lower end of the shaft of the index finger is the set-down disc assembly, under the base plate, as shown in Fig. 8A.

The set-down disc assembly and the pickup-arm raising disc work together with a set-down lever to manipulate the set-down indexing. The set-down lever has a roller mounted on one end which contacts the cycling cam. Its action is similar to that of the rocker-arm assembly previously discussed. As the change cycle starts, the pickup is lifted from the record and is moved out by action of the pickup-arm raising lever and its associated mechanism, as previously described for other models. The vertical cycling-cam action against the roller causes the set-down lever to move up into one of the grooves in the set-down disc assembly. The groove into which it moves is dependent upon the setting of the index finger.

If the index finger is all the way in (no records on the spindle), the set-down lever will slide into the left-hand groove. Going to the right, the other grooves correspond to 7- and 10-inch records, and the portion on the right end corresponds to the 12-inch position. The pickup-arm raising lever follows the outside edge of the cam groove for all positions due to spring tension.

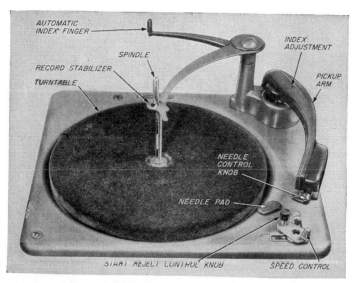

Fig. 7. This changer with spindle-type drop utilizes an automatic index finger to control the combination indexing. (Howard W. Sams photo)

With 7-inch records on the stack, the set-down disc assembly is fully counterclockwise. The set-down plate does not contact the pickup-arm raising disc under this condition, and the cycling cam controls the set-down position.

With 10-inch records on the stack the set-down disc position is as shown in Fig. 8B. Now as the pickup-arm raising lever returns the pickup-arm raising disc and pickup arm toward the set-down point, the end of the set-down plate contacts the stop ear on the set-down disc assembly, stopping the pickup arm in the proper horizontal position.

The index assembly is designed so that the same stop ear is used for both 10- and 12-inch records. The index finger and thus the set-down disc assembly are further clockwise for the 12-inch record, shortening the inward (clockwise) movement of the pickup-arm raising disc and pickup arm.

After the last record has been played, the index finger is furthest counter-

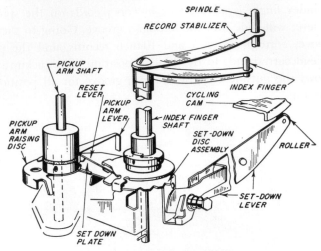

(A) SET-DOWN MECHANISM

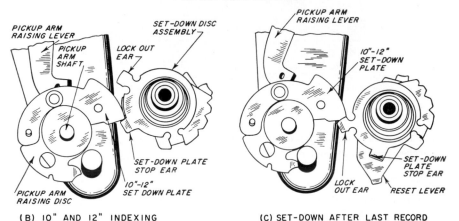

(B) 10" AND 12" INDEXING

(C) SET-DOWN AFTER LAST RECORD

Fig. 8. The set-down disc assembly rotates with the index finger. The set-down lever is raised by the cycling cam during the change cycle so that the set-down disc assembly is held in place. This stops the set-down plate for proper indexing

clockwise. This rotates the set-down disc assembly so that the lock-out ear now stops the set-down plate when the pickup arm is over the pickup-rest post as shown in Fig. 8C. The reset lever which is a part of this assembly is used to reset the trip mechanism. Such action is discussed in another chapter.

Combination Cycling—Lift-mechanism Troubles. The lift mechanism here, as in most changers, is a simple lever system using a cam to initiate the action. Only two adjustment limits are involved. The pickup-arm lift must not be so great that the pickup arm hits the unplayed records on the record support. On the other hand, the lift must be enough so the needle clears the top record when the entire stack is on the turntable.

Dried lubrication or dirt may cause the pickup-arm shaft to bind. In this case the shaft will have to be removed from the assembly for cleaning with carbon tetrachloride, then polished with a very fine emery cloth or crocus cloth. The shaft hole should also be cleaned by saturating a small cloth with carbon tetrachloride and poking it through the hole with a screwdriver. If necessary, gently run a very small file through the hole to remove any dirt that still adheres. Care should be used as no metal should be removed. The shaft can then be tried for a fit. If it is free, remove and reassemble after applying a little Lubriplate or STA-PUT.

It is generally sufficient for the needle to clear the top record of a full turntable stack by $\frac{1}{16}$ to $\frac{1}{8}$ inch. To adjust the lift, trip the mechanism and rotate the changer through a cycle until the pickup arm has risen to its maximum height above the turntable but has not yet begun to move out. It is simple to stop at this point if the turntable is rotated by hand.

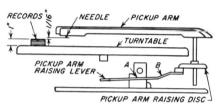

Fig. 9. Adjustment of the clearance between the needle and the records in a combination indexing changer is made by bending the pickup-arm raising lever. The lever should be held at point A and bent up or down as required at point B by use of pliers

A typical method of making this adjustment, shown in Fig. 9, involves holding the pickup-arm raising lever at point A and bending it at point B. Use either long-nose or duck-bill pliers. Bending upward at B will raise the pickup arm. Care should be taken so that the lever is not twisted during this effort. No attempt should be made to move the pickup-arm raising disc either up or down.

Combination Cycling—Indexing Adjustment. It is a common practice to use some sort of cam arrangement to provide indexing adjustment. This is frequently located in the pickup-arm assembly. Figure 10A illustrates one such arrangement.

The pickup-arm shaft is rigidly fastened to the pickup-arm hinge so that when the shaft rotates, the hinge (and pickup arm) rotates. The pickup arm has a plate fastened to it on the inside providing a sturdy mounting surface. The hinge is fastened to the pickup arm or plate with one fixed screw located at the rear. The other fastening screw is an eccentric. The screw shaft centers in a hole in the plate. The eccentric portion fits into the hinge. The relative position of the hinge and the plate depends on the position of the eccentric. Adjustment moves it back and forth.

If the eccentric screw does not give enough correction when in its extreme position, return the screw to its middle position so it will be useful in the future. Now put the record-selector post in the 10-inch position. Operate the mechanism by revolving the turntable by hand until the needle drops to within ⅛ inch of a 10-inch record on the turntable. Locate the two screws that control pickup-arm position, illustrated in Fig. 10B. Using

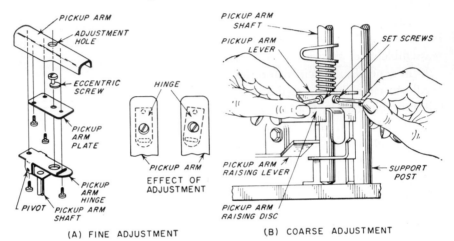

(A) FINE ADJUSTMENT   (B) COARSE ADJUSTMENT

Fig. 10. The fine indexing adjustment is a cam-operated lever available through the top of the pickup arm. The coarse indexing adjustment is made by alternately adjusting two screws on the pickup-arm shaft below the base plate

the right size of Bristol wrench, alternately loosen one and tighten the other until the needle is brought to the desired point. Check the adjustment by changing the record-selector post to the 12-inch position and watching the needle drop point on a 12-inch record. When this adjustment is finished, be sure that both set screws are tight. Since this entire action is accomplished by the pressure of the screws against the sides of V-shaped grooves, both screws must be tightened simultaneously or the index point will change.

Combination Cycling—Pickup Arm Drops off Rest. When the pickup arm is moved to the rest position, the projection of the pickup-arm raising disc should rest in the groove formed when the inside bevel of the pickup-arm shaft bracket touches the support post in Fig. 3. When the bracket is properly adjusted, there should be 0.01 inch clearance between the lip of the pickup-arm raising disc and the bottom of the groove.

If this clearance is too large, the pickup arm may fall off the rest position when coming down on it after the last record is played. To correct the clearance, adjust the bracket. First loosen the two set screws on the pickup-arm raising disc. With the bottom of the pickup-arm shaft resting on the chassis and the pickup arm on the rest post, set the clearance properly and tighten the set screws. It will now be necessary to check the indexing on a record and possibly readjust it as previously described. Be sure that the set-down of the needle on a 12-inch record is checked, taking care that the projection of the pickup-arm raising disc does not hit the beveled side of the bracket.

Lubrication of Combination Mechanism. Apply SAE 10W oil to the bottom bearing point of the pickup-arm shaft where it passes through the pickup-arm shaft bracket and where it goes through the base plate. Lubriplate should be applied to the pivot points of the pickup arm and on the sharply beveled edge on the end of the pickup-arm raising lever. The tracks of the cycling cam, the bearing surfaces of the pickup-arm raising-lever assembly, and the pivot of the pickup-arm raising lever should be lubricated with Lubriplate or STA-PUT.

Independent Set-down Mechanism. In one of the earlier changers, the raising and lowering action of the pickup arm is independent of the indexing action. Figure 11A is an underneath view of this changer, showing those parts which are directly concerned with the horizontal positioning of the pickup arm. The index finger on the pickup-arm return lever is in contact with the larger portion of the cam segment. This is the position when the record-shelf support has no records on it and it has been allowed to rise.

When the shelf support has records on it, the record-support shaft will drop down, and the index finger will ride in over the top of this cam and come to rest against the support shaft. The pickup-arm feed-in spring is fastened to the base plate at one end and so placed that it will keep the index finger pressed against either the cam segment or the support shaft unless some force is exerted in a direction opposite to its pull.

As the needle enters the eccentric groove of the record, the pickup-arm lever is quite close to the pickup-arm rotating lever. When the mechanism is tripped, the drive gear starts to rotate, causing the pickup-arm rotating lever, which is contacting the cam track of the drive gear, to move outward. The lower left end moves in a counterclockwise direction. This motion continues until the pickup-arm rotating lever contacts the stud on the pickup-arm lever, forcing the pickup-arm lever to move clockwise. Since the pickup-arm lever is fastened to the pickup-arm shaft, the pickup arm is moved out from underneath the stack of records yet to be played.

As the outward movement is continued, the stud on the pickup-arm lever moves the pickup-arm return lever far enough so that the index finger leaves the support shaft for a short distance. All levers are held momentarily in this position until another record has dropped.

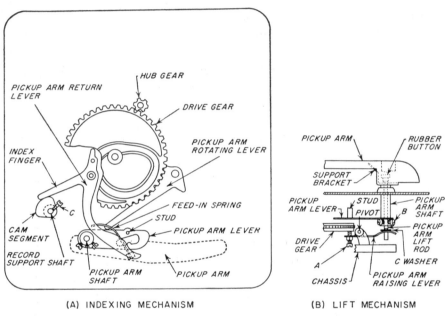

(A) INDEXING MECHANISM   (B) LIFT MECHANISM

Fig. 11. The pickup-arm lift and indexing mechanism in a changer where the actions are governed independently

After the new record is on the turntable, the cam track moves the pickup-arm rotating lever to its neutral position, which is in toward the center of the drive gear. The feed-in spring on the pickup-arm return lever causes the pickup-arm lever to move in until the index finger again contacts the support shaft.

Since the stud of the pickup-arm lever was resting against the pickup-arm return lever, the pickup-arm return lever will cause the pickup-arm lever to be moved in too. When the index finger is stopped by the record-support shaft, the pickup-arm lever is in the correct position for the needle to be set down on the record.

The feed-in spring, attached to the pickup-arm return lever, will exert just enough inward pressure on the stud of the pickup-arm lever to make the needle enter the first playing groove of the record, even when the record has no lead-in groove.

Independent Pickup-arm Lift Mechanism. The pickup arm is fastened to a hollow pickup-arm shaft, as shown in Fig. 11B. The pickup-arm lift rod goes through the center of this hollow shaft and has at its top end a rubber button. At the bottom end of this lift rod is the pickup-arm raising lever, its pivot support, and the adjusting screw A, which rides against the drive gear. The pickup-arm raising lever is slotted at the point where the pickup-arm lift rod extends downward through it. As the pickup-arm raising lever rises, contacts a C washer that is locked on the pickup-arm lift rod and pushes against this washer to raise the pickup-arm lift rod and the pickup arm.

A support bracket is used to stop the downward movement of the pickup arm so that the needle will never touch the base plate of the changer. This is a preventive measure, as jeweled needles can easily be chipped by coming in contact with a hard surface. If the needle touches the base plate, the bracket should be adjusted by bending so that the needle clears by approximately $3/32$ inch.

As the needle enters the eccentric groove at the end of the record and trips the mechanism, the drive gear starts to rotate. The adjusting screw A is forced down almost immediately by the downward incline on the bottom face of the drive gear. Since the pickup-arm raising lever is pivoted in the middle, this causes the other end of the lever to rise against the C washer on the pickup-arm lift rod. The rod then rises until its rubber top button pushes up the pickup arm. The lift mechanism remains in this position until the rest of the cycling movement has been completed. Then, as the drive gear comes into the neutral position, the adjusting screw A is allowed to rise up another incline on the drive gear, relieving the upward pressure exerted through its associated mechanism. The right end of the pickup-arm lift rod moves down and the pickup sets down on the record.

Independent Lift Mechanism—Lift Adjustment. This changer has a screw adjustment for lift. For this, loosen the locknut and adjust the screw A until the distance between the turntable top and the needle tip is not less than $1 3/16$ inches. This will now give the correct adjustment for the proper rise of the pickup arm to clear a full load of records. If the adjustment is made so that the pickup arm rises somewhat higher, no harm is usually done. However, make sure that the top of the pickup does not strike the bottom of a stack of records loaded on the mechanism.

In record changers, never tighten seemingly loose screws unless you first make sure that tightening can do no damage. As an example, tightening the shaft screws marked B in Fig. 11B can cause binding between the pickup-arm lift rod and the hollow pickup-arm shaft through which it runs. Excessive tightening of the screws here can cause the pickup-arm shaft to be distorted and forced out of round.

Pickup-arm Pivot Screw. In this mechanism one of the pivots which supports the pickup arm is an adjustable screw. If screwed in too far, it will make the pickup arm move up and down very stiffly. If too loose, it will allow the pickup arm to move back and forth without the pickup-arm support shaft moving and could possibly interfere with the tripping mechanism. This pivot must be adjusted so that the pickup arm is firmly held yet has complete freedom of vertical movement. After making the adjustment, look for a set screw or locknut which acts on the screw. If one is there, tighten it to lock the pivot in position.

Independent Set-down Mechanism—Troubles. If the pickup-arm return-lever spring is loose or missing, the needle may set down off the edge of the record. To remedy this condition, the loose end of the spring must be replaced on its anchoring post or hole and the loop tightened so that it cannot come off again.

If it is necessary to replace the spring, use one just strong enough to insure consistently correct set-down. This may involve trying a few different sizes of spring. Too strong a spring will cause too much binding or straining of the parts. Too weak a spring causes wrong set-down.

Binding of the pickup-arm return lever on its pivot can cause wrong set-down also. If there is an accumulation of hardened lubrication in the stud hole of the pickup-arm lever or on the stud itself, wash it off thoroughly with carbon tetrachloride and polish the adjacent stud and lever surfaces with a very fine emery or crocus cloth. Clean again to remove emery particles, then lubricate with a light grease such as STA-PUT.

Binding of the pickup-arm shaft in its bushing is another cause of erratic set-down in this mechanism. To fix, loosen the two screws marked B in Fig. 11B, and remove the pickup-arm lever from the shafting. Now remove the pickup arm by loosening the one pivot that is a screw. The spring toward the rear of the pickup-arm assembly, which acts as a counterbalance, must be unhooked at either end to free the pickup arm. Leave the pickup wire connected.

The lift rod can now be removed from the pickup-arm shaft. If dried lubrication or some foreign matter is causing the binding, a thorough washing with carbon tetrachloride will remove it. If necessary, use very fine emery cloth or a file to get out hardened pieces of grease. The shafting should be tried in the shaft hole until the proper fit is obtained, then lubricated with STA-PUT or Lubriplate.

If the set screws that attach the pickup-arm lever to the pickup-arm shaft are loose, the pickup arm and shaft may move regardless of whether or not the pickup-arm lever moves. This is another cause for erratic set-down of the pickup arm. To remedy this, trip the changer and rotate the turntable by hand until the pickup needle is just barely down at the start of a record. Adjust the pickup arm so the needle is about ⅛ inch in from the edge of the record, then tighten the set screws (marked *B* in Fig. 11B). This will give the proper set-down position for the needle. If tightened too much, these set screws may distort the hollow pickup-arm shaft and cause binding of the pickup-arm lift rod. The shaft will then have to be replaced as repair is usually too difficult.

Since the stud on the pickup-arm lever is definitely a determining factor in the positioning of the pickup-arm assembly, its position is quite critical. Normally it should be fastened in a perpendicular position on the pickup-arm lever. A bent stud could cause set-down off the record or in beyond the first grooves. Use pliers carefully to straighten a bent stud.

A loose stud could also give erratic indexing. To tighten the stud, remove the pickup arm lever from the pickup-arm shaft, and place the top of the stud on the anvil part of a vise or on some solid block of metal. With a ball-peen hammer tap that part of the stud which protrudes through the hole of the pickup-arm lever until the stud is firmly seated in its hole. The pickup-arm lever can then be replaced on the pickup-arm shaft and the needle set-down position adjusted.

The index finger, which is part of the pickup-arm return lever, must be in such a position that it rides directly on the center of the large section of the cam segment with no records on the record shelf. If the index finger is bent, straighten it with duck-bill pliers or other smooth-jawed pliers.

If the cam segment is too high or too low, remove all records and loosen the set screw on the cam (marked *C* in Fig. 11A). Move the cam segment so that the pickup-arm return lever rides on the middle of the segment. Now rotate the entire cam until it is in such a position that the pickup-arm return lever will never ride off either end when the record-separator post is rotated during the cycle. Finally, check the pickup-arm return lever to see that it rides in over the top of the cam when the record shelf is depressed. The set screw *C* can then be retightened.

When the pickup arm is moving toward set-down, the stud of the pickup-arm lever is in contact with the edge of the pickup-arm return lever and must move along this surface. If there are any burrs or rough spots on the edge of the pickup-arm return lever, or if the stud itself is rough, binding may occur and cause erratic set-down. Remove these burrs or rough spots with a fine file or a very fine emery cloth, then apply a small amount of Lubriplate or STA-PUT to these surfaces to further reduce friction and wear.

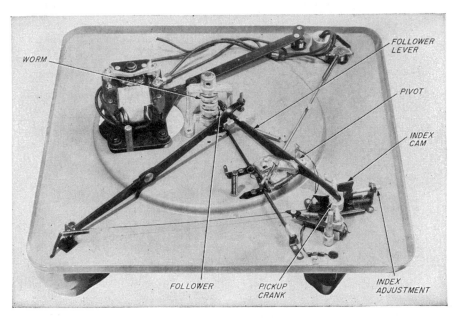

Fig. 12. Bottom view of independent changer with worm drive showing the linkage to the pickup-arm lift and indexing assembly. (Howard W. Sams photo, courtesy of V-M Corp.)

Independent Cycling Type—Lubrication. Apply SAE 10W oil on the pickup-arm pivots, the pickup-arm raising lever, the pivot of the pickup-arm return lever, and the pickup-arm lever. STA-PUT or Lubriplate is recommended on the drive-gear cam surface which the adjusting screw A contacts, on the contact points between the pickup-arm return lever and the pickup-arm lever stud and on the contact points between the segment cam (and record-support shaft) and the index finger. Lubriplate or STA-PUT may be used to lubricate the pickup-arm lift rod and the bushing of the hollow pickup-arm shaft.

Independent Non-intermix—Cam Indexing Mechanism. In one changer using a worm-drive mechanism, a flat cam provides proper indexing during set-down. The bottom view of this mechanism is shown in Fig. 12. During the change cycle, power is transmitted from the spindle worm gear through the follower.

When the follower trip is actuated at the end of a record, the follower contacts the worm and moves downward. Since the follower lever is pivoted near the center, the other end moves upward. This far end is located under the trip crank and lift-rod assembly, causing the lift rod to move up. As the assembly raises, the arm of the trip crank contacts the inclined portion of the index cam and rides up the incline as in Fig. 13. The trip crank pivots about the lift rod rotating the pickup crank which in turn moves the pickup-arm shaft. This causes the pickup arm to swing out clear of the turntable.

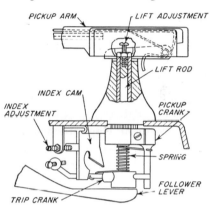

After the next record has dropped, the follower reverses its direction, moving up the worm. The trip crank and lift-rod assembly therefore move down, following the face of the index cam so as to lower the pickup at the proper position on the record.

This record-changer mechanism is not of the intermix variety. To adjust for record size, the record shelf is set. This moves the index cam to ad-

Fig. 13. A cut-away view of the independent set-down changer illustrating the cam and other parts involved in the indexing of the pickup arm

just for the proper set-down. When the index cam is toward the center, the pickup arm will set down properly on the 10-inch size. When the index cam is toward the outside, the pickup arm sets down at the end of the 12-inch record.

Independent Non-intermix—Indexing Adjustment. The indexing of this unit is adjusted by loosening the locknut on the indexing cam (Fig. 12) and turning the index adjustment screw. Clockwise adjustment moves the pickup toward the center. Counterclockwise adjustment moves the pickup away from the center. The adjustment may be made with either 10- or 12-inch records and should be correct for both.

If the pickup arm or pickup crank are loose due to mishandling, it will be necessary to set the arm before adjusting. To do this, loosen the set screw in the pickup crank. Next, turn the crank until the screw in the base plate stops it. Move the pickup arm to about ¼ inch from the spindle, tighten the set screw, then make the index adjustment.

If it is necessary to adjust the lift of the pickup arm, loosen the locking nut and then turn the adjusting screw at the top of the lift rod. When the screw is turned clockwise, the pickup arm will be lowered. After the adjustment has been completed, tighten the locking nut.

Independent Non-intermix—Improper Indexing. If the needle set-down point is incorrect, it can be checked to determine whether it needs adjustment or whether other troubles exist. With the changer in the 10-inch position push the index cam in with the fingers as far as it will go, and check the indexing. Set to the 12-inch position, and hold the index cam as far out as possible while checking the set-down. If the indexing is not satisfactory, adjust it.

If the indexing is satisfactory, check to see that the index cam does not creep or bind. Check the trip crank and index cam where they meet, looking for burrs or worn grooves. Smooth any rough surface by filing if necessary and then polishing with a crocus cloth. Clean off well, and lubricate with Lubriplate or STA-PUT.

Independent Non-intermix—Lubrication. The lift rod, the portion of the index cam where the trip crank contacts it, and the contact surface between the trip crank and the pickup crank should be lubricated with Lubriplate or STA-PUT. A small amount of SAE 10W oil should be applied to the index where it slides in its bracket.

Independent Intermix—Cam Indexing. The simple indexing arrangement of Fig. 14 serves for one type of changer employing independent intermix operation. When the drive gear rotates, the roller on the lift arm follows the heart-shaped cam. The outside end of the lift arm has an inclined surface which pushes on the pickup-arm lift rod. As the end of the lift arm moves, the relative height of the inclined surface changes. As the cycle starts, this causes the pickup-arm lift rod to rise, lifting the pickup arm from the record. As the lift arm moves, the end hits the stud on the circular pickup-arm rotating lever and rotates the pickup arm.

During the change cycle, the index finger and pickup-arm rotating lever come into contact. These parts are notched and mesh during this part of the operation. After half of the cycle has been completed, the index-finger spring causes the index finger to return, and it comes to a stop against the index cam. This establishes the index point.

The index cam is manually set for the type of records being played. There are two positions—one for 7-inch records and one for 10- and 12-inch records. In the latter position the pickup normally sets down in the 10-inch position.

The 12-inch set-down adjustment is built into the pickup arm and is shown in Fig. 15. This consists of a spring-loaded trip mechanism. The trip arm, called the set-down actuating lever, extends out beyond the pickup arm on the inner portion so that when a 12-inch record drops, the outer edge of the record strikes the lever, causing the pickup to set down for a 12-inch record.

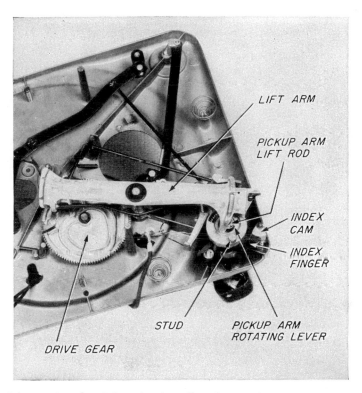

Fig. 14. A bottom view of an independent intermix set-down mechanism using a cam on the end of the lift arm for both lift and indexing. (General Electric photo)

The mechanism shown in Fig. 15 consists of an inner and an outer section mounted concentrically. A catch contacts a rest stop setting the relative position of these two. The inner section rotates as determined by the indexing mechanism underneath the chassis. The outer section is free to rotate a small amount in either direction with respect to the inner section.

As the pickup arm moves counterclockwise to clear the record stack during the normal change of 10-inch records, the motion of the outer section is restricted by means of a stop not shown. The inner section rotates more but has a stud that eventually contacts the illustrated stop. The right end of the catch is released and the spring causes it to rotate counterclockwise to a point opposite the 10-inch step.

When a 12-inch record drops, the edge strikes the set-down actuating lever. A projection on the right end of this lever catches a stud on the set-down cam so that they move together. The rising cam surface contacts the lower end of the catch, causing it to slide into the 12-inch step. Hence, the outer section moves counterclockwise.

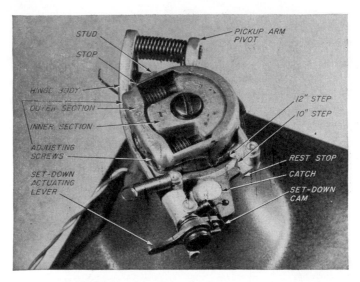

Fig. 15. A 12-inch index mechanism located in the pickup arm. The 12-inch record strikes the set-down actuating lever when it drops, actuating the index mechanism. (Courtesy of V-M Corp.)

Since the inner section of the mechanism is fixed in position, the position of the outer mechanism determines the position of the pickup arm. When the catch is in the 10-inch step, the outer section (and the pickup arm) is in the maximum clockwise direction. The pickup arm is therefore closest to the spindle, as required for 10-inch set-down. When the catch is in the 12-inch step, the outer mechanism is in the maximum counterclockwise direction so that the pickup arm sets down further out from the spindle for 12-inch set-down.

Independent Intermix—Adjustment of Pickup Arm. The indexing adjustment is made by means of two screws, as shown in Fig. 15. These adjust the relative position of the inner and outer sections. If the needle sets down too far out on the record, it is necessary to rotate the outer section clockwise with respect to the inner section. This is done by loosening the back (upper) screw and then tightening the front (lower) screw. Adjustment of about ¼ turn at a time is suggested.

If the needle sets down too far in on the record, the reverse is necessary. Loosen the front screw and tighten the rear. In either case both screws must be tightened equally upon completion. The same adjustment serves for all sizes of records.

Height of the pickup arm is adjusted by a screw on the top of the pickup-arm lift rod as described for other changers.

Independent Intermix—Set-down Trouble. If the pickup does not set down properly, check to see if this happens for all sizes of records. If it happens only on 7-inch records, the index finger is likely to be bent or damaged. Straighten it with a pair of long-nose or duck-bill pliers, or replace it.

If the trouble occurs on 12-inch records, check to see if the record hits the set-down actuating lever when it drops to the turntable. If it does not, it is probably due to an undersize record, an oversize center hole in the record, or a defective stop on the hinge body. If the record hits the set-down actuating lever, check to see that the lever stays down. If it doesn't, stop the changer before the pickup arm starts to move in over the record. Check the catch to see that it can move freely. Any binding due to dirt can be cleared by washing thoroughly with carbon tetrachloride. Any burrs must be removed by filing lightly and polishing with a crocus cloth. Another possible trouble is that the catch doesn't go into the 12-inch step. This can be checked by stopping the pickup arm in its outermost position and manually tripping the set-down actuating lever. Binding of the catch so that it doesn't rotate or binding between the set-down cam and the catch can cause this trouble. Remove any burrs by filing lightly, polish with a crocus cloth, and clean with carbon tetrachloride.

If indexing is not proper for 10-inch records or for all sizes and adjusting the set-down doesn't cure the trouble, it is likely that the trouble is in the combination of the pickup-arm rotating lever and index finger. When the lift arm starts to operate the lift rod, the index finger must mesh with the pickup-arm rotating lever. To check this, stop the changer at this point and swing the pickup arm toward the spindle. If the mesh releases when the pickup arm is about halfway in, attention is required. Check for dirt, burrs, or other foreign particles which may keep these parts from meshing, and remove the cause of the difficulty. There are notches in both which give the meshing action, so care must be taken not to smooth off these surfaces.

Independent Intermix—Slide-type Indexing Mechanism. With the slide mechanism of Fig. 16A an inclined surface on the end of the cycling slide serves for raising the pickup arm. As the inclined surface of the slide forces

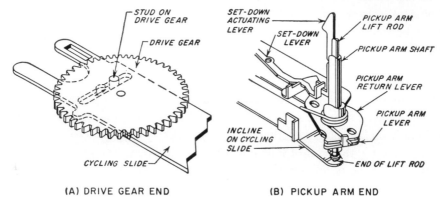

(A) DRIVE GEAR END   (B) PICKUP ARM END

Fig. 16. The rotation of the drive gear causes the slide to move to and fro, operating the pickup-arm lift and indexing mechanism at the other end of the slide

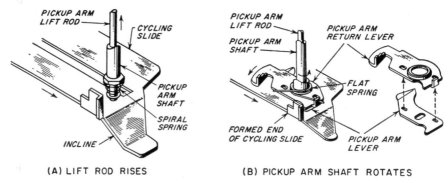

(A) LIFT ROD RISES   (B) PICKUP ARM SHAFT ROTATES

Fig. 17. The outward motion of the cycling slide causes the lift arm to be raised by the incline and the pickup-arm shaft to be rotated by the formed end

the pickup-arm lift rod to rise (Fig. 17), the force of the spiral spring causes the pickup-arm lever to be carried along. As the pickup-arm lever raises, the two dimples on it mate with the corresponding holes in the pickup-arm return lever. The protrusion on the formed end of the cycling slide contacts and pushes against the pickup-arm lever so that it rotates in a counterclockwise direction. This swings the pickup arm out beyond the turntable so that the next record may be dropped.

When the record drops to the turntable, a tab on the drive gear pushes down on the inside end of the set-down lever, as in Fig. 18. Since the set-down lever is pivoted in the middle, the outer end is raised and latches on the edge of the set-down actuating lever.

The cycling slide now reverses its direction. As it moves back, the formed end allows the pickup-arm return lever to rotate clockwise. The tension in the flat spring provides the force. This rotation continues until the pickup-arm return lever contacts the set-down lever. When these two come into contact, the pickup arm is directly above the indexing point for a 10-inch

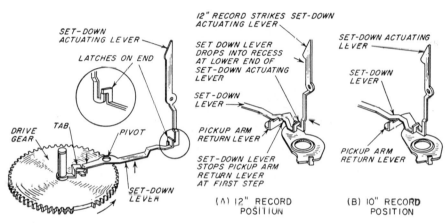

Fig. 18. A tab on the cycling gear causes the set-down lever to latch the end of the set-down actuating lever

Fig. 19. Indexing for the 10-inch and 12-inch record is determined by the relative position of the pickup-arm return lever. This is controlled by the position of the set-down lever which in turn is controlled by the set-down actuating lever

record. The pickup-arm lift rod now slides down the inclined surface, thereby allowing the pickup needle to drop into the starting groove. The slackened pressure of the spiral spring relieves the contact between the pickup-arm lever and the pickup-arm return lever so that the pickup arm is free to rotate.

When a 12-inch record is played, it strikes the set-down actuating lever as it drops to the turntable. This causes the upper portion of the lever to move outward, as illustrated in Fig. 19A. Since the lever is pivoted in the middle, the lower end moves in, and the set-down lever seats itself down in the recess. As the pickup-arm return lever rotates clockwise, the lower step contacts the set-down lever. Now the pickup arm is not allowed to move as far inward and therefore sets down further out. With 10-inch records, the next step of the pickup-arm return lever contacts the set-down lever, as shown in Fig. 19B.

Independent Intermix—Slide-type Adjustment. Adjustment of the pickup arm is made by means of adjustments located on the pickup-arm assembly above the base plate as shown in Fig. 20.

The assembly has a cam coupling arrangement between the pickup-arm shaft and the pickup-arm hinge. This is adjustable by means of the index adjustment screw and determines the indexing.

On the underside of the pickup arm is an adjustment screw which varies the height. The lift rod pushes against it during the change cycle. Clockwise adjustment moves the screw into the pickup arm so that it lowers the arm. Counterclockwise adjustment raises the pickup arm. As customary, the lift should be adjusted so the pickup arm will raise up off a full stack of records when placed on the turntable yet will not hit the underside of a record on the support shelf.

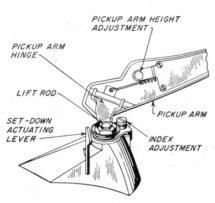

Fig. 20. Index and lift adjustments in an independent intermix-type set-down mechanism

Independent Intermix—Slide-type Troubles. Proper adjustment of set-down will work for both 10- and 12-inch records. If proper set-down does not occur on 12-inch records only, check to see that the set-down actuating lever is tripped when the 12-inch record drops to the turntable. An undersize record or one with an enlarged center hole may not hit this lever. Such records must be played manually or discarded. If the set-down actuating lever is hit but does not function, check for binding in its pivot, between it and the set-down lever, or between the set-down lever and the steps on the pickup-arm return lever (Fig. 19). If binding is evident, clean off any dirt or foreign material with carbon tetrachloride. Remove any burrs by filing lightly, polishing with a crocus cloth, and cleaning thoroughly with carbon tetrachloride.

Other causes of improper set-down may be binding in the pickup-arm hinge, between the pickup-arm shaft and the housing, between the pickup-arm lift rod and the pickup-arm shaft, between the bottom of the pickup-arm lift rod and the inclined surface of the cycling slide, or between the pickup-arm lever and the pickup-arm return lever. Such troubles should be remedied as just described.

Lubrication. Lubriplate or STA-PUT should be applied to the pivot on the pickup-arm hinge. It should also be used on the cycling slide where it contacts the pickup-arm lift rod, the pickup-arm lever, and the pickup-arm return lever. SAE 10W oil should be applied between the pickup-arm lift rod and the pickup-arm shaft. Do not overlubricate. Wipe off excess oil.

Independent Non-intermix—Variation of Slide-type Indexing Mechanism. In the slide mechanism shown in Fig. 21, the rotating drive gear causes the cycling slide to move out and then in. The pickup-arm lift rod extends from the pickup arm and down through the cycling slide. As the cycling slide moves outward, the depressed incline pulls down on the pickup-arm lift rod. The downward force on the rear of the pickup arm behind the hinge causes the pickup end to rise and clear the record.

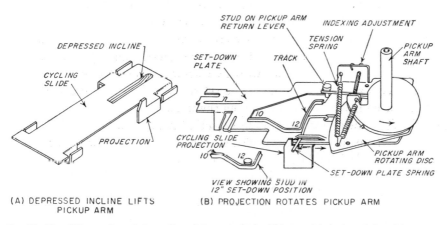

Fig. 21. The sliding action of the cycling slide controls the lifting and indexing of the pickup arm

The motion of the cycling slide also causes the cycling-slide projection to contact the curved end of the pickup-arm rotating disc. This gives the pickup assembly a counterclockwise motion, causing the pickup arm to move out beyond the edge of the record.

The projection on the cycling slide also contacts the set-down plate spring and carries the set-down plate with it. The stud on the pickup-arm return lever is thus forced against the track on the set-down plate. The pressures caused by the track and the cycling-slide projection force the pickup-arm rotating disc and the stud on the pickup-arm return lever apart, and the tension spring is expanded. As the cycling slide moves inward, the tension spring pulls these two pieces together. The amount the pickup-arm rotating disc is pulled back is determined by the adjustment screw. The landing position is thus established.

On the bottom of the pickup-arm rotating disc is a stud which contacts the selector cam when the cycling slide is moving outward, as shown in Fig. 22. Contact between the two causes the pickup-arm set-down plate to stop. The position of the selector cam is determined by the size of the record being played and acts as a gage to position the set-down plate. If the smaller radius of the selector cam is toward the stud, the pickup-arm rotating disc moves furthest out, and the stud on the pickup-arm return lever will ride on the portion of the track marked 10 in Fig. 21B. The pickup will then land on the 10-inch record. When the larger radius of the selector cam is toward the stud, the set-down plate is stopped sooner, and the stud on the pickup-arm return lever will ride on the portion of the track marked 12. The pickup will now land properly on the 12-inch record.

Independent Non-intermix—Slide-type Adjustment. In this changer the pickup-arm pivot is located directly under the record-selector post, and the pickup-arm lift rod passes up through the pickup arm. Just above the pickup arm is a collar, fastened with a set screw, that determines the amount of lift. To adjust the lift, loosen the set screw and move the collar up or down the desired amount and tighten the screw.

To adjust the indexing, the indexing-adjustment screw of Fig. 21B should be used. If this does not give sufficient range, turn it clockwise as far as it will go, then back off 2 or 3 turns. Put a 12-inch record on the turntable, set the record-support post for 12-inch, and cycle the mechanism by hand until the pickup is about to land on the record. Just below the pickup arm is a collar which is a part of the pickup-arm hinge. Loosen the two set screws which hold this, and put the needle in the starting groove. Tighten the set screws and cycle the changer. Adjust the indexing as necessary by means of the indexing-adjustment screw.

Independent Non-intermix—Slide-type Troubles. Binding in the pickup-arm shaft, between the pickup-arm return lever and the pickup-arm rotating disc or between the track of the set-down plate and the stud of the pickup-arm return lever will cause improper set-down. Remove any dirt, dried grease, or foreign particles by washing thoroughly with carbon tetrachloride. Where necessary disassemble the parts to accomplish this. Burrs may be removed by filing lightly, polishing with a crocus cloth, and washing with carbon tetrachloride. Lubrication is indicated below.

Loose, defective, or missing springs are other possible causes of trouble. If loose, replace the ends in the holes or on the studs and pinch the end loops to assure that the trouble will not recur. Where the spring must be replaced try several if necessary to find one that gives consistent indexing every time yet does not cause the operation to slow down during the change cycle.

A loose stud on the set-down plate or a loose selector cam will give improper indexing, as would be suspected when viewing Fig. 22. To tighten the stud, the set-down plate must be removed from the changer. Place the stud on a heavy metal vise, and hammer the rolled-over end of the stud with a ball-peen hammer until it fits tightly. The selector cam is rigidly fastened to the selector shaft. At the top of the selector shaft is a selector arm fastened with two set screws. If the cam is loose, these should be tightened. The sides of the selector cam should be parallel with the guide rails.

Lubrication. STA-PUT or Lubriplate should be used on sliding surfaces such as on the track of the set-down plate, the guide rails, and the pickup-arm lift rod.

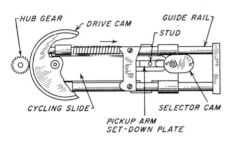

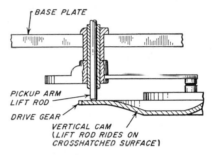

Fig. 22. As the cycling slide moves outward, the slud on the pickup-arm set-down plate contacts the selector cam causing the set-down plate to stop. The position of the selector cam is determined by the size of the record being played, thereby acting as a gage

Fig. 23. An independent-type set-down mechanism uses a cam to actuate the lift rod. It is now in the uppermost position, having followed the top side of the crosshatched cam surface

Independent Non-intermix—Vertical-cam Lift. Figure 23 illustrates the action of a vertical cam on the pickup-arm lift rod. As shown the lift rod is pushed up, so the pickup arm is off the record. The pickup-arm lever has been moved so the pickup arm is off to the side. When the record has dropped to the turntable, the stud on the pickup-arm lever is allowed to follow the receding surface of the set-down cam which is part of the drive gear. This is illustrated in Fig. 24. The pickup-arm return lever exerts a spring pressure causing the pickup-arm lever, and thus the pickup arm, to move in toward the edge of the record. The set-down point is determined by contact of the pickup-arm return lever with the set-down lever, which in turn is set by the position of the record-selector arms. These are set manually since the changer is not of the intermix variety.

In the position shown, the pickup arm will set down for a 12-inch record.

When the record-selector arms are set for playing 10-inch records, the set-down lever is moved to the left. The 10-inch record-stop recess in the pickup-arm return lever now contacts the set-down lever. Since the 10-inch recess is greater than the 12-inch recess, the pickup arm will be allowed to move in further on the record when in the 10-inch position. This is as it should be.

On top of the drive gear is the retard lever, which is spring-loaded near the pivoted end. The other end is shown protruding in Fig. 24. The spring exerts a slight outward pressure against the pickup-arm lever when it rides

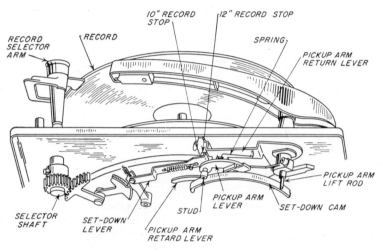

Fig. 24. The stud on the pickup-arm lever follows the surface of the set-down cam as it recedes. The pickup arm moves in over the set-down point. The spring action of the pickup-arm index finger keeps the two in contact

off the cam surface of the drive gear. This prevents the pickup-arm lever from swinging in too rapidly and holds it at the radius determined by the pickup-arm return lever until the pickup is set down on the record. The set-down is accomplished by the vertical cam following the reverse of the action shown in Fig. 23.

After the needle touches the record, the booster spring exerts a slight inward pressure, causing the needle to enter the starting groove. This tension was constantly exerted, but the slight outward pressure of the retard lever previously counteracted it. Since the drive gear has rotated to a point where the retard lever slides off the stud of the pickup-arm lever, the booster spring is now allowed to act without any counteracting force.

Independent Non-intermix—Vertical-cam-type Adjustment. The lift of the pickup arm is again adjusted by means of a screw at the top of the lift rod. In this case the screw goes into the pickup-arm bracket rather than into the lift rod. As a result, turning the adjustment screw clockwise causes the pickup arm to be lowered.

Indexing is accomplished by positioning the pickup arm with respect to the pickup-arm lever. An Allen-head screw is used. Cycle the changer until the needle is just about to set down on the record. Loosen the set screw on the pickup-arm lever, move the pickup arm to the correct indexing position, and tighten the adjusting screw. Check to be sure that the pickup-arm lever is high enough on the pickup-arm shaft to allow the pickup-arm lift rod to operate properly.

Set-down Troubles. Near the pickup-arm shaft is a spring which pulls the pickup-arm return lever in against the set-down lever. If this spring is missing or is too weak, proper indexing will not occur, and the motion of the pickup arm may be erratic during the change cycle. When replacing, find a spring that gives good consistent operation but does not slow down the mechanism.

If there is excess play in the pickup-arm hinge, the pickup arm may be allowed to wobble horizontally giving improper indexing. In this changer the pickup arm rides on a knife edge, held in V seats in the pickup-arm hinge by spring tension. The sides of the hinge must be bent inward by use of long-nose or duck-bill pliers if the pickup arm tends to shift. In many changers adjustable pivot screws are used and must be tightened, so as to eliminate any wobble in the pickup arm but not cause any appreciable friction.

Binding between the stud on the pickup-arm lever and the set-down cam, between the pickup-arm return lever and the set-down lever, or in the retard-lever pivot are possible causes of trouble. Dirt and foreign materials may be removed by washing thoroughly with carbon tetrachloride. To remove burrs, file lightly, polish with a crocus cloth, and clean with carbon tetrachloride.

Independent Non-intermix—Vertical-cam Lubrication. The pickup-arm lift rod, the stud on the pickup-arm lever, and the cam surface of the drive gear should be lubricated with Lubriplate or STA-PUT.

Muting. During any change cycle there is considerable meshing of metallic parts. This is not particularly noticeable to the ear, but it is possible for the pickup to be jarred so that noise is fed to the amplifier. To avoid the resulting amplified noises, a few record changers utilize a muting switch. This switch either shorts or places a low-impedance capacitor across the amplifier input during the change cycle.

Operation of one muting switch is shown in Fig. 25A. The drive gear keeps the switch open during normal play. When the change cycle starts, the drive gear rotates and the switch closes when the muting cam moves away.

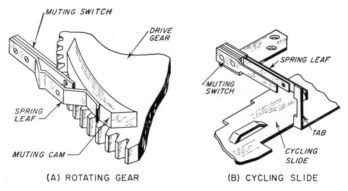

(A) ROTATING GEAR   (B) CYCLING SLIDE

Fig. 25. The muting switch is held open as shown when the drive gear or cycling slide is in the rest position. During the change cycle the spring leaf slides off the cam or tab, and the switch closes shorting the amplifier input

A similar arrangement is used for a changer with a cycling slide. This is shown in Fig. 25B. During normal play the tab on the cycling slide holds the spring leaf so that the switch is open. During the change cycle the cycling slide moves to the left and the muting switch closes.

Repairing Muting Switch. If the customer complains that muting does not occur during the change cycle, first make sure that the record changer is supposed to provide muting. Most record changers do not include this provision.

Where muting is not functioning, the switch should be checked first. The important point is that the contacts operate properly. By tripping the changer and watching the switch during the change cycle, it can be determined whether or not the switch is operating. Generally, the switch should close during the change cycle and remain open during the record play. The opposite operation is possible, but in either case the switch contacts will be caused to move during the change cycle.

If the switch operates but no muting is obtained, the connections to the wires should be checked, and the wires checked for a possible open circuit. A continuity check between the switch contacts and the muting wires will indicate this. Figure 26, which is a typical schematic diagram for the muting section, will aid in checking this.

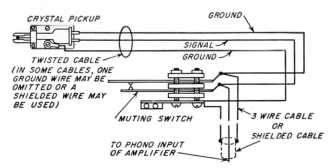

Fig. 26. The schematic diagram of a record changer showing the wiring of the muting switch

On occasion, the switch contacts will require cleaning. A piece of fine sandpaper or crocus cloth may be used if the contact surfaces are rough or pitted, but generally carbon tetrachloride will suffice.

QUESTIONS

1. What common operator mistake often causes the cycling mechanism to be strained?
2. Describe the difference between a combination cycling changer and an independent cycling type.
3. How is the difference in index-spring tension used to change the indexing?
4. How does the indexing finger change the indexing in a spindle-drop changer?
5. How is an eccentric used for fine adjustment of the indexing point?
6. When is it necessary to make the coarse indexing adjustment?
7. Describe the use of a cam to lift the pickup arm in an independent cycling mechanism.
8. Where would you lubricate an independent cycling mechanism?
9. If the indexing adjustment is not located in the pickup arm, where is it likely to be?
10. What are the usual methods of adjusting the amount of pickup-arm lift?
11. If you think that a changer is of the intermix type, where will you look for the indexing actuator?
12. How is muting obtained?

11

Shutoff Mechanisms

Introduction. Some modern record changers will repeat the last record until the mechanism is shut off by the operator. Others, usually deluxe models, are designed to shut off the record changer automatically upon completion of the last record. If the automatic-shutoff type of changer is designed into the amplifier equipment, the entire system could be shut off automatically, but this is seldom done. However, the use of an automatic shutoff on the changer avoids the annoyance of repetition of the last record.

Four different types of shutoff mechanisms are in common use. These are: (1) Sliding-spindle shutoff for pusher-type changers; (2) Selector-post shutoff for slicer-type changers; (3) Stabilizer-arm-actuated shutoff; (4) Spindle-stabilizer arm shutoff for spindle-drop-type changers.

Shutoff by Pickup Arm. In one common type of changer mechanism the weight of the pickup arm presses an OFF button as the arm comes down in its rest position after the last record. Figure 1A shows the switch mechanism in the OFF position.

To start the record changer, the ON-REJECT button is pressed downward. This causes the shutoff-actuating lever to rotate counterclockwise about the pivot or fulcrum. The upper tip, called the shutoff-actuating-lever finger, contacts the shutoff-trip lever which operates the switch. Thus the mechanism is switched on, and the motor begins to rotate.

During the starting action, the shutoff-actuating lever is moved away from the toggle, allowing the toggle to move. The toggle is pivoted in the middle, and the spring pulls it in a counterclockwise direction. The toggle stop limits the movement. The left end of the toggle now holds the stud on the shutoff-actuating lever so that the lever is held in the on position as shown in Fig. 1B.

To shut the mechanism off, it is necessary to push the off button down. When this is done, the left end of the pawl catches the right end of the toggle forcing it down also. The left end of the toggle thus moves up releasing the shutoff-actuating lever. The spring on the on button shaft forces the shutoff-actuating lever to rotate clockwise shutting the switch off.

When the off button is released, it is forced up by the spring. The pawl then slides past the toggle so that it is in position to operate when it is again depressed.

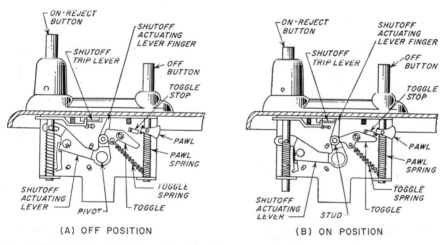

Fig. 1. The ON-OFF mechanism used with a sliding-spindle shutoff. The weight of the pickup arm on the OFF button causes the changer to shut off after playing the last record

When a rest-position button is used for automatic shutoff, the changer must bring the pickup arm to the rest position automatically after playing the last record. One way of doing this will now be taken up.

Sliding-spindle Control of Shutoff after the Last Record. The rocker-arm type of change mechanism uses the center post or spindle to control the automatic shutoff, as in Fig. 2. When one or more records are on the spindle, it is forced downward against the end of the shutoff-lock lever. This lever is pivoted between the ends, and the other end is raised so that it is free of the pickup-arm raising disc.

During the change cycle the pickup-arm raising lever is moved by the cycling cam. The pickup-arm raising disc is contacted by the sharp beveled edge of the pickup-arm raising lever and, because of the friction between the two, the pickup-arm raising disc is lifted and rotated. Since it is attached to the pickup-arm shaft, the pickup arm is cycled. When the last record is dropped to the turntable, the weight of the shutoff-lock lever causes the spindle end to rise, and the other end drops so that it is on the same level as the pickup-arm raising disc. Now, as the pickup arm starts to move in toward the spindle, the hook on the end of the shutoff-lock lever catches the end of the pickup-arm raising disc, as in Fig. 2A, keeping it from rotating. The pickup-arm raising lever thereby slides across the pickup-arm raising disc and the pickup arm does not move horizontally. This holding action takes place when the pickup arm is over the pickup-arm rest post (OFF button). The pickup-arm raising lever then lowers the pickup arm onto the OFF button shutting off the changer motor.

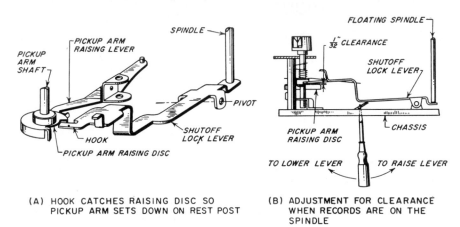

(A) HOOK CATCHES RAISING DISC SO
PICKUP ARM SETS DOWN ON REST POST

(B) ADJUSTMENT FOR CLEARANCE
WHEN RECORDS ARE ON THE
SPINDLE

Fig. 2. The sliding-spindle type of automatic shutoff as used in a pusher-type changer. The lack of records on the spindle causes the pickup arm to set down on the rest post

Repair of Sliding-spindle Shutoff Mechanism. If a record changer with the button-type switch does not shut off after the last record, it should first be checked to determine whether it is the switch mechanism or the pickup-arm indexing that is at fault. If the pickup arm sets down properly on the OFF button, then the switch mechanism is at fault. If not, the trouble is obviously in the indexing. It should be definitely determined that the record changer has automatic shutoff before proceeding with repairs to the indexing.

Failure of Switch Mechanism. Since it is necessary for the OFF button to be depressed before the switch can be actuated, there is little problem of premature shutoff. However, a weak toggle spring (Fig. 1) may allow the switch to shut off as soon as the ON button is released.

Failure to shut off may be caused by binding of the OFF button shaft, the pawl, toggle, shutoff-actuating lever, or the ON-REJECT button shaft. Weak springs on the two button shafts may also cause failure to shut off.

The spring on the shaft of the OFF button serves only the purpose of returning the button to a raised position. Since the weight of the pickup arm must depress the button, the spring must be rather weak. Perhaps the best method of checking for binding is to prod the individual parts slightly with the finger or a tool to get the feel of the freedom of motion. Cleaning with carbon tetrachloride is the routine for clearing binding due to grime and dirt. Burrs must be removed by use of a fine file. Then polish with a crocus cloth and clean with carbon tetrachloride.

The bracket which holds the switch mechanism is U-shaped, having bends at the top and bottom for support of the button shafts. Should either or both of these shafts bind, it is necessary to bend the bracket very slightly. This may be done with long-nose pliers, taking caution to move the bracket only enough to line up the upper and lower holes through which the shafts pass. The idea here is to correct the upper bend of the bracket without warping the vertical portion. The experience gained in making such an adjustment will assure careful handling of this type of changer thereafter in order to prevent any weight from bearing on this bracket when the changer is laid down.

Failure of Sliding-spindle Mechanism to Index in Rest Position. In the event the pickup arm does not set down on the OFF button after the last record has played, see whether the floating spindle will move up and down. If not, the reason for binding must be found and corrected. This spindle rests on the end of the shutoff-lock lever. The other, or hook, end of the shutoff-lock lever should catch the pickup-arm raising disc at the beginning of the cycle if the pickup arm is to set down on the OFF button. With no records on the spindle the hook should clear the pickup-arm raising disc by about $\frac{1}{32}$ inch when the mechanism is not cycling. This is illustrated in Fig. 2B. If this clearance is not proper, it must be adjusted by bending the triangular projection on the bottom of the chassis. Provision is made for insertion of a screwdriver blade. The pickup-arm raising disc should not be adjusted to correct this.

Lubrication of Sliding-spindle Shutoff Mechanism. For the most part, there is no lubrication required in this portion of the mechanism. Smooth surfaces, such as in the sliding spindle and the shutoff-lock lever pivot, will operate without lubrication. Use of lubrication may impair the operation since dust and dirt will stick and accumulate. If lubrication is present, wash it off with carbon tetrachloride and check to assure that there is no binding.

Selector-post Shutoff in Slicer-type Changer. Automatic shutoff in a slicer-type record changer is shown in Fig. 3. When one or more records are located on the selector arms, their weight depresses the shutoff button. With the shutoff button down, the lever is raised on the left side, and the shutoff shaft and shutoff cam are in the raised position illustrated by the dotted lines. The shutoff cam will not contact the shutoff-cocking lever in this position. After the last record has dropped, the force of gravity pulls the shutoff shaft and the shutoff cam down. The shutoff cam is now on a proper level so that the stud on the shutoff-cocking lever may contact it.

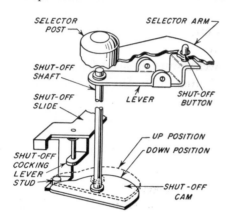

With reference to Fig. 4, as the drive gear rotates during the cycle, the stud which is a part of it runs off the shutoff-actuating lever, allowing the lever to be moved in toward the drive gear by its spring. At this time, action of other portions of the mechanism causes the pickup arm to move out to the rest position. It is locked in this position by contact between the shutoff-lock lever and the pickup-arm lever.

Fig. 3. The shutoff cam in a slicer-type changer is held in the raised position when a record is on the shelf, but is allowed to drop and contact the shutoff-cocking lever when there are none to be played.

The selector gear, which is a part of the record-dropping mechanism, is rotated by action of the drive gear through various levers and cranks. The shutoff cam also rotates and contacts the stud on the shutoff-cocking lever, causing the lever to rotate. The tension created in the spring connected between the shutoff-cocking lever and the shutoff slide forces the slide to move to the left.

A projection on the shutoff slide contacts the shutoff release and moves it slightly clockwise releasing the shutoff link so that it may align itself with the shutoff-actuating lever, as shown by the dotted outline. The end of the shutoff slide moves in to the dotted position at the left so that the right end of the shutoff-lock lever is held in position. Now, when the pickup-arm release lever is engaged by the cam on the outer edge of the drive gear, the pickup arm will not be unlocked as is usual, and the pickup arm remains in the rest position.

As the drive gear finishes its clockwise cycle, the stud on it pushes the shutoff-actuating lever out, or up. Since the shutoff-actuating lever and the shutoff link are engaged, the shutoff lever is pushed up. The fulcrum of the shutoff lever is at the right end so the left end moves upward, pulling the shutoff-trip lever with it. This moves the power switch to the OFF position.

Repair of Selector-post Shutoff. In Fig. 3 it is shown how the shutoff cam drops due to gravity, to be in position to contact the stud on the shutoff-cocking lever. In either the 10- or 12-inch position of the selector arms, there must be no lateral pressure between the shutoff cam and the stud to restrict free up-and-down motion. In addition, when a record is on the shelves, the shutoff cam must clear the top of the stud or shutoff will occur prematurely.

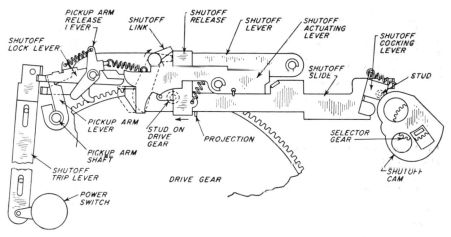

Fig. 4. The selector-post shutoff mechanism is cocked by movement of the shutoff slide to the left. This locks the pickup arm in the rest position. It also links the shutoff-actuating lever and shutoff lever so the stud on the drive gear pushes them up. The shutoff-trip lever is moved up, actuating the switch

When the shutoff-actuating lever is resting against the stud on the drive gear, the tail of the shutoff-actuating lever must clear the formed-down lip (shown as point 1 in Fig. 5) on the shutoff slide when the shutoff-actuating lever is moved manually. However, this clearance must be sufficiently small so that the shutoff slide cannot move forward far enough to take up the clearance at points 2 or 3. Lack of clearance at point 2 would actuate the shutoff release. Loss of clearance at point 3 would block the movement of the pickup-arm lock lever.

When the stud on the drive gear has rotated just far enough into the change cycle so as to move out of contact with the shutoff-actuating lever, the lever has rotated to its extreme position against the stud on the chassis. Now there is additional clearance at point 1, and it must be sufficient to fulfill two conditions.

First, it must allow the shutoff slide to actuate the shutoff release at point 2. If the clearance at point 1 is too small to allow sufficient motion of the shutoff slide, it will not completely clear the shutoff link, and the shutoff release may fail to operate. The shutoff slide must move far enough so that the shutoff release completely clears the shutoff link, and the link is free to rotate against the stop.

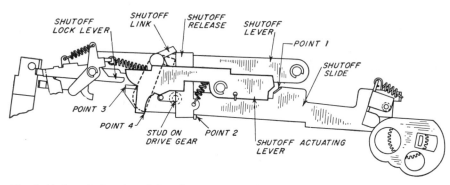

Fig. 5. Various check points of the selector-post shutoff mechanism which provide ready analysis of any trouble

Second, the clearance at point 1 must now be sufficient so that the shutoff slide block the shutoff-lock lever at point 3. Excessive clearance at this point, however, will allow the shutoff-lock lever to be partially disengaged by the rotation of the drive gear. Insufficient clearance might cause a wedging action which would prevent smooth operation of the shutoff slide.

The point of contact between the shutoff-actuating lever and the shutoff link is point 4. In the position shown by the dotted outline of the shutoff link, it is necessary that there be sufficient clearance between the formed-up end of the shutoff-actuating lever and the end of the shutoff link at point 4 so that the shutoff link can assume the position shown.

As the automatic-shutoff cycle progresses, the drive-gear stud rotates until it strikes the shutoff-actuating bracket and the cam action forces it out toward the edge of the changer. This results in the shutoff link completely clearing the shutoff release as shown in Fig. 6. The maximum outward motion of the shutoff-actuating lever and the shutoff lever must be sufficient so that the shutoff link is carried far enough to completely clear the shutoff release at point 5.

Failure of the shutoff link to return to the position shown in Fig. 5 will result in repeated automatic-shutoff cycles. This condition may result from insufficient clearance at either point 4 or point 5.

In the AUTOMATIC position the tip of the shutoff lever must permit free movement of the shutoff-trip lever into the REJECT position. During the shutoff cycle the shutoff lever must move the shutoff-trip lever into OFF. Incorrect clearance at point 6 will result in either moving the shutoff-trip lever too far into MANUAL or moving the lever too little and leaving it in AUTOMATIC.

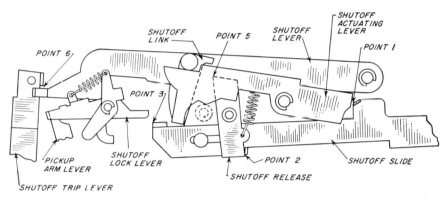

Fig. 6. Additional check points on the selector post shutoff mechanism are also used later in the cycle

Lubrication of the Selector-post Shutoff. SAE 10W oil should be sparingly applied to the shutoff shaft and the pivots of the shutoff-cocking lever, shutoff-actuating lever, shutoff lever, and shutoff link. Lubriplate or STA-PUT No. 512 should be applied to the sliding surfaces such as the stud on the shutoff-cocking lever, the bearing surfaces of the shutoff slide and shutoff-trip lever, and the mating surfaces of the shutoff lever and shutoff-trip lever. Take care not to overlubricate as this is as detrimental as lack of lubrication.

Stabilizer-arm-actuated Shutoff on Slide-type Cycling Mechanism. The automatic shutoff for a slide-type cycling mechanism is shown in Fig. 7A and utilizes the record stabilizer for control. At the midway point of the change cycle the cycling slide is in the outermost position. As the slide moves inward (to the right) to the normal out-of-cycle position, the hooked end of the shutoff-lock lever drops through a hole in the cycling slide. Since the fulcrum of this lever is in the middle, the opposite end rises. This is better viewed in Fig. 7B. If any record other than the last one is dropped during the cycle, the pickup-arm return lever passes over the left end of the shutoff-lock lever. The pickup is thus allowed to set down on the record.

After the last record has dropped to the turntable, the stabilizer arm drops over the spindle shelf, as shown in Fig. 7C. This downward motion is transmitted by the stabilizer shaft and rotates the shutoff-actuating lever

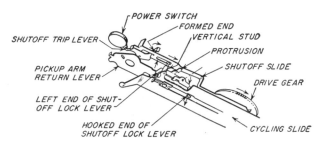

(A) ACTUATING MECHANISM

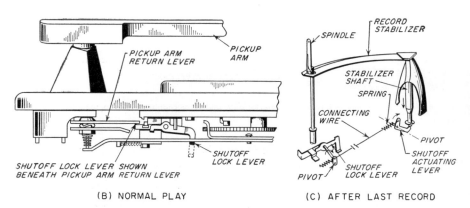

(B) NORMAL PLAY   (C) AFTER LAST RECORD

Fig. 7. The shutoff mechanism in a slide-type cycling mechanism utilizes the return movement of the cycling slide to pull the shutoff slide, rotating the shutoff-trip lever which trips the power switch. The shutoff-lock lever cocks the shutoff slide after the last record has played and stops the pickup-arm return lever in the rest position

a little in a clockwise direction. The resulting pull on the spring and connecting wire causes the shutoff-lock lever to rotate about its fulcrum. During the next change cycle this extra force on the shutoff-lock lever causes it to rotate more than usual so the right end extends further below the cycling slide. The left end, therefore, raises further and stops the pickup-arm return lever so that the pickup arm is over the rest post.

As the left end of the shutoff-lock lever raises, a protrusion on it pushes the shutoff slide up. This is best viewed in Fig. 7A. As the cycling slide moves back toward the spindle, the raised shutoff slide is pulled along with it because the shutoff slide contacts the built-up end of the vertical stud. The formed end of the shutoff slide pushes the shutoff-trip lever causing it to rotate in a clockwise direction. The other end of the shutoff-trip lever actuates the power switch shutting off the motor.

Repair of Stabilizer-arm-actuated Shutoff. Common troubles in shutoff mechanisms actuated by the stabilizer arm are illustrated in Fig. 8A. If the changer does not stop automatically, it may be due to the failure of the record stabilizer to drop over the spindle. This may be caused by a binding between the stabilizer and the spindle or by binding in the stabilizer shaft.

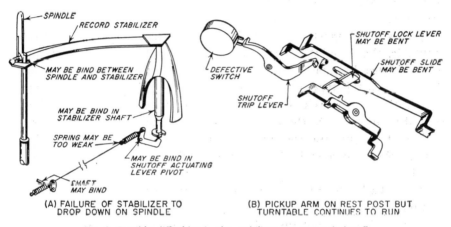

Fig. 8. Possible difficulties in the stabilizer-arm-actuated shutoff

Binding in the shutoff-actuating lever bearing or in the shaft of the shutoff-lock lever may also prevent automatic stopping as would a weak shutoff-actuating lever return spring. On the other hand, an overly strong spring on the shutoff-lock lever may also result in failure to shut off.

Binding due to accumulation of dirt and grime may be eliminated by washing thoroughly with carbon tetrachloride. Lubrication may be required at pivot points. Should binding be a result of burrs, remove them and then polish the surface with crocus cloth. Clean off any filings with carbon tetrachloride.

Failure of Turntable to Stop. If the pickup arm sets down on the rest but the turntable continues to rotate, a check should be made to determine if the switch is actuated. If it is, then the difficulty lies therein. If not, the points indicated in Fig. 8B should be checked to determine the cause of the difficulty. If the pieces do not mesh properly because of bent parts, they must be restored to their proper shape. Do this carefully without putting in additional bends.

Automatic Shutoff before Completion of Record Stack. The possibility also exists that premature shutoff may occur so that the entire stack of records is not allowed to play. The most logical source of trouble here is a binding in the shutoff-lock lever, particularly at the fulcrum. The usual technique of liberally applying carbon tetrachloride is the first step required followed by a light application of lubricant.

Lubrication of Stabilizer-arm-actuated Shutoff Mechanism. SAE 10W oil should be used sparingly on the shutoff-trip lever pivot, the shutoff-actuating lever pivot, and on the stabilizer shaft. Other lubrication is not necessary.

Spindle–Stabilizer-arm Shutoff. After the last record has dropped to the turntable, the record-stabilizer arm of some spindle-drop changers drops a little farther down on the spindle so as to restrict the travel in the pusher. A changer of this type is shown in Fig. 9. After the last record has been played, the change cycle is actuated and the lift arm rotates clockwise as viewed from below. As the roller on the spindle pusher rides up the cam surface of the lift arm, the spindle housing cannot retract completely as during other change cycles because the stabilizer arm restricts the pusher travel.

On the back side of the lift arm there is attached a shutoff rod with the end protruding upward. This is shown in Fig. 9A. This end usually clears the spindle housing, but since the spindle does not retract completely, it now engages the shutoff rod when the roller reaches the top of the cam surface. The shutoff rod is rotated 90 degrees by this action.

The other end of the shutoff rod is also bent. When a record is on the spindle, this end lies horizontally and provides no action. After the last record it is rotated 90 degrees as just described, so that it now protrudes upward (downward when viewed from below). As the lift arm reverses its motion, this end rides in a slot in the shutoff-trip lever as shown in Fig. 9B. As the lift arm nears the end of its rotation, the end of the shutoff rod contacts a stud on the shutoff-trip lever, causing the lever to rotate. Since one end of the shutoff-trip lever is connected to the switch in the customary manner, the motor is shut off.

The same stud on the shutoff-trip lever flips the shutoff rod over at the start of the next cycle so as to return it to its ready position.

Repair of Spindle–Stabilizer-arm Shutoff. If this type of record changer does not shut off after playing the last record, two points should be checked.

First, the record support should drop and rest on the offset shoulder of the spindle. If this does not happen, the record support must be checked to determine where binding occurs. Removal of any burr by use of a fine file or crocus cloth may be necessary. Any grime or dirt may be washed away by use of carbon tetrachloride.

The second point to check is the shutoff rod located along the lift arm. The end nearest the center should contact the shoulder on the spindle-pusher housing. If this does not occur, the spindle should be checked to ascertain that it is held in place properly by the set screws. The lift arm should also be investigated to assure that it is held tightly by its screw. Another possibility is that the shutoff rod may require replacement due to a short turned-up end.

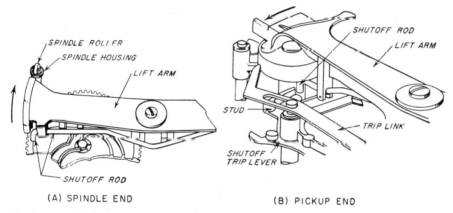

Fig. 9. A spindle-drop mechanism where the depressed spindle housing flips the shutoff rod. The opposite end then presses against a stud on the shutoff-trip lever and moves it, shutting off the switch

Spindle–Stabilizer-arm Mechanism—Premature Shutoff. If an old record is used which is too thick, a spindle-drop changer will shut off instead of drop. Another cause of premature shutoff is a weak roller spring or excessive compression of it. This spring is located within the spindle assembly and may be checked by watching the relationship between the roller and the pusher housing as the changer is being cycled. The pusher housing should stop its upward motion just before the top of the lift-arm cam action is reached. The roller should continue its upward motion just a trifle (about 0.005 inch) during which time the roller spring is compressed.

A weak spring requires replacement of the spindle assembly. If the spring compresses too much, the fiber washer between the lift arm and the steel washer under it should be removed. This will drop the lift arm so it does not push up as much on the spindle.

Premature shutoff also occurs if the shutoff rod is not reset. This may be due to poor tension in the lever spring so that the shutoff rod does not snap into place. If this is the case, remove the rod and bend the spring slightly to increase tension. The bearings and the surface around the lever spring should be lubricated with Lubriplate or STA-PUT to assure easy motion. The clearance between the end of the shutoff rod and the shutoff-trip lever stud should only be sufficient to allow the shutoff rod to flip over when actuated.

Lubrication of Spindle–Stabilizer-arm Shutoff Mechanism. All points of sliding contact should be lubricated with a film of Lubriplate or STA-PUT No. 512. This includes the bearings for the shutoff rod and between the shutoff rod and the lever spring which loads it. For other bearings, such as lever pivots and the shutoff-trip lever bearing, use light oil such as SAE 10W.

QUESTIONS

1. Name four types of automatic-shutoff mechanism.
2. How does a sliding spindle shut off a changer?
3. Where would you lubricate a selector-post shutoff mechanism?
4. How would you check to see if the stabilizer arm is used for shutoff actuation?
5. If you think that a changer is of the automatic-shutoff type, where will you look for the actuator?
6. In the above situation, how can you check to see if shutoff is used?

12

Special 45-rpm Changers and Spindles

Introduction. Record changers that play only 45-rpm records use much the same dropping, set-down, and trip mechanisms as other changers. They do have several unique features, however, that justify consideration in a separate chapter. The information here will therefore be a review of familiar mechanisms as used in an unfamiliar and highly compact special changer.

Physical Features of 45-rpm Records. The 45-rpm record is 7 inches in diameter with a microgroove recording area near the outer edge and a center hole 1½ inches in diameter. The record thus fits over a spindle which is sufficiently large so that the changer mechanism can be located inside.

The cross section of the record, as indicated in Fig. 1, is such that the record is thinner near the spindle as well as in the recorded area. A mid-section is the thickest portion. The records can thus be stacked without having the recorded surfaces rubbing together.

The 45-rpm record changer utilizes separating slicers protruding from the spindle. Because of the thin area on the record next to the spindle, the separator slicers move into an air space between records. The slicers merely support the record stack when the shelf moves from under the bottom record.

Physical Features of Record Player. Modern record changers are primarily of the three-speed type. Special changers are made that play only 45-rpm records. Because the 45-rpm record changer operates at only one speed and the records are small and light, the changer is considerably smaller and less complicated. Since only one size of record is used, the indexing is relatively simple. Also, the pickup arm does not have to move as far and the resulting size of the various parts is smaller. As a result, it was possible to design

217

the changer with a very rapid changing speed. The time required from the entrance of the needle into the eccentric finishing groove to the indexing on the next record is only about 1⅓ seconds.

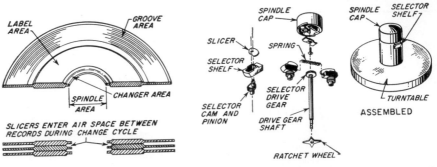

Fig. 1. The physical features of the 45-rpm record

Fig. 2. The changing mechanism of a 45-rpm record changer is of the slicer type but is contained within the spindle

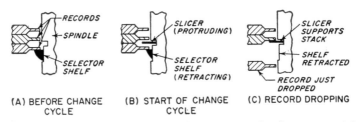

Fig. 3. Record-dropping action of a 45-rpm record changer. As the slicer comes out to support the record stack, the shelf retracts allowing the bottom record to drop

Dropping Action. The record-changing mechanism of the 45-rpm changer is of the slicer type housed entirely in the spindle assembly, as shown in Fig. 2. Two slicers and two selector shelves are used, located on opposite sides of the spindle assembly.

The records rest on the selector shelves. During the normal playing portion of the cycle the slicers are within the spindle. This and the following motions are shown in Fig. 3.

When the changer mechanism works, the slicers come out from the spindle, entering the air space above the lowest record. At the same time the selector shelves are drawn back into the spindle. The slicers support the record stack while the selector shelves move away from under the bottom record, allowing it to drop to the turntable. The selector shelves then come back out from within the spindle and the slicers withdraw, allowing the record stack to drop down onto the shelf. The stack is then ready for a repetition of this action.

Dropping Mechanism. The changer mechanism consists of a shaft which runs through the center of the spindle assembly. Underneath the turntable and on the end of the shaft is a ratchet wheel.

Near the head of the spindle assembly and attached to this shaft is a selector drive gear which meshes with two others diametrically opposed. These two selector gears have a cam arrangement, as shown in Fig. 4, in which a selector shaft or stud protrudes from the upper side of the selector gear. This arrangement is known as the selector cam.

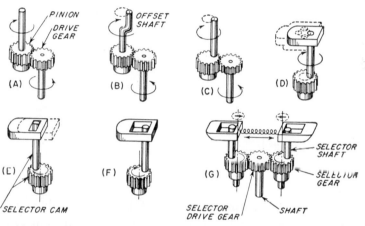

Fig. 4. Operation of dropping mechanism in a 45-rpm record changer illustrating how a rotating shaft movement is changed to a to-and-fro shelf motion. (A) Rotation of the selector drive gear causes the pinion gear to rotate. (B) The end of a crank on the pinion gear describes a circular motion. (C) The same motion is obtained by placing the shaft off center on the gear. (D) A shelf with a hole to fit the shaft will be caused to follow the shaft. (E) A slotted shelf will move back and forth but not sideways. (F) The same motion is obtained with a larger hole if the shelf is pushed to the left. (G) A dual arrangement of the same type with a compression spring pushing out

As the drive gear rotates, it causes the selector cam to rotate. This causes the stud to revolve in an eccentric manner. The record shelves are placed in a position so that the selector shaft fits in a slot. As the selector shaft rotates in its eccentric manner, it imparts a sliding motion back and forth to the shelf.

In operation the entire turntable assembly including the spindle rotates. The drive and pinion gears, as well as the drive-gear shaft and ratchet wheel, all rotate simultaneously, and there is no relative movement between the drive gear and the selector gear.

The trip mechanism causes the ratchet wheel to be stopped when a record has been played. As a result, the shaft and associated drive gear stop. The outer spindle shell continues to rotate, moving the shelves with it. This causes the selector shaft and gear to rotate about the selector drive gear. The record shelf first moves inward and then out again. Once the cycle is completed, the ratchet wheel is released, allowing the selector drive gear and shaft to rotate with the spindle assembly.

The slicers are connected to the opposite support shelves as indicated in Fig. 5 so that as the record shelves move inward, the slicers are pushed outward. As the selector shaft reverses the direction of the shelves, they move outward and the slicers are pulled inward.

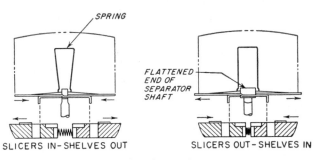

Fig. 5. Slicer action

Drive and Trip Mechanisms. Because of the small turntable and relative simplicity of the changer the drive mechanism is of the rim type in all 45-rpm changers. The motor drives a rubber-tired idler wheel, which in turn drives the inside of the turntable rim.

In some 45-rpm changers the drive gear is connected directly to the turntable shaft. The drive gear therefore makes a complete revolution during the change cycle while the turntable makes one revolution. This gives a very quick change cycle.

In other 45-rpm changers a knurled hub gear is attached to the turntable shaft and in turn drives the drive gear.

The trip mechanism in all 45-rpm changers is of the position type, but various models differ slightly in construction. In that shown in Fig. 6, the pickup arm is attached to a pickup-arm lever which moves inward with the pickup arm as the record is played. The record has its eccentric groove so located that the pickup arm moves to within $1\frac{9}{32}$ inches of the center of the record.

When the pickup arm reaches the eccentric groove, the pickup-arm lever contacts a stud on the drive gear. The fast-finishing groove of the record causes the pickup arm and pickup-arm lever to move inward so that the pickup-arm lever pushes against the stud, rotating the drive gear so that the gear teeth come into contact with the hub gear which is attached to the turntable assembly. A spring holds the drive-gear mechanism against the hub gear. The drive gear is attached to a slider so as to change the rotary motion into lateral motion. A mutilated section of the drive gear allows the hub gear to rotate when the record is being played. A bracket, illustrated in Fig. 7, keeps the drive gear away from the roller when in the playing position. The mechanism has no shutoff.

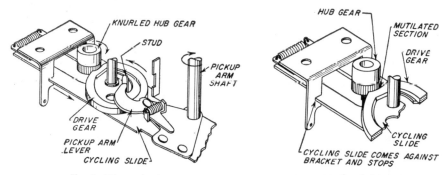

Fig. 6. Trip mechanism   **Fig. 7.** Mutilated drive gear

In the mechanism of Fig. 8 the trip mechanism is slightly different. In this case the pickup-arm lever contacts the clutch pawl when the pickup arm enters the eccentric finishing groove of the record. The clutch pawl is caused to rotate in a counterclockwise direction when viewed from the top so that the upturned left end moves in the path of a stud which is located on the bottom of the turntable, as in Fig. 8A.

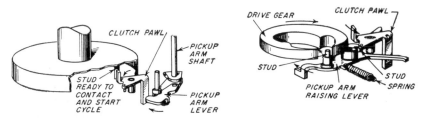

(A) INITIATED BY PICKUP ARM LEVER   (B) PAWL FORCES RAISING LEVER INTO CAM

Fig. 8. A position-type 45-rpm trip mechanism. The pickup arm and lever rotate the clutch pawl until a stud on the turntable hits it. This forces the raising lever to rotate until a stud on it enters the opening in the drive gear

Thus, as the turntable rotates, the stud contacts the clutch pawl, carrying it along for a short distance. A stud on the lower portion of the clutch pawl is forced against the pickup-arm raising lever, as illustrated in Fig. 8B. Since the pivot or fulcrum of the pickup-arm raising lever is to the left of the stud on the clutch pawl, this motion causes the pickup-arm raising lever to rotate slightly in a clockwise direction. The force is applied until a stud on the top of the pickup-arm raising lever is forced through the slot on the drive gear, which is connected to the turntable shaft. The stud moves through this slot and then follows the contour of the cycling cam due to the tension of the spring pulling on it.

During the cycle the pickup arm is moved back to the outside of the turntable, and the pickup-arm lever releases the contact with the clutch pawl. When the drive gear has completed its rotation, the spring is allowed to pull the pickup-arm raising lever away from the drive gear as the stud on the pickup-arm raising lever slips through the open slot.

Indexing. The pickup-arm action in a conventional drive-gear-cam cycling equipment is illustrated in Fig. 9A. As the stud on the pickup-arm raising lever follows the contours of the inside of the drive gear, it is first caused to rotate in a clockwise direction. As the stud on the left-hand end moves away from the muting switch, the switch is allowed to close. At the same time a stud on the right-hand end of the pickup-arm raising lever pushes against the pickup-arm lift lever, causing it to rotate in a clockwise direction. The right end of the pickup-arm lift lever bears against the pickup-arm lift rod. The pickup arm is pivoted to the right of the pickup-arm lift rod. As the pickup-arm lift lever applies a force in the left-hand direction, the pickup-arm lift rod is forced to the left causing the pickup arm to rotate upward.

Figure 9B shows that the tip of the pickup-arm raising lever contacts the stud of the pickup-arm lever, moving the pickup arm outward from the center of the record. As this motion is occurring, the stud on the pickup-arm lever contacts the pickup-arm return lever forcing it clockwise against the tension of the spring shown in Fig. 9C.

When the pickup arm reaches the outermost position, the clamping latch of the pickup-arm return lever hooks around the stud on the pickup-arm lever and locks it in position. When the pickup-arm raising lever reverses its motion due to the change in the cam position, it still retains contact with the stud on the pickup-arm lever as in Fig. 9C.

Since the pickup-arm return lever is exerting an inward force on the pickup arm due to the spring tension, the motion of the pickup arm is stabilized by contact between the two parts. A stud on the left-hand end of the pickup-arm return lever comes into contact with an eccentric stud (indexing adjustment), as in Fig. 9D, stopping the inward movement of the pickup arm directly above the landing position of the pickup arm. The position of the indexing adjustment can be changed by rotating the eccentric stud, providing a fine adjustment for the proper set-down position.

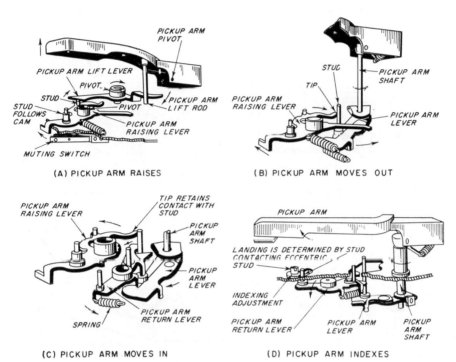

Fig. 9. Indexing in the conventional drive-gear-cam type of 45-rpm record changer

The stud on the right side of the pickup-arm raising lever still contacts the pickup-arm lift lever (as in Fig. 9A) as its position is reversed, thus lowering the pickup arm so that the needle contacts the record at the start.

Indexing in Slide-type Mechanism. In the slide-type mechanism, a knurled hub gear drives the drive gear during the change cycle. The drive gear is pivoted off center and is mounted on the cycling slide, as illustrated in Fig. 10A, so that as the distance between the drive-gear pivot and the knurled roller increases, the slide is pushed to the right toward the pickup-arm shaft. In the course of this action the tension of the return spring is increased, and in addition the muting switch is allowed to close.

As the motion of the slide continues, the incline on the cycling slide causes the pickup-arm lift rod to rise, lifting the pickup arm. This is shown in Fig. 10B. The stud on the pickup-arm lever contacts the side of the cycling slide so that as the slide continues to move to the right in Fig. 10C, the pickup-arm lever is pushed in a counterclockwise direction. The eccentric indexing-adjustment stud, which is attached to the pickup-arm lever, moves against the pickup-arm return lever.

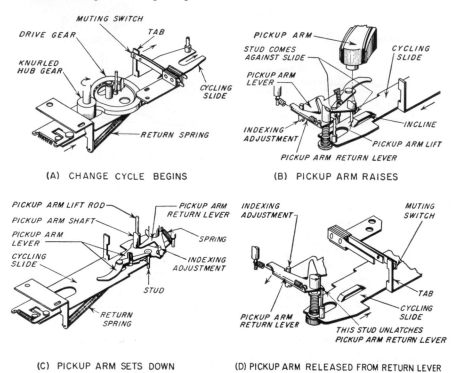

(A) CHANGE CYCLE BEGINS

(B) PICKUP ARM RAISES

(C) PICKUP ARM SETS DOWN

(D) PICKUP ARM RELEASED FROM RETURN LEVER

Fig. 10. The indexing mechanism of a 45-rpm slide-type changer. Mechanism shown from two different sides for clarity

After the next record has dropped to the turntable, the cycling slide moves away from the pickup-arm shaft. This is possible since the drive gear has rotated so that its smaller-diameter side is against the knurled hub gear. The return spring keeps them in contact, assuring the return motion of the cycling slide.

As shown in Fig. 10C, the spring tension on the pickup-arm return lever causes it to stay in contact with the indexing-adjustment stud on the pickup-arm lever. Thus the other stud on the pickup-arm lever follows the slide as it moves.

When the indexing-adjustment stud contacts the curved stop on the end of the pickup-arm return lever (as illustrated in Fig. 10C), the pickup-arm lever no longer moves. This is the set-down position. When the cycling slide moves so that the pickup-arm lift rod slides down the incline, the pickup is lowered to the start of the record.

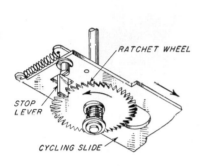

Fig. 11. The ratchet wheel of a slide-type changer is stopped by a stop lever on the end of the cycling slide

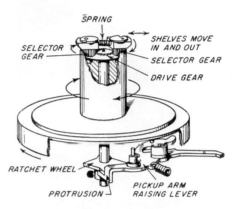

Fig. 12. The ratchet wheel of the drive-gear-cam-type changer is stopped by a protrusion on the bottom of the pickup-arm raising lever thus initiating the drop mechanism

As the cycling slide returns to its rest position, a stud on its extreme end moves the pickup-arm return lever away from the indexing-adjustment stud, as in Fig. 10D. The pickup arm and pickup-arm lever are then free to follow the record grooves. In addition, a tab on the slide opens the muting switch so that the output of the pickup will be fed to the amplifier.

Ratchet Wheel. The position-trip mechanism of the slide-type 45-rpm changer causes a ratchet wheel to be stopped, stopping the spindle mechanism so that the record shelf is actuated. The ratchet wheel shown in Fig. 11 is attached to the spindle shaft and normally rotates with the turntable. When the cycling slide moves to its extreme position during the change cycle, a stop lever on the innermost end engages the ratchet, causing it to stop.

A variation is shown in Fig. 12 and is used in the drive-gear-cam type of 45-rpm changer described. The pickup-arm raising lever moves the pickup arm out from the center of the record. As this occurs, the left-hand end of the pickup-arm raising lever, which extends below the base plate, contacts the ratchet wheel and stops it, as illustrated.

Repair of 45-rpm Record Changers. Since the mechanisms of these 45-rpm record changers are similar to those discussed in previous chapters,

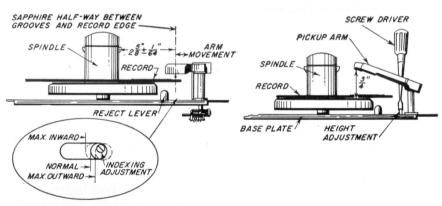

Fig. 13. Pickup-arm height and indexing adjustments on the drive-gear-cam-type 45-rpm changers. (Howard W. Sams photo)

detailed steps for repair are not repeated. Problems result from the same types of difficulties, namely, dirt, grime, burrs, loose studs, bent parts, and weak or missing springs. Usual techniques must be applied to correct these, but diagnosis of the trouble should be considerably easier because of the simplicity of the mechanism.

Adjustments. The principal adjustments are the pickup-arm height and indexing adjustments. The locations of these for the more conventional drive-gear-cam mechanism are shown in Fig. 13. Both adjustments are on the top side of the base plate near the pickup arm.

The indexing adjustment is generally required most frequently of all in record-changer repairs. The position at which the pickup should set down is 2⅝ inches from the spindle. This is halfway between the edge of the record and the first music groove.

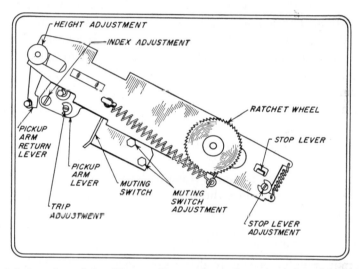

Fig. 14. A bottom view of the slide-type 45-rpm changer shows the cycling slide and various adjustments

The landing or indexing adjustment is a cam with a slotted stud to permit use of a screwdriver. If the indexing and pickup-arm mechanism is properly assembled, the correct adjustment should be near the center of the cam adjustment as indicated in the illustration. Some variation may be expected, but if it is necessary to adjust very near either extreme, the mechanism should be inspected.

The height adjustment is a cam located near the rear of the base plate. To check it, the mechanism should be started through its change cycle by hand. When the pickup arm has reached its maximum height, there should be ¾ inch between the turntable and the needle. The pickup arm should rise during clockwise adjustment of the eccentric on the pickup-arm lift lever. If the adjustment is turned too far, back it up and repeat the adjustment.

In the cycling-slide mechanism the indexing adjustment is a cam on the pickup-arm lever. Figure 14 shows this and other possible adjustments. The height adjustment is checked in similar fashion as described above, also, but the proper spacing is $1\frac{1}{8}$ inches. The location of the knurled adjustment nut is at the upper left end of the slide. The muting switch may be adjusted by loosening two screws and moving it.

To correct for records dropping on the pickup arm, the stop-lever adjustment should be utilized. Likewise, the trip point is conveniently adjusted. Trip should occur when the needle is $1\frac{9}{32}$ inches from the spindle.

Lubrication. The motor bearings on both units should be oiled with SAE 10W oil. On other bearing or sliding surfaces STA-PUT or Lubriplate are recommended. STA-PUT No. 320 or its equivalent is recommended for the bearing surfaces, and STA-PUT No. 512 or its equivalent is recommended for the sliding surfaces. Once again, if any oil or grease gets on rubber parts it should be thoroughly washed off immediately with alcohol.

45-rpm Spindles on Three-speed Changers. Many three-speed record changers use a single spindle of conventional diameter. In order to play 45-rpm records on such changers, it is necessary to use the snap-on spiders on each record. These reduce the size of the center hole to fit the conventional spindle.

Other changers use changeable spindles. To play the 45-rpm records, a large-diameter spindle plugs into the turntable and works very much like the 45-rpm spindles previously described. No ratchet wheel is used. Instead the drop is actuated by the spindle shaft being pushed upward as in the spindle-drop mechanism. By use of a beveled cam surface at the top of the spindle shaft the slicers and selector shelves are caused to operate.

QUESTIONS

1. How do the 7-inch records differ from others?
2. How does the 45-rpm spindle differ from the conventional spindle?
3. What are the unique features of a 45-rpm changer?
4. Describe the dropping action of a 45-rpm changer.
5. What type of trip mechanism is normally used in a 45-rpm changer?
6. What is the purpose of the ratchet wheel?
7. What is the difference between the spindle of a 45-rpm changer and the 7-inch changeable spindle used on three-speed changers?

13

Amplification and Compensation

Need for Amplifier. The electrical signal developed by the pickup in a record changer is of a low level, generally under 3 volts. In order to convert this to an audible sound, amplification is needed. The audio amplifier used in reproduction of recordings is essentially the same as that used in amplifying the radio and television sound but may have special features to give higher fidelity and to compensate for the varying characteristics of recordings.

Amplifiers. A simple audio amplifier consists of a voltage amplification section and a power amplification section. One such unit is shown in Fig. 1. This gives an output sufficient to drive a loudspeaker so that the recorded information is audible to the listener.

More elaborate amplifiers are used to give more output, wider frequency response, and less distortion. A common method of producing more power and less distortion is to use a push-pull output circuit, as shown in Fig. 2. As would be expected, more output power is available since two output tubes are used. In addition, the even harmonics oppose each other in the primary of the output transformer and are effectively canceled. Thus, there is less distortion present.

Negative Feedback. The frequency response of a resistance-coupled amplifier is definitely limited. This may be extended by the use of negative feedback, and at the same time distortion is very greatly reduced. More expensive amplifiers nearly always use negative feedback.

It is generally customary to use about 20 db of feedback, which reduces the distortion to about 10 per cent of the value without feedback. A resistance-coupled amplifier with feedback is shown in Fig. 3. More elaborate

229

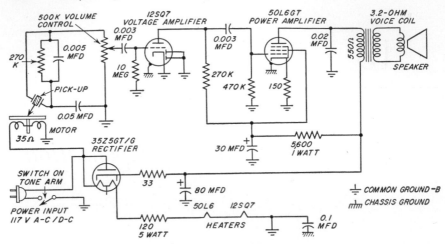

Fig. 1. A simple amplifier consisting of a voltage amplification section and a power amplification section. A rectifier supplies B + voltage

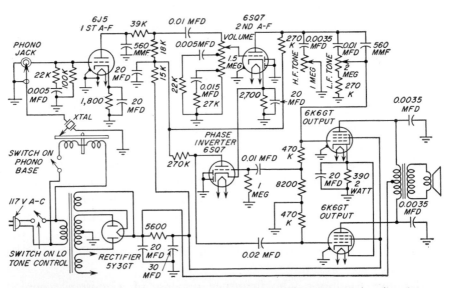

Fig. 2. A push-pull amplifier (2 6K6's) provides considerable output with low distortion

amplifiers may use other types of coupling as well as feedback to give still better results. Figure 4 is a transformer-coupled amplifier.

Negative feedback also serves to reduce the output impedance of the amplifier. This helps to damp out unwanted transients in the loudspeaker. These transients might be defined as short-lived distortions of an irregular type.

Relation of Cost to Design. Inexpensive amplifiers may be of the a-c/d-c or transformerless variety. This is definitely a money saver. It is likely that only moderate d-c filtering will be used as well. As an amplifier design is improved to provide less distortion, power supply filtering is usually improved, too. In the case of an elaborate design regulation may be employed to maintain a relatively constant B+ supply, even though the line voltage may vary. As one phase of a circuit is improved, other aspects must be improved as well. Cost thus goes up rapidly with improvement in characteristics.

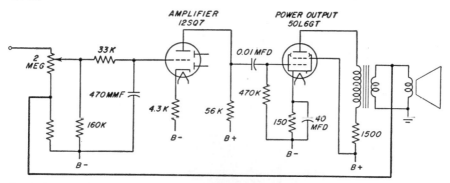

Fig. 3. Negative feedback extends the frequency response and greatly reduces distortion in an amplifier. The heavy line shows the path of the signal fed back

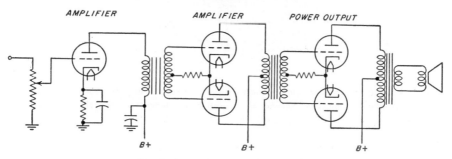

Fig. 4. A transformer-coupled amplifier

Preamplifiers. Magnetic pickups generally have more desirable characteristics than the crystal types. The price that is paid for this is a considerably reduced output. As a result, it is usually necessary to use a preamplifier to raise the magnetic-pickup output to the proper input level for the average amplifier. If the amplifier is designed for the pickup, the two may be combined by adding an extra stage or two. On the other hand, the preamplifier may consist of a small supplementary chassis as shown in Fig. 5. This particular amplifier includes compensation at low frequencies.

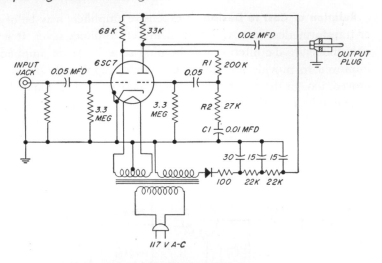

Fig. 5. A supplementary preamplifier chassis used with a regular amplifier when a GE variable-reluctance pickup is used. Low-frequency compensation is included consisting of R1, R2, and C1. (GE photo)

Use of Compensation. The customary method of recording commercial records is to use a varying frequency characteristic. Surface noise in a disc occurs primarily above 1,000 cps. To reduce the effect of this in the reproduction, it is common to accentuate the high frequencies when recording and to correspondingly attenuate the high-frequency response of the pickup. This gives a constant output and an improved signal-to-noise ratio.

The N.A.B. (National Association of Broadcasters) standard lateral-recording characteristic is shown in Fig. 6. Over most of the low-frequency range the recording amplitude varies inversely with the velocity of the modulated record groove. This means that regardless of the frequency the recording amplitude remains constant. At the lowest frequencies pre-emphasis is introduced. In a manner similar to the high-frequency pre-emphasis, this tends to reduce line frequency hum and turntable rumble.

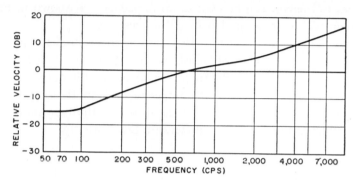

Fig. 6. The N.A.B. (National Association of Broadcasters) recording characteristics

In order to give an audible output which is the same as that originally produced for recording, it is necessary to provide characteristics opposite to these recording characteristics. This is illustrated in Fig. 7. For this reason compensation is introduced.

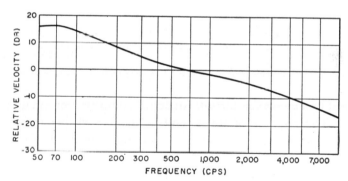

Fig. 7. Over-all audible response desired to correct for N.A.B. recording characteristics so as to make playback the same as the original sound recorded

Compensation is the act of correcting or replacing something that is lost. Generally it is spoken of very loosely as any change which is made in the response. Figure 8 shows several simple *RC* compensation circuits that are frequently encountered. In Fig. 8A is shown a series *RC* circuit with the output taken across the resistor R. With this the low-frequency response falls off below a certain frequency.

Another combination frequently encountered is the parallel *RC* circuit shown in Fig. 8B. The equivalent stray capacitance across the plate load resistor of a resistance-coupled amplifier gives this arrangement, which causes the output (or impedance) to drop off at high frequencies.

A series *RC* circuit can be used as an impedance, as shown in Fig. 8C. This circuit will increase the low-frequency response.

The parallel *RC* circuit of Fig. 8B can be used in series to give a rising high-frequency effect. Figure 8D illustrates this. Since the impedance of the parallel portion decreases as the frequency increases, the output resistor R_2 is a greater percentage of the total impedance. Thus the output rises, as at f_a. However, R_2 and C_1 form a series divider of the type shown in Fig. 8A. The effect of this is to add a downward break, as at f_b.

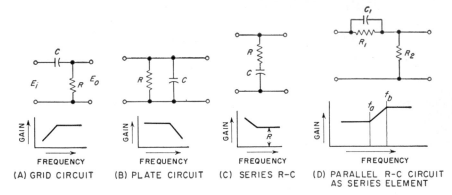

Fig. 8. Simple RC combinations give various frequency-response changes as illustrated

Practical Compensation Circuit. An actual compensation circuit is shown in Fig. 9. The response of this circuit is about 3 db per octave. If one section is applied to the response of recording, a relatively flat output is obtained.

Combining Characteristics. Where one circuit does not load down another, they may be combined to give improved results. Thus two compensation sections may be cascaded, as in Fig. 9, and the results will be essentially twice that of one alone.

Compensating for the Pickup Cartridge. In addition to compensating for the recording characteristic, it is often necessary to compensate for the pickup. Crystal pickups, for example, are frequency-sensitive because of internal capacitance. A Rochelle salt crystal has high internal capacitance and a PN type (ammonium dihydrogen phosphate) has low internal capacitance.

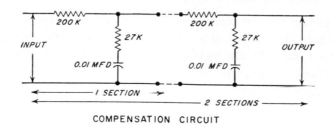

COMPENSATION CIRCUIT

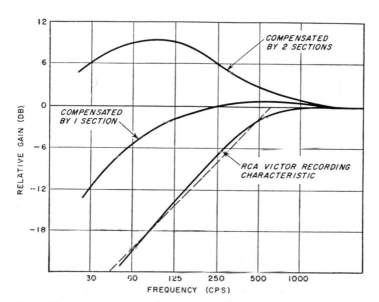

Fig. 9. The RCA Victor recording characteristic and compensation of the circuit

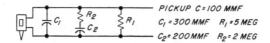

PICKUP C = 100 MMF
C_1 = 300 MMF R_1 = 5 MEG
C_2 = 200 MMF R_2 = 2 MEG

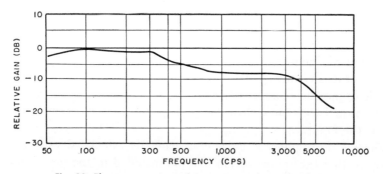

Fig. 10. The response curve of a compensated crystal pickup

235

The pickup may be represented as a voltage generator in series with a capacitance. The value of this capacitance is about 1,000 micromicrofarads ($\mu\mu$f) for a Rochelle salt pickup and approximately 100$\mu\mu$f for a PN cartridge. Figure 10 shows the circuit of a compensated crystal pickup and the over-all response. The pickup has a capacitance of about 100$\mu\mu$f as indicated. C_1 is the capacitance of the cable, R_2 and C_2 make up a compensation circuit, and R_1 represents the grid resistor of the amplifier input.

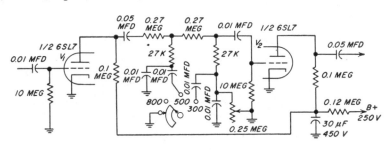

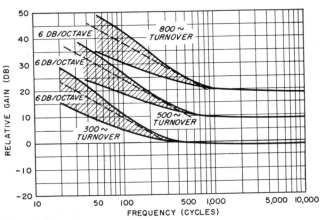

Fig. 11. A circuit with compensation inserted between stages. The switch allows selection of any one of three characteristics. The shaded areas indicate the variation provided by the potentiometer

Location of Compensation Circuit. In order to provide compensation, a convenient means must be used to incorporate it in the circuit. It is readily possible to put such compensation in the amplifier circuit. Since amplifiers are often used with more than one pickup, the compensation is put in at or near the input.

Where a preamplifier is used, it is generally associated with a specific pickup so that the compensation may be included in the preamplifier circuit. Figure 11 shows such an arrangement where the compensation is included between two sections of a 6SL7 or 6SC7. In this case provision is made to select various types of compensation to match recording characteristics.

Insertion Loss. All compensation circuits have an insertion loss which must be made up by the amplifier.

Amplifiers frequently use bass and treble controls so that the listener may vary the response of the circuit. These controls are a part of circuits which are compensation circuits. Control of the bass notes, or bass boost as it is often known, is made by means of an *RC* circuit of the type already discussed. Control of the high notes is accomplished by means of a circuit which attenuates the low frequencies more than the highs. Figure 12 shows a circuit containing both treble and bass control. As with previous cases of compensation circuits, insertion loss exists.

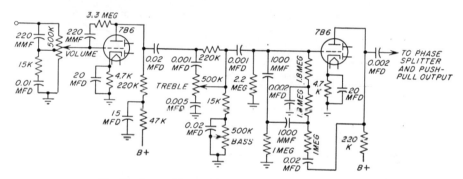

Fig. 12. An amplifier with both bass and treble tone control

Since tone-control circuits have insertion loss and also serve to change the gain at certain frequencies, many tone controls will have an effect on the volume. Likewise, a volume control is usually part of a frequency-sensitive circuit such as an *RC* coupling arrangement and will therefore affect the frequency response. It is possible, however, to rather simply obtain a tone-control circuit which does not materially affect the frequency response.

More important is the consideration of the hearing characteristics of the listener. The level of sound at which a person begins to feel the sound as well as hear it is known as the threshold of feeling. At this level the response of the ear is nearly uniform over the entire hearing range. As the volume is reduced, however, the ear is more sensitive to the mid-frequency range. This means that if one is to hear the sound in proper proportion, the high and low frequencies must be amplified more than the mid-frequencies. This effect becomes progressively pronounced as the volume is decreased as shown in Fig. 13.

Until recently a volume control with these characteristics was very elaborate, as might very well be expected. A relatively simple arrangement is now available and is illustrated in Fig. 14. The characteristics show that, in general, this arrangement does a very acceptable job at a reasonable price.

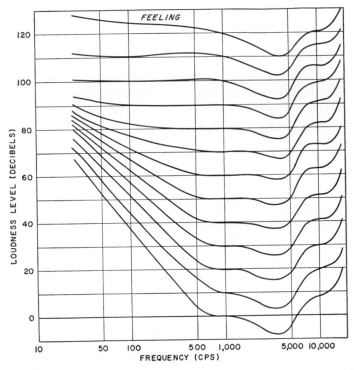

Fig. 13. Fletcher-Munson curves showing the response of the ear at various sound levels

Adding a Compensation Circuit. It is generally possible to add compensation to the circuit by connecting it between the record-changer output and the amplifier. Figure 15 shows the method of connecting two such circuits to compensate for a crystal. Such a practice is not indiscriminately recommended but demonstrates adjustments which can be made and suggests an experiment for familiarization. In Fig. 15A, R_1 will vary the low-frequency response. The lows are increased by making the value larger. With R_1 removed, the low frequencies are a maximum. The output is controlled by R_2. A smaller value gives an increased output. An increase in C_1 will increase the high frequencies.

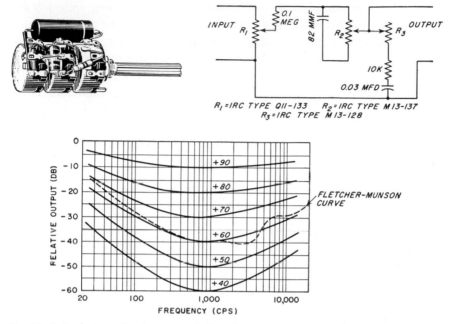

R_1 = IRC TYPE QII-133 R_2 = IRC TYPE M 13-137
R_3 = IRC TYPE M 13-128

Fig. 14. A simple type of volume control gives close approximation to Fletcher-Munson curves. The solid lines show the results obtained at various settings of the IRC type LC-1 control

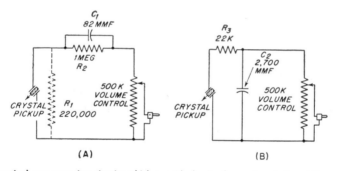

(A)   (B)

Fig. 15. Practical compensation circuits which provide basis of experimentation. (A) provides both bass and treble compensation, and (B) reduces needle scratch. The circuitry is usually built into the amplifier but may be put on a supplemental chassis

Where needle scratch is prevalent, it may be controlled by the circuit of Fig. 15B. To increase the highs, C_2 may be decreased. If R_3 is increased, the highs will be decreased and the volume reduced.

Volume Expansion. If the full volume range were recorded the lateral groove variation would be very large. On loud passages, the groove would cut through to the adjacent one unless considerable space were left between grooves. This would limit the amount that could be recorded.

To avoid such problems, volume compression is used when recording. Electronic circuits are used to limit both the loud and the soft passages so as to reduce the range of volume changes. In most recordings this is of little consequence. In operatic recordings, however, a high-fidelity enthusiast will notice the difference. To overcome this, a volume expander is used. This reverses the effect of volume compression so that the soft passages are made softer, and the loud passages are made louder. This might be viewed as the opposite of automatic volume control (a.v.c.) as used in radios.

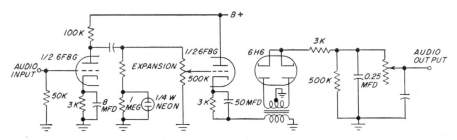

Fig. 16. A volume-expander circuit

Volume expansion is usually built into the amplifier and consists of one or more stages of action. It is possible to use a separate volume expander by connecting it between two amplifier stages. A typical volume expander is shown in Fig. 16.

Connecting a Record Changer to an Amplifier. The record changer usually has a shielded cable with a single center conductor coming from the pickup cartridge. The shield is a metal braid surrounding the center conductor which is the signal lead. The shield is connected to the ground side of the cartridge and to the metal plate or chassis of the record changer.

The shielded cable is usually terminated by a simple plug-in or screw-on connector. The outer shell of the connector is used for the ground or shield connection and the center contact for the signal connection. A mating connector is provided on the amplifier.

If the amplifier uses screw connections, the ends of the shielded cable can be slipped under the screws and fastened securely, or spade lugs can be attached to the end of the shielded cable. If the loose ends are fastened directly, they should be tucked under the screw head and bent around the screw in a clockwise direction. Then as the screw is tightened, the wire will tend to wrap around the screw rather than squirm out.

Connecting a Record Changer to a Radio. Many radios have provisions for connecting a record changer directly to them. If this is not the case and such a connection is desired, it will be necessary to add a connector and a switch and to rewire a portion of the circuit. The basic requirement is to open the circuit of the radio at the output of the second detector and insert a switch which can be used to select either radio or phono. The connection is shown in Fig. 17.

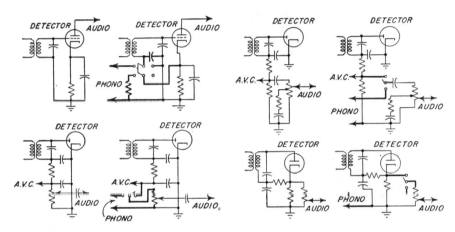

Fig. 17. Various radio-detector circuits (left) and the corresponding manner in which a record-changer attachment may be made (right). The ground connection in an a-c/d-c set must be isolated from the chassis by a capacitor

The input to the amplifier section is connected to the selector arm of the switch. The record-changer input is connected to one switch position, and the second detector output is connected to the other.

The record-changer or phono lead from this switch should go to a connector mounted at the rear of the chassis. Since the volume level at this point is very low, shielded cable must be used. Since two connections are made, either two pieces of shielded cable may be used or a single piece of two-conductor shielded cable. The following descriptions will be based on use of a single piece of two-conductor shielded cable.

If it is possible, a combination connector and switch assembly is recommended for convenience. If not, separate units can be used but will necessitate additional work. The switch may be a single-pole double-throw

(S.P.D.T.) toggle switch. The connection of the connector and switch are shown in Fig. 18A, and a commercial version is outlined in Fig. 18B.

The switch or assembly should be fastened to the radio cabinet by means of a bracket in a convenient position. The upper-rear edge of the cabinet is a convenient spot. Where a plastic cabinet is used, the bracket must be fastened to the chassis. Soldering or use of self-tapping screws may be convenient.

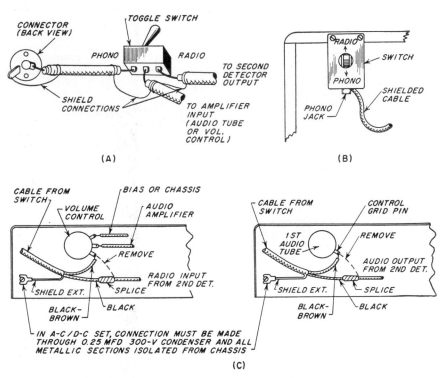

Fig. 18. Circuit connections to modify a radio for record-changer input. (A) Connection of the connector to the switch, showing the use of single-conductor-shielded cable. (B) A commercial switch and connector combination that utilizes double-conductor-shielded cable. (C) Methods of connecting the switch of (B) to the circuit

If the set is a-c/d-c, the connector and switch should be isolated from the chassis by means of a block of wood or other suitable insulator. Caution must be taken that there is no metallic connection between the hot chassis and the shields on the cables. Keep the shield on the cable well away from the chassis, and make the chassis connections through a 0.25-microfarad 300-volt condenser.

Figure 18C shows the physical connections of the switch to the radio circuit. To determine where the connection is to be made, the circuit must be inspected to find the lead which goes from the second detector to the audio tube or the volume control. In most radios the connection will be made to the volume control.

QUESTIONS

1. Why is an amplifier necessary?
2. What is the advantage of negative feedback?
3. Why is compensation used?
4. What is the purpose of volume expansion?
5. How do you connect a record changer to an amplifier?
6. Where do you break a radio circuit to connect a record changer?

14

Fault Location and Tests

Approach to Repair. The knowledge you now have about basic mechanisms is the important factor in isolating troubles and making repairs of record changers. Background knowledge is most valuable, however, if it is put to use in a logical manner. This is most important in a new or unfamiliar model of changer.

The best way to get acquainted with a record changer is to study the mechanism for a few minutes when it is idle, then rotate the turntable by hand and watch the various actions as the mechanism slowly goes through a cycle.

Location of Key Parts. When the changer is idle, look for the motor, the method of turntable drive, the method of coupling power to the cycling mechanism, the type of drop mechanism, the controls, and other easily recognized parts. A general familiarization is thus established. Now, when the cycling is actuated by use of the REJECT button and the turntable is rotated by hand, the combined action of the various parts can be more easily studied. Go as slow as is necessary to study individually the actions that occur simultaneously. With this approach, the familiar basic mechanisms can be readily recognized and a thorough understanding gained even on a changer you have never before worked on.

Segregation of Actions. While studying the changer mechanism, it helps to mentally separate the trip, drop, indexing, and drive sections. The automatic shutoff may also be checked if present. Certain obvious features can conveniently be used to isolate these sections quickly, as shown in Fig. 1.

The cycling power drive comes from a single source so this may be located first. Suppose it is a large drive-gear cam driven by the turntable. This would

244

then be connected in some manner to the pickup arm so as to raise and rotate the arm. Having located the lift rod, the linking mechanism between the drive gear and the lift rod can easily be traced.

The method of dropping the record to the turntable can just as easily be determined by inspection. You know that the base of the record-selector shaft must be linked to the drive gear so look for the drop actuator first. Trace the links from here to the drive gear and you have covered the record-dropping section.

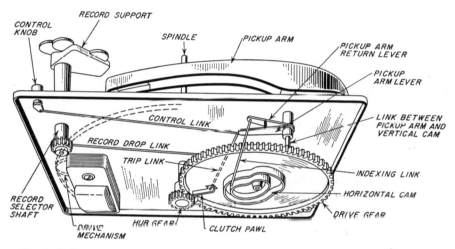

Fig. 1. Easily recognizable parts of a record changer assist in analyzing the actions involved

By inspection of the drive gear and its clutch pawl the clutch mechanism can be located. This can then be traced back to the pickup-arm lever which will work in unison with the pickup arm. The connecting link between these can often be clarified by checking the tie-in with the REJECT control knob, which will also actuate the clutch.

Once the actions are determined, investigation of any trouble may be made. Where this is an improper action or a missing action, such as two records dropping at once or none dropping, the improper operation of the mechanism is usually obvious. The first step in finding the cause of the trouble is determining how the mechanism is supposed to work. Here your knowledge of the basic mechanisms is of prime value. Any information gained through experience or from changer service manuals will also be of assistance.

Classifying Troubles. Most record-changer troubles can be classified according to the section in which they occur, such as motor, drive, trip, drop, set-down or indexing, shutoff, or pickup. Some troubles involve more than one section of the mechanism. In addition, there are a few general troubles such as rumble, wow, jamming, glide-in, and skipping.

Troubles pertaining to individual sections of the record changer have already been covered. This leaves only the general troubles and those applying to more than one section. Procedures for recognizing and fixing these will be taken up one by one in this chapter.

Visual Tests. Examination of a defective record changer is the simplest method of locating the trouble since no special equipment is necessary. Do this in a logical order, checking each important part of the mechanism in turn, as follows.

First, check the operation of the control knob or selector switch. When in the MANUAL position no changing action should take place, and you should be able to move the pickup arm freely back and forth across the record by hand. Any catching or binding that may exist in the pickup-arm shaft may be detected by doing this carefully.

Next, shut off the changer and return the pickup arm to its rest post. Then place several records on the record changer. Now set the control knob or selector switch to AUTOMATIC, and push the control knob to REJECT. The pickup arm will lift off the rest post and probably swing in and then out again before the next record drops. A check should be made to see that clearance exists between the top of the pickup arm and the bottom of the unplayed record stack. As the pickup arm comes down on the record, watch carefully to see if the set-down point is correct. To save time, lift the pickup carefully, and move it in toward the spindle slowly so as not to actuate the trip. Some changers are so sensitive that you cannot do this without actuating the trip; hence you will have to wait for playing of the entire record. After the needle has been replaced in the groove about two-thirds of the way in, watch the pickup arm again to assure that the trip is actuated when the needle is in the eccentric finishing groove but not before. The cycling should then repeat.

If the changer has more than one speed, check it on all speeds. Try it with all sizes of records as well.

A check should be made with a full stack of records on the turntable to assure that the pickup will raise sufficiently high to clear the stack and not hit the edge of the records.

If the record changer has automatic shutoff, see that it works and that the pickup arm sets down in the rest position after the last record has been played.

Test Records. Special records are available to aid in testing record changers. Frequency response, wow, rumble, and tracking can be checked by means of a single test record. These tests can be made by other means, but a test record combines many of them in a convenient manner.

Frequency response is indicated by a series of recorded notes covering the frequency range from about 50 cps to 10 kc. They follow the normal recording technique of constant amplitude below 500 cps and constant velocity above this. A rough idea of the over-all system performance can be obtained by ear, and this is usually sufficient. By use of a cathode-ray oscillograph or vacuum-tube voltmeter connected across the amplifier output, the exact performance can be plotted. These instruments may be connected across the speaker as a substitute, but unless the speaker is replaced by a resistor of equal ohmic value, the readings may sometimes be misleading because of the voice-coil inductance.

Use of a high-sensitivity meter or cathode-ray oscillograph to measure the pickup output will give a check on it. Another method of doing this is to use a test amplifier of known frequency response. A response curve can be obtained by feeding a constant value audio signal of varying frequency into the amplifier and measuring the output. An audio oscillator is a good signal source for this. Now when a response curve is made of the over-all system, the difference between the two curves is the response of the pickup.

Wow can be tested by use of a steady frequency tone on a test record. Any variation can be noted by the ear. A signal in the range of 1,000–3,000 cps is usually used. A stroboscope card gives the same results and also indicates the turntable speed.

A groove of varying volume levels will give an indication of the tracking. A single frequency is used in one test record, and the volume level changes in steps. Variations in volume or tone or presence of a fuzziness while on a single step will indicate tracking difficulty. You can readily detect skipping of grooves or gliding in if such troubles exist.

Rumble, noise, and scratch can be detected by use of a groove with no sound modulation. This is available on the starting and finishing groove of a record, but these are usually too short for a good check. Hum can be determined by turning up the volume of the amplifier before playing the record. It is a low-frequency noise. Place the needle on the record, but leave the turntable stationary. Any new noise is probably caused by poor shock mounting of the record player. Check to make sure the record changer is floating. Now place the needle in the unmodulated groove. Any new noise is either rumble or scratch.

Types of Test Records. There are a number of manufacturers of test records, and most make more than one type. Dubbings has a 12-inch 33⅓-rpm microgroove test record which includes the following:

Frequency response: 30, 50, 100, 250, and 400 cps constant amplitude; 700 cps, 1, 2, 4, 6, 8, 10, and 12 kc constant velocity

Wow: 3-kc tone for 45 seconds

Rumble: unmodulated 45-second groove

Tracking test: 5 levels of 400 cps tone.

Clarkstan has two somewhat similar test records, one for 78 rpm and another for 33⅓ rpm.

Dubbings has another test record to check compensation or equalization of a system. If properly compensated, the amplifier output as measured with a vacuum-tube voltmeter will be very nearly flat. The test record contains test sections for several different record compensations.

Test records are available through most radio-parts jobbers.

Turntable Speed. The speed of the turntable may be checked by means of a stroboscope card placed over a record. If the speed of the turntable varies, the wow will be detected as a variation in the rotation of the bars or dots on the stroboscope card.

Check the speed first with one record and again with a full stack on the turntable to determine the effect of loading. Since some variation will occur with loading, it is desirable that the speed under light load is slightly fast and that under full load it is slightly slow.

Needle Pressure. Needle pressure is important because it affects the tracking and wear of the records. If the pressure is not great enough, the needle may skip over grooves. If the pressure is too great, undue wear may occur in either the record or the needle. Needle pressure is covered in the chapter on needles and pickups. Needle pressure, vertical friction, and horizontal friction should not be taken lightly. Checking is a simple routine which will pay dividends in added repair work and customer satisfaction.

Rumble and Wow. Rumble is caused by mechanical vibrations which are coupled into the pickup from the motor. Most of this rumble is suppressed when the base plate of the record changer is floating properly on its springs or rubber cushions.

When shipping new changers, it is customary to fasten the base plate down tight with screws. These are sometimes inserted through the spring supports. In this case the screws must be loosened and left in place. In some cases these shipping screws are located under the turntable and must be removed. Such screws can usually be identified by the large slotted head so that the appearance is that of a wood screw rather than a machine screw.

If these shipping screws are not removed, rumble will exist. This and other causes of rumble are shown in Fig. 2.

Excess vibration originates primarily in the drive system. Wobble in the drive wheels due to loose bearings, uneven surfaces, and a bent or warped turntable are possible causes of this.

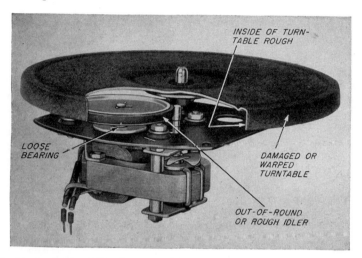

Fig. 2. Rumble, feedback, and howl are caused by mechanical vibrations being transmitted to the pickup. (General Industries photo).

Wow is due to variations in turntable speed. It causes the pitch of the resulting sound to change continuously. Binding or slipping of the turntable drive system are causes of this, as illustrated in Fig. 3.

Gumming or lack of lubrication is one possible cause. On the other hand, the presence of lubrication on friction elements such as the idler, drive wheel, or turntable rim may cause slipping. Motor difficulty or loose springs may also be the cause.

A missing washer in the bearing assembly can cause wow. If the friction is excessive as a result of this, the wow may very well change to a rumble. Caution should be used when removing the turntable since a washer will very often cling to it and drop off unnoticed later.

Jamming. Jamming of the mechanism may occur in almost any section of the record changer. Two of the most likely causes are improper record dropping and improper handling of the pickup arm. When a record fails to drop clear, it may be squeezed, such as between slicers in a two- and

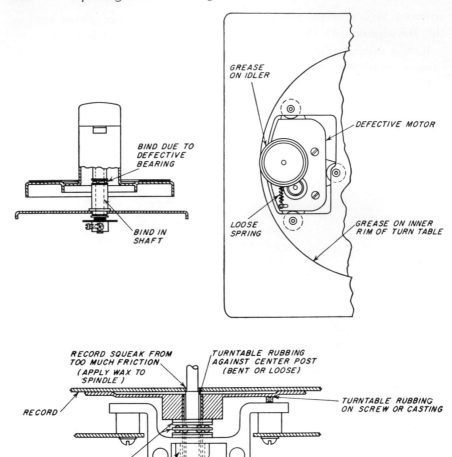

Fig. 3. Various causes of wow (speed variation)

three-shelf slicer-type mechanism, thus restricting the movement of the parts.

The pickup arm can cause jamming if the trip is actuated when the pickup arm is picked up. In this case the action of the mechanism is faster than the hand, causing undue force to be applied to the set-down mechanism.

Excess friction between parts, such as that caused by lack of lubrication or a scraping because of a burr, can also be a cause of jamming.

To free a jammed mechanism, rotate the turntable by hand in a backward or counterclockwise direction. Once the mechanism is free, it should be inspected for damage and recycled by hand to ascertain that it will not jam again.

When the mechanism is jammed, the motor is usually stalled. The motor is generally designed so that it is not damaged under these circumstances. On the other hand, it is possible for the motor to rotate and slippage to occur elsewhere, such as between the motor shaft and the idler wheel. This may wear an indentation into the idler causing a repeated thump or rumble when operated again.

Many record changers were designed for 78-rpm operation and the 33⅓- and 45-rpm speeds added without redesign of anything but the drive mechanism. The flywheel effect of the turntable is dependent upon the weight, size, and speed of rotation. As a result of the slower speed and therefore less flywheel energy, it is possible for the mechanism to slow down and possibly stop during cycling at 33⅓ rpm yet operate satisfactorily at other speeds. This slowdown can result from excess friction of moving parts. It may also be due to weak tension in the idler spring, permitting slippage in the drive mechanism.

Stalling of the record changer can occur if the temperature is so low that the grease congeals. Low line voltage is another cause of stalling. The motor will generally not operate too well at a voltage of less than 105 volts.

Improper Tracking. Improper tracking may be a skipping of grooves or a repetition of the same groove. Assuming that the record is not at fault, difficulty may be due to an unlevel mounting, insufficient slack in the pickup leads, or a binding in the pickup-arm bearing. A turntable can be checked to see that it is level by using a pocket-size level faced in two directions at right angles to each other.

Glide-in is a common type of trouble. It occurs when the needle does not follow the starting groove but rather slips across (or glides in) several grooves. Generally this is caused by improper indexing action.

Record Defects. Faulty records are often the cause of difficulty and should be investigated immediately if there is any doubt. Records that are too thin or too thick may cause trouble in slicer- and pusher-type drop mechanisms.

Improper-size center holes may cause problems where spindle support or drop is used. Spindle drop often causes rapid wear of the center groove.

Lack of a finishing groove, as on old records, will result in loss of trip action.

Warped records can cause improper drop, slow speed, wow, skipping of grooves, and improper trip.

Cleaning and Lubrication. Parts needing cleaning should be thoroughly wiped, brushed, or rinsed with carbon tetrachloride. This is a solvent for the accumulation of dirt and grease. Naptha and alcohol are suitable substitutes. It is essential to the proper operation of a record changer that the parts are either clean or adequately lubricated. Rubber parts, in particular, must be kept clean and free of grease and oil. Lubricants deteriorate rubber. Do not use carbon tetrachloride to clean off rubber as it is a solvent. Use alcohol to clean dirt or lubricants from rubber. Be careful not to breathe the fumes as they are dangerous.

Many parts are designed to operate without lubrication. Certain items, such as the friction portion of a velocity trip, must not be lubricated.

Those parts of a record changer which should usually be lubricated are listed below. Lubricants are of two types; a light oil such as SAE 10W and a heavier quality grease such as STA-PUT or Lubriplate.

SAE 10W
Drive-motor bearings
Pickup-arm shaft
Felt lubricating washers
Ball bearings
Trip-rod bearings
Turntable and spindle bearings

STA-PUT No. 320 or Lubriplate 105
Bearing surfaces
Cam bearing
Record-shelf assembly
Gear teeth
Hinge bearing
Turntable ball bearing

STA-PUT No. 512 or Lubriplate 105
Worm threads
Other surfaces

No Lubrication
Slicer separator shaft
Friction connections

To be certain of the lubrication procedure, the manfacturer's manual should be read, and the instructions followed for the particular unit involved. Figure 4 shows an example of such information.

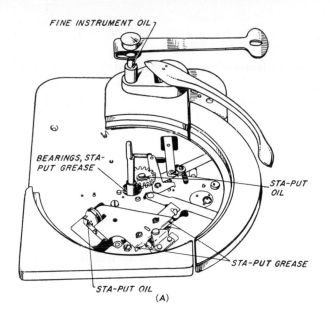

FINE INSTRUMENT OIL

BEARINGS, STA-PUT GREASE

STA-PUT OIL

STA-PUT GREASE

STA-PUT OIL

(A)

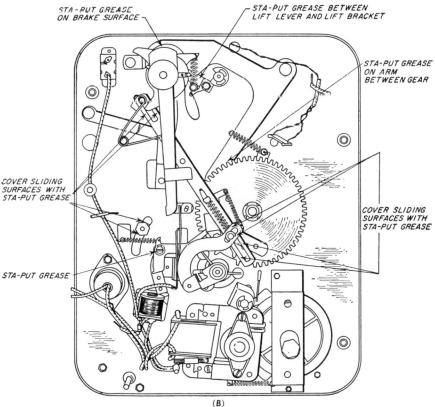

STA-PUT GREASE ON BRAKE SURFACE

STA-PUT GREASE BETWEEN LIFT LEVER AND LIFT BRACKET

STA-PUT GREASE ON ARM BETWEEN GEAR

COVER SLIDING SURFACES WITH STA-PUT GREASE

COVER SLIDING SURFACES WITH STA-PUT GREASE

STA-PUT GREASE

(B)

Fig. 4. Lubrication points of a record changer. (A) Top view. (B) Bottom view

253

Assembly and Disassembly of Mechanism. Certain precautions should be observed during repair work on record changers. A lot of effort is expended in disassembly and reassembly of mechanical parts. Proper caution will give good results with a minimum of effort.

First, proper tools should be used. This applies particularly to screwdrivers. Use of a Phillips screwdriver of the proper size to remove Phillips-head screws, and use of the proper blade size to remove slotted-head screws is essential to avoid stripping or gouging the head.

The proper blade size is the one which fits the head snugly. In this manner the force is applied evenly through the slot rather than at isolated spots. When tightening machine screws, only moderate pressure should be exerted. Excess pressure may shear the screw or make it difficult to remove.

When disassembling a mechanism, it should be inspected thoroughly before removing any screws. Careful scrutiny will probably reveal the points at which the mechanism separates. In some instances removal of the wrong screw will allow an undesired assembly to come apart. Thus caution must be used. Where several screws hold the assembly, partial loosening of all of them will allow checking to assure that only the necessary ones are taken out.

Assembly of a mechanism is sometimes complicated if one of several screws is put in and tightened completely. Because of mechanical tolerances necessary for economic construction, all of the holes may not line up exactly. If all of the screws are put in only part way and then alternately tightened a few turns each, the assembly will pull together properly. Finally, each screw can be tightened firmly.

Since a record changer is floating on spring supports, it is necessary that it be held in position so that it cannot fall out in transporting. Frequently a pivoted mounting clip is used with a stud or bolt for this purpose. This is illustrated in Fig. 5. To release the changer from the mounting springs, an upward pressure must be applied to the slotted ends of the clips. When enough pressure is applied, the clips will snap into a vertical position. When installing the record changer, the clips must be pivoted back to the holding position.

Disconnecting Wires for Replacement of Parts. In the process of repairs it is often necessary to remove leads from cartridges, switches, and other electrical parts. Where more than one wire is used, color coding is frequently used. This is to distinguish between the connections. When removing the wires, it is well to take note which wire is connected to each point. If immediate replacement is not made, a sketch is usually advisable. This assures that proper installation is made later. Where more than one person may work on the equipment, such notation is essential.

Removing Burrs. Since most actions depend on smooth operation of several interrelated mechanical parts, it is essential that frictionless motion be approached. A nick or burr is a common cause of trouble. To smooth such a surface, a file or crocus cloth must be used. If the burr is heavy, a file is desirable. It should, however, be of a coarseness consistent with the roughness of the piece. In most cases a rather fine file is desirable.

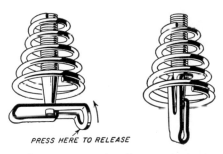

PRESS HERE TO RELEASE

Fig. 5. A popular support spring uses a mounting clip to retain the changer in place. To remove, an upward pressure must be applied until the clip snaps into the vertical position

After the burred surface has been evened off, the crocus cloth should be used to polish it. Since the burr was probably caused by rough contact between the parts, they should be polished extra well to avoid repetition. Cleaning of the surface with carbon tetrachloride will allow careful inspection of the surface so the condition can be determined.

Bending Metallic Pieces. Relatively long, flat pieces of metal are often used in record changers. Repairs occasionally require slight bending of such parts to correct for warping caused by jamming, excess pressure, or other similar reasons. Extreme care must be used in straightening such pieces in order to avoid causing more damage.

Since it is seldom convenient to remove the piece and flatten it in a vise or with a mallet, it is necessary to use one or two pliers. The piece should be grasped with as broad a grip as possible, using the broadest portion of the pliers. Easy force should be applied so as to bend the part gently and not too much. Patience is a virtue under such circumstances. The force must be applied in only the one direction so that the part is not twisted. Skill is vital, but until it is acquired extra care must be used to supplant it.

QUESTIONS

1. How would you determine the trip mechanism in an unfamiliar record changer?
2. How would you make a visual inspection of a changer to locate trouble?
3. What can you check with a test record?
4. What is the purpose of a stroboscope card?
5. Name some causes of rumble and wow.
6. How would you free a jammed mechanism?
7. How can you level a record changer?
8. What parts of a changer should be lubricated?
9. How do you remove burrs?

15

Magnetic Tape Recorders

Introduction. Although magnetic tape recorders are not of the automatic-change type, their use has become sufficiently widespread to warrant consideration. On the whole, they will be found easier to repair than record changers.

Magnetic tape recorders are designed to operate for periods up to and over one hour without changing spools of tape so that the need for automatic changing devices is not present. The principle parts of a typical tape recorder are shown in Fig. 1.

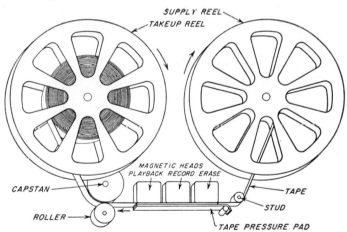

Fig. 1. A typical tape recorder showing principal parts. The tape is moving from right to left

The long, flat tape is wound on a reel. During the process of recording or playback the tape is wound off this supply reel and onto an identical takeup reel. Between the two reels is a drive mechanism used to move the tape at a constant speed. The drive is called the capstan, and the tape is squeezed between it and a roller. The mechanism is similar to a rim-drive mechanism. The capstan drives the tape past one to three magnetic heads used for erase, record, or playback. The capstan and head are usually enclosed for protection against dust or physical damage. A drive mechanism must be used to turn the takeup reel so it will wind up the moving tape. Most home tape recorders record on only one-half of the tape so that when the reel is run through, it can be turned over and the other half used. The two tracks are side by side. This is called dual-track recording.

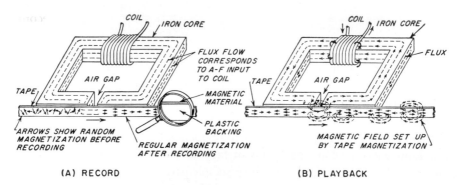

(A) RECORD   (B) PLAYBACK

Fig. 2. Electrical variations are changed to magnetism by the coil when recording. The magnetism flows through the iron and tape, magnetizing the latter. The process is reversed when played back. The direction of the arrows on the tape shows the polarity of the magnetization, and the number of arrows indicates the volume

The chief advantage of a magnetic recording is that it may be replayed thousands of times with little wear, yet the tape may be magnetically erased and used over again.

Tape may be stored indefinitely without ill effect and will not rust in damp climate. It may be stored in cardboard containers and will not be magnetically damaged if dropped. Because of its strength the tape can be operated at higher speed for rewinding and cueing.

How Magnetic Recording Works. When recording, the audio signal is fed from an amplifier to a coil in the recording head. This coil is wound around a magnet with a very small air gap, as shown in Fig. 2. The changing current in the coil causes flux to flow around the magnetic circuit consisting of the magnet and air gap. Since the reluctance of air is very great, the flux will flow through a magnetic tape instead, providing the tape is placed close to the poles of the magnet. When demagnetized, the molecules of the tape are arranged at random, as shown to the left of the gap. When exposed to a magnetizing force, the molecules will line up. It is the property of a magnetic material that as the magnetizing force is removed, the molecules will remain lined up and retain some of the magnetism. When the tape moves past the gap, that portion to the right of the gap is removed from the magnetizing force and retains the recording.

The direction of the arrows shows the direction of the magnetizing force. The closer the arrows are together, the stronger is the force. In the unmagnetized region of the tape the molecules are not lined up, and the arrows indicate this by their random direction.

Playback is simply the reverse of this process. The changes in the tape magnetization change the reluctance of the magnetic circuit so that current is caused to flow in the coil.

Construction of Tape. Tape consists of a strong plastic base about ¼ inch wide. On one side of this is applied an even layer of finely powdered crystalline magnetic particles. The base of the tape provides the strength and traction required to pull it through the drive mechanism.

Recording Speed. For a particular length of tape, the slower the recording speed the longer the recording capacity. Tape speed is directly related to frequency response, so the penalty of slow recording speed is a lower high-frequency response. A tape speed of 7½ inches per second can, with proper design of the head and amplifier compensation, provide a satisfactory reproduction up to about 15,000 cps. A tape speed of 3¾ inches per second will give 8,000 cps response. Since the quality of speaking is acceptable with 4,000 cps response, a tape speed of 1⅞ inches per second is also used. In high-quality professional recording work, such as transcriptions, tape speeds of 15 and 30 inches per second are used. For the sake of comparison the average groove speed of a 78-rpm record is about 29 inches per second.

Biasing of Head. As the magnetizing force applied to a magnetic material increases, the magnetization of the material increases. This is not linear, however, since the powdered magnetic material tends to saturate at higher levels. This means that beyond a certain point further increases in the magnetizing force give very little more increase in magnetization of the tape.

As the magnetizing force is reduced, the material retains some of the magnetism so that the tape still has some magnetization when the magnetizing force is brought down to zero. This effect is called hysteresis and would cause distortion in magnetic recording if not corrected.

To obtain undistorted output in magnetic recording, high-frequency bias is used to offset hysteresis. The bias frequency is usually several times the maximum audio frequency so that it cannot cause audible interference. The high-frequency bias and audio signal combine in a manner similar to modulating an r-f signal for radio transmission.

The reason for the excellent results achieved with high-frequency bias is not fully understood, but here is a general idea of what goes on. As the tape leaves the gap in the recording head, demagnetization occurs. More demagnetization takes place at the high frequencies than at the low frequencies so that the bias frequency disappears in the magnetic recording. This leaves the desired audio signal on the tape. With no audio signal, the tape is nearly completely demagnetized. As a result, the noise level is low.

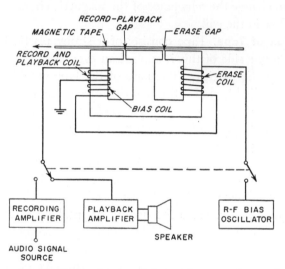

Fig. 3. A diagram of a combination head used for erasing, recording, and playback. Radio frequency is used for erasing and for recording bias

Use of the proper level of bias gives low distortion. The correct value of bias is dependent upon the type of recording material and the speed. Bias is not used during playback.

Construction of Heads. Separate heads are used for recording and for playback in more expensive professional-type equipment. In the more reasonably priced tape recorders such as will be encountered by servicemen, however, a combination head generally serves both functions. An example using two coils wound on a common laminated core is shown in Fig. 3. One coil is used for both recording and playback and is wound on one leg of the core.

The erase coil is wound on another leg and supplied with erase current from a high-frequency oscillator. The same high-frequency source provides bias for recording, so a portion of the erase coil is wound on the same leg as the record-and-playback coil to accomplish this. The middle leg of the core is used as a common magnetic path. The erase gap is generally about ten times the length of the record-playback gap.

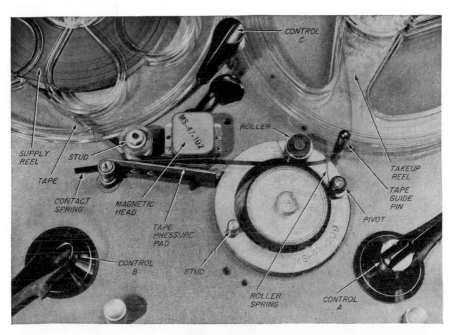

Fig. 4. A home tape recorder showing the tape-handling mechanism with the head and capstan housings removed. (Masco photo)

The record-playback gap determines the frequency response. As the gap size is increased, the lows increase and the highs decrease. A compromise is therefore chosen, making the gap one to two thousandths of an inch.

The direction of travel of the tape is such that it is erased before recording. This assures a clear tape with which to work.

Tape Recorder. Figure 4 shows the face of a tape recorder with the head exposed. This unit is intended primarily for home entertainment purposes. It is a dual-track unit with a combination record-playback-erase head. The equipment will operate at either 3¾ or 7½ inches per second tape speed. It has a fast forward speed feature that allows the user to proceed rapidly to a particular spot on the tape. It also has a rewind feature so that the tape may be backed up. Construction is such that the tape cannot accidentally be erased or damaged. Provisions are made for recording from a record changer, radio, or microphone. The latter two are included in the unit illustrated. The audio amplifier is self-contained. Provisions are made for monitoring the recording and a glow-lamp level indicator is built in. A remote speaker may be plugged in. Seven-inch tape reels may be used giving 1 hour of recording at 7½ inches per second or 2 hours at 3¾ inches per second. This requires reversing the tape at the mid-point.

Fig. 5A. The operating portions of the tape recorder. Tape routing when control A is set for RECORD-PLAYBACK. (Masco photo)

Preparation for Use. A reel of tape must first be placed on the spindle marked SUPPLY REEL in such a manner that the reel unwinds counterclockwise. The tape must then be unwound so that about 2 feet extend from the reel. It is then dropped into the tape slot and run around the front of the tape-guide pin located at the right of the housing.

The free end of the tape should next be inserted in a slot on the takeup reel which has been placed on the takeup-reel spindle. A few turns of tape should be wound on the takeup reel by rotating it counterclockwise by hand. Caution should be taken to assure that the tape is not twisted along the exposed section.

Figure 4 shows the face of the recorder with the tape loaded and the housings over the head and capstan removed. This is the tape position when loaded and with the two control levers in the OFF position. When the right-hand control lever A is rotated to the RECORD-PLAYBACK position, the tape is moved to the position shown in Fig. 5A.

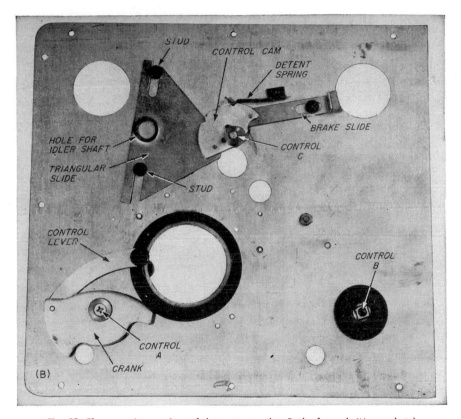

Fig. 5B. The operating portions of the tape recorder. Back of panel. (Masco photo)

The mechanism under the panel for moving the tape to the operating position is shown in Fig. 5B. When control A is rotated from OFF to RECORD-PLAYBACK, the lever rotates the capstan ring in the correct direction to press the tape against the magnetic head. The tape then passes over the stud on the capstan assembly, between the spring-loaded roller and the capstan and around the fixed tape-guide pin to the takeup reel. The spring-loaded roller maintains its tension by means of the hair spring attached to the pivot.

Drive Mechanism. The tape recorder being used as an example has two four-pole motors. One is used to drive the supply reel or the tape capstan, and the other drives the takeup reel. Both drive mechanisms use an idler wheel in a manner similar to that used in a rim-drive record-changer drive mechanism. Two forward tape speeds are provided, 3¾ inches per second and 7½ inches per second.

Fig. 6. The drive mechanism of a tape recorder. (Masco photo)

Normal Forward Speed. When the tape-recorder controls are set for operation at the forward tape speed of 3¾ inches per second, the tape capstan and the takeup reel are rotated by the motor mechanisms. To drive the takeup reel, the normal idler, shown in Fig. 6, engages both the takeup-motor shaft and the takeup reel. The supply reel rotates due to the pull of the tape.

The takeup-motor shaft has two diameters. For 3¾ inches per second the normal idler contacts the smaller diameter on the shaft. The brake pad, provided to keep the tape taut during rewind, is retracted during play so the takeup reel is free to rotate.

During play the capstan idler wheel is in a position where it contacts both the drive-motor shaft and the capstan. The speed pushbutton is in the depressed position so that the spring-floated motor subchassis is depressed and the smaller diameter on the drive-motor shaft is opposite the capstan idler wheel.

For a tape speed of 7½ inches per second, the speed pushbutton is left in the up position. The drive-motor shaft is therefore up, and the large diameter contacts the capstan idler wheel.

In both cases a brake with light spring action is held against the supply reel to keep the tape taut.

Fast Forward Speed. When the operating controls are set for FAST FORWARD, the normal idler is disengaged from the takeup-motor shaft. Control C causes the fast idler to be moved in so that it engages the takeup reel and the larger diameter of the takeup-motor shaft. The tape capstan and supply reel operate as in the case for normal forward speed.

Control A is in the OFF position so that the tape is not in contact with the tape capstan. The takeup reel therefore provides the tape drive even though the capstan is rotating.

Rewind Action. After the tape has been entirely wound on the takeup reel, it may be desirable to rewind it for playing or rerecording. For this the controls allow the tape capstan and takeup reel to run freely, while the supply reel is driven by the motor. Only light brake action is applied to the takeup reel to prevent it from whipping. The capstan idler wheel has been moved so that it contacts the drive-motor shaft and the supply reel. The tape is hence wound back on the supply reel.

Position of Mechanism in OFF Position. When the controls are set to OFF positions, the normal idler is engaged and both the supply and takeup reels are completely disengaged and braked. The controls move levers or studs that press against the brake pads and brake springs to achieve the desired heavy braking action.

Amplifier. The audio amplifier used in a tape recorder is essentially conventional. Some models include a radio tuner. Provision is often made to allow use of an external amplifier or an external speaker if desired. Radio, phono, or microphone input may be used. A typical frequency response for a home unit is from 80 to 8,500 cps at a tape speed of 7½ inches per second and 80 to 5,000 cps at 3¾ inches per second. Some manufacturers have approached a response of about twice this range. The speaker or a plug-in headset may be used to monitor when recording.

Magnetic Head. The magnetic head of a tape recorder generally has one portion for erasing and the other for recording and playback. A 52.5-kc signal is used for both purposes in one particular recorder. The erase head is energized in the recording position to automatically clear the tape in the event it was previously used.

Wire Recorders. For a time wire recorders were as popular as tape, but the quantities made were small. The advantages of tape over wire have obsoleted the latter. It is possible that an occasional service call may be required on wire recorders. The principle is the same. With home wire recorders, the wire drive is usually applied to the takeup reel. To prevent pile-up of wire, a level-wind guide is used to move the wire up and down over the takeup spool as it winds.

Maintenance of Tape Recorders. Tape recorders are in many respects simpler than disc record changers. The mechanical features are mostly concerned with the drive mechanism, and these are lubricated and serviced essentially the same as record changers.

Replacing the Magnetic Head. The magnetic head of a tape recorder is changed in much the same manner as a record-changer cartridge is changed. It is customary to use a hood to cover the head so as to shield it from stray fields and to protect it against damage. One or more accessible machine screws will hold it in place, and removal of these screws allows the hood to be lifted from place. The magnetic head can then be removed. It is held in place either by a screw or two, or it is of a plug-in variety. By inspecting the head, it can be determined where the screws are located. The mounting plate may be adjustable. Do not move the adjustment screws or it may require more work when testing. If there are several, it is likely that the larger ones will hold the head in place and the others are used for assembly. Careful scrutiny will help to confirm this.

Where the magnetic head is held by machine screws, it is likely that the leads will have to be unsoldered. Careful attention must be given to the color coding so that the replacement is properly connected.

Plug-in units are becoming popular as would be expected. Here the electrical connections and support are both made through the pins which plug into corresponding sockets. Steady pressure should be used in removing or inserting a head. The head should be pulled straight out when removing so as to avoid breaking the pins. It is always a good policy not to force any item. If moderate force does not move it, it is likely that it is held captive, and an inspection should be made to locate the guilty screw or pin.

Cleaning the Magnetic Head. Dirt, gum, and other foreign material are likely to accumulate in the gap of the head. Carbon tetrachloride should be used to clean it and can be applied by means of a rag or a cotton swab wrapped on the end of a stick. Under no circumstances should a metallic object be used.

It will be found that the capstan in a tape recorder will also become dirty with use and therefore must be cleaned. If the capstan has a rubber tire, clean with alcohol.

Johansson Effect. Johansson Blocks are precise metal blocks used by machinists to calibrate gages. The surfaces are so smooth and accurate that if one is placed on another they will stick.

After considerable use the magnetic heads are likely to get polished by the tape so that the two stick together. This has been called the Johansson Effect. In early stages it may cause a squeal. Later it may stall the tape recorder or break the tape. Cleaning the head only makes it worse. Rubbing the head with crocus cloth will actually roughen it sufficiently to correct it. Then clean it with carbon tetrachloride. Some high-quality tapes are designed to minimize this effect.

Use of Test Tape. Several test tapes are available to check the recorder's operation and aid in correction. Audio Devices has a test tape designed for alignment of the heads and usable at either 7½ or 15 inches per second. Dubbings has two test tapes for these speeds but includes information to allow checking of head alignment, maximum recording level, tape speed, wow and flutter, frequency response, and signal-to-noise ratio.

A test tape should be recorded on a material which does not stretch. To use it, a vacuum-tube voltmeter, or equivalent, is required. The meter must be accurate up to the maximum audio frequency used.

Wow and Flutter. Wow and flutter are variations in sound. If the wavering is low in frequency, it is called wow, while a high-frequency wavering is called flutter.

To check wow and flutter, a constant-frequency recorded signal is required. When this is played back, it should not change pitch. The ear can generally detect a change in pitch of ½ per cent. A good-quality machine is better than this. It is possible to introduce wow by touching the supply reel during operation. If the equipment has very little wow, a light touch of the hand should increase the wow considerably. If wow is detected with the tape running free and does not increase when the supply reel is touched lightly, the wow is excessive.

If a test tape is not available, an audio tone from a signal generator may be recorded on the equipment and played back. A steady frequency of about 3,000 cps is suitable. Since the stability of the signal generator and the type of tape will affect the results, this should be considered a stop-gap procedure.

Wow and flutter are due to uneven tape speed and will be caused by the rotating portions of the tape drive. Eccentric or worn idlers and capstan, defective motor, and warped reel are possible sources of trouble. To correct these, replacement is likely to be required. Slipping due to oily surfaces or weak spring tension are other possible causes.

Frequency Response. To test the frequency response, a test tape includes a series of tones covering the frequency spectrum. Dubbings' tapes cover 30–7,500 cps and 30–15,000 cps for 7½- and 15-inch per second speeds, respectively. Each frequency step lasts several seconds and all are recorded at the same level. By measuring the output at the speaker by use of a vacuum-tube voltmeter, the readings indicate the frequency response.

In addition to the effect of the amplifier response poor low-frequency response may be caused by low bias. High bias may give poor high-frequency response. If the head is worn, or if the tape does not make good contact with the head, the high-frequency response will deteriorate. In the former case, replacement of the head is necessary. In the latter case, the tape pressure pad may not keep the tape against the head, or the head needs cleaning. The specifications for the recorder will indicate the frequency response.

Signal-to-noise Ratio. The signal-to-noise ratio may be determined by finding the signal level at which the signal and noise are equal. The Dubbings' tapes have a series of 400-cps tones that are recorded at different levels. Each level is 5 db below the previous one. When the vacuum-tube voltmeter, connected across the speaker, shows the tone and the unrecorded portion to be equal in output, the announced level is the measure of the performance. The lowest recorded level is 50 db below normal recording level. If the 400-cps note is stronger than the noise at this level, the performance is excellent. A home recorder will have a signal-to-noise ratio of 40–45 db at 7½ inches per second. The ratio will be about 5 db lower at a speed of 3¾ inches per second.

Head Alignment. For proper operation the record head and the playback head must have the same relationship to the tape. In order that a tape may be played on more than one machine, this requires that the gap be set at 90 degrees to the edge of the tape. An alignment error of ½ degree will cut the output by one-half. To check azimuth alignment, it is desired to use as high a frequency as is convenient. At 7½ inches per second tape speed Audio Devices uses 7½ kc, and Dubbings uses 5 kc.

The technique of adjusting the head is to set it for maximum signal by adjusting the head mounting screws. To check the setting, a nonmetallic object may be used to tilt the tape with respect to the head. A plastic alignment tool can be used for this. Touch the top of the tape adjacent to the playback or combination head lightly. Repeat, touching the bottom of the tape. This causes the tape to run at a slight angle down or up. Maximum signal should be obtained when the tape is running naturally, and the signal level should drop when the tape is guided up and down.

Also make sure that the tape is touching both sides of the gap. This can be done by visual inspection or pressing the tape with the finger on either side. A variation in level indicates incorrect horizontal alignment. Make sure there is no difference in tone obtained by the latter method as this indicates that the tape speed is being changed and the test results may be erroneous.

If the equipment has a separate record head, record a tone of the same frequency on a piece of scrap tape. Play it back, tilting the tape up and down with the plastic alignment tool. If the recording head is properly aligned, maximum output will be obtained when the tape is running free.

It is likely that a tape guide will be used just before the tape reaches the heads. It is then easiest to tilt the tape where it comes off the head. In order to do this, it is necessary to remove any housing over or near the heads. Be sure that the tape pressure-pad tension is not removed when this is done as the output will drop and the frequency response may change. If the tape pad tension is removed, it will be necessary to hold the tape pressure pad against the heads lightly. Never touch the tape with a magnetic material as it will tend either to erase the tape or make it noisy. An alignment tape should not be subjected to high-speed rewind.

Recording Level. The Dubbings' tapes give two recording-level signals, one at maximum recording level and one 10 db below this, corresponding to normal level. The volume control settings for either maximum or normal setting can be determined by the following procedure. Play the test tape at a normal volume, and note the volume setting. Use another tape, and record a 400-cps tone using the presumably proper level as shown by the meter or glow lamp. Now play this last tape back with the volume control set to the level previously noted. The volume should again be normal. If too high in level, try again using a lower recording level. If too low a level, repeat using a higher recording level. Note the proper recording level.

By using this method for both maximum and normal levels as recorded on the test tape, the proper maximum and normal recording levels can be determined. Thus the meter or glow lamp can be properly interpreted for future use.

Tape Speed. Tape speed can be checked by use of time beeps recorded at fixed intervals on a machine that is known to run at exact speed. By timing these when played back, the speed of the tape mechanism is readily determined. If the playback takes longer than it should, the recorder being tested is running slow and vice versa.

Demagnetization. If any of the heads become magnetized, they will deteriorate the performance of the recorder. The tape will be partly erased or become noisy. Such heads must be demagnetized. To prevent possible damage to the test tape, all recorders being tested should be demagnetized before checking. Audio Devices markets a head demagnetizer especially for this purpose. It is an a-c magnet with two long pole pieces bent at the end so that they may be placed adjacent to the head. To prepare for use, it is necessary to cover the demagnetizer pole tips with Scotch tape to prevent scratching the head. Then plug the cord into the a-c line. Place the tips of the demagnetizer against the head and move over the entire surface of the head for about 1 second. Then slowly move the demagnetizer away from the head. Disconnect the power cord.

Do not check a magnetic head by measuring the resistance, as this will magnetize it. If inadvertently done, demagnetize it as just explained.

Noisy Recording. In addition to noise due to magnetization of the heads other precautions are necessary. Some manufacturers recommend erasing a new tape completely before recording even though the tape is erased again just before the recording-head action. When a tape has been stored for several months without being used, it is recommended that it be rewound before use.

Noise may be due to a faulty bias shape. The bias signal must be sinusoidal and can be viewed by connecting a cathode-ray oscilloscope across the resistor in the erase-head circuit. Since such difficulty is likely to be the oscillator tube, try replacing it first when you have noisy operation.

Defective filter capacitors are also likely to give excess noise. If the normal signal-to-noise ratio is about 35 db, the noise will be very apparent with such a trouble.

Lubrication. General lubrication instructions apply. Lubriplate, STA-PUT, or equivalent should be used on worm and other gear assemblies. Pulleys, idlers, and other rotating bearing surfaces should be lubricated with SAE 10W grade oil. Oil or grease should be removed from rubber surfaces by the use of alcohol. Some units use oilless bearings and do not require lubrication. Where doubt exists, the manufacturer's instructions should be consulted.

QUESTIONS

1. How is sound recorded on tape?
2. What are the common recording speeds of tape recorders?
3. What is the purpose of biasing of a head?
4. Name three functions of magnetic heads.
5. What type of drive mechanism is used in a tape recorder?
6. How do you clean a magnetic head?
7. What can you check with a test tape?

Index